Healthy Dining
in San Diego

Seventh Edition

Restaurant Nutrition Guide

Featuring Healthy Entrées from
Popular San Diego Area Restaurants

Including:

✓ Calories   ✓ Cholesterol
✓ Fat   ✓ Sodium

Fruit & Vegetable Servings,
Protein, Carbohydrate & Fiber Information

by

Accents On Health, Inc.

Authors and Contributors:
Anita Jones-Mueller, M.P.H.
Esther Hill, Ph.D.
Erica Bohm, M.S.
Nicole Quartuccio, R.D.
Susan Goldstein
Karen Busch

Healthy Dining
in San Diego

Seventh Edition, Second Printing

Restaurant Nutrition Guide
by
Accents On Health, Inc.

Authors and Contributors:
Anita Jones-Mueller, M.P.H., Esther Hill, Ph.D., Erica Bohm, M.S.,
Nicole Quartuccio R.D., Susan Goldstein, and Karen Busch

Published by:

Healthy Dining Publications
Accents On Health, Inc.
8305 Vickers Street, Suite 106
San Diego, CA 92111
(858) 541-2049
FAX (858) 541-0508
www.healthy-dining.com

Cover graphics by Sprokkit Web Technology & Marketing Services and Cindy Kendrick, logo by Cindy Kendrick, staff photos by Michael Ross, clip art by Microsoft.

Copyright © 2005, 2006 by Accents On Health, Inc.
Published in U.S.A.

Library of Congress Cataloging in Publication Data
Jones-Mueller, Anita
Healthy Dining in San Diego
1. Nutrition.
2. Diet.
3. Restaurant Food.
91-71724
ISBN 1-879754-06-1

Table of Contents

Welcome to **Healthy Dining**   iv
10 Ways You Can Help **Healthy Dining** Grow in Your Community   vii
About **Healthy Dining** and Accents On Health   viii
Foreword by The American Cancer Society   x
Preface by Dr. Donald Lyman, California Department of Health Services   xi
People are Talking about **Healthy Dining**   xii
Thank You's and Recognitions   xiv
Healthy Dining Extravaganzas   xv
Sign Up for *Cuisine Connection* e-newsletter   xvi

Part I   Healthy Dining Tips: Realistic Guidelines and Practical Information   1
   Introduction   How to Use This Book   3
   Chapter 1   Health, Every Day Makes a Difference   7
   Chapter 2   Dining Out Challenges   11
   Chapter 3   Do Your Calories Have a Purpose?   17
   Chapter 4   Fat – the Good, the Bad, & Stuff Your Mother Didn't Warn You About   21
   Chapter 5   Cholesterol – Where, What and How?   25
   Chapter 6   Sodium – To Salt or Not to Salt?   28
   Chapter 7   Protein, Carbohydrates, and Fiber   31
   Chapter 8   Fruits & Vegetables – Nutrition Heavyweights   34
   Chapter 9   Additional Tips for **Healthy Dining**   38
   Appendix   Analysis Methods, Accuracy and Disclaimer   40

Part II   Healthy Dining Menus (Restaurants Arranged Alphabetically)   43

Part III   Chefs' Recipes   123

Part IV   Health Resource Guide   181

Part V   Distinguished Advisory Board   195

Part VI   Additional Information   201
   Healthy Dining in Orange County Participating Restaurants   202
   Healthy Dining in Los Angeles Participating Restaurants   203
   Questionnaire   205
   Book Order Form with $5.00 Discount   206
   "Thank You" Notes to Restaurants   207
   "Please Join" Notes to Restaurants   209

Part VII   Restaurant Coupons   213

Part VIII Restaurant Indexes   225
   Cuisine   226
   Location   228
   Alphabetical   232

Introduction

Welcome to Healthy Dining

◆ **Are you striving to eat healthier?**
Are you trying to eat more fruits and vegetables? Are you attempting to eat less fat and/or refined carbohydrates? Perhaps you are committed to losing weight or are following a special diet to reduce cholesterol, lower blood pressure or control diabetes. Maybe you are physically active or an athlete and know that what you eat directly affects your performance.

◆ **Do you read the nutrition facts labels on food products?**
Do you check for serving size information, calories, fat grams, sodium content, etc.? These labels provide valuable information to assess how food products impact your diet and influence the achievement of your nutrition goals.

◆ **Do you eat away from home often?**
Does your business, social life or hectic lifestyle require you to eat out frequently?

◆ **Do you love to dine out?**
Is dining out a wonderful treat for you? Do you love to experience the vast array of world cuisines available here in Southern California? Do you delight in tasting the fabulous flavor of dishes specially created for your enjoyment by talented chefs?

**If you answered YES to any of the above questions,
you will LOVE this book!**

Now, imagine sitting at your favorite restaurant perusing the menu. What will you order? How will this restaurant meal add up in terms of calories, fat, protein, fiber, carbohydrates, and fruit/vegetable servings? Generally, nutrition information is not available for restaurant meals, so how do you know? Well –

We have GOOD NEWS & BAD NEWS for you ...

First, the BAD NEWS

Most restaurant meals are very high in calories and fat. In fact, **most restaurant meals have 1,000 to 2,000 calories and 50 to 100 grams of fat**. For most people, that's over a full day's allowance of fat – in just one meal. To put that in perspective, one stick of butter has 800 calories and 88 grams of fat, so in many cases, **one restaurant meal has as much fat as a whole stick of butter!** And worse, those figures are for the meal itself – they don't include the chips, bread and butter, beverages, desserts, etc.! Read on, however, because we also have GOOD NEWS for you!

The GOOD NEWS

In Southern California, over 250 popular chefs and restaurants care about your health and participate in the **Healthy Dining** Program. These restaurants agree to offer a selection of menu items that meet nutrition guidelines recommended by leading health organizations, such as the U.S. Surgeon General's Office, the U.S. Department of Agriculture, the U.S. Department of Health and Human Services, the American Cancer Society, the American Heart Association, the 5 A Day For Better Health Program and others.

Now you may be thinking: **Healthy** – is that the dry, skinny chicken breast with "floppy" broccoli on the side? Or, perhaps, here in Southern California, healthy has a more "tempeh, tofu, raw" meaning. Recently, some restaurants have promoted as "healthful alternatives: the low carb, high saturated fat items such as a "Supersize Bun-less Cheeseburger" (490 calories, 37 g fat, 16 g saturated fat) or a Low-Carb Breakfast Bowl (900 calories, 73 g fat, 33 g saturated fat!) – which are **definitely not healthy**! Just what is healthy and how does it taste?

The EXCITING NEWS

Through the **Healthy Dining** Program, chefs are applying their artistry and creativity in developing **great-tasting, vibrantly beautiful** menu items with health **and** taste buds in mind. Innovative techniques employed by the chefs in creating healthful dishes include: using **lean** proteins to provide the foundation for the meal; adding **fresh and seasonal ingredients**; combining **bold** seasonings and spices; incorporating **flavorful fruits and vegetables** as main ingredients in sauces, stocks and purees; including **wholesome** grains and **disease-fighting produce** as vital components of the meal.

> These healthful ingredients and techniques generate delicious and colorful dishes that **tantalize** taste buds, **dazzle** senses and **whittle** waistlines.

This **Healthy Dining** book provides you with everything you need to eat out and eat healthfully. This book guides you to restaurants that care about your health, identifies which menu items are healthiest, provides nutrition information for every menu item featured, and in some cases includes "Special Request" instructions.

We invite you to step out of your usual dining "rut" (you know, going to the same couple of restaurants and ordering the same few dishes, time and time again). Now, with the **Healthy Dining** book, you have a whole new world of sensational dining to explore. We know you will be wonderfully surprised as you use this book and discover how magnificent **healthy** can be.

Bon Appetit!

Our Vision

The **Healthy Dining** Program was founded in the early 1990s to enhance the health and well-being of Americans by propelling a shift toward healthier restaurant cuisine. Our team of health and nutrition professionals is dedicated to motivating chefs and restaurateurs to create and offer dishes that emphasize fruits and vegetables, lean proteins and whole grains. If chefs continue to create such healthful and appealing "masterpieces," this can influence both our choices when dining out and also how we cook at home and teach our children to cook and eat – and that will ultimately and significantly impact the health status of our nation!

It is our dream that **all restaurants offer a selection of appealing, healthy menu items** with corresponding nutrition information. This will enable Americans to make wise choices when eating away from home. Although this sounds reasonable and achievable, it is actually quite a challenge!

We Need Your Help

We want you to know how very influential you – as a customer in the restaurant – are to the **Healthy Dining** Program. More than anything, restaurants want to please their customers. They want you to come back more often, and they want you to tell your friends and family about their restaurant. It is your voice that can make a difference! Please tell the restaurants you patronize that **Healthy Dining** is important to you. If the restaurant is featured in this book, give them a big THANK YOU for caring about the health and well-being of their customers. Be sure to order the **Healthy Dining** menu items and use the coupon in the back of the book (when available). If a restaurant is not featured in this book, most likely, we have invited them to be a part of **Healthy Dining** and they have declined. So, please tell the restaurant owner or manager that **Healthy Dining** is important to you and you hope they will join in this growing community effort. "THANK YOU" and "PLEASE JOIN" cards are provided in the back of this book (pages 207 and 209). Please tear them out of the book, make additional copies if you wish, and leave one with the owner or general manager of each of your favorite restaurants.

You Can Make a Difference!

It is essential that restaurants see an increasing demand for healthier cuisine – or they will not continue to provide healthy menu items. We invite you to help us – in every way you can. The following page identifies suggestions and strategies for helping **Healthy Dining** to expand in your community. Thank you for your support.

Working together, we can make California the healthiest place to live and eat!

10 Ways You Can Help Healthy Dining Grow in Your Community

Welcome to the **Healthy Dining** "family." This program has grown from San Diego to Orange County to Los Angeles. More than 2000 individuals have participated in this effort, including restaurant chefs and management, health professionals, and members of community organizations. You, the **Healthy Dining** reader and restaurant diner, are also an essential "ingredient."

Why? Because restaurants are responsive to their customers. They need to hear from you that healthy menu items and nutrition information are important to you.

Here's how you can help **Healthy Dining** grow in your community:

1. Dine at the restaurants listed in the book and tell the restaurant staff and owners that you appreciate and value their participation in **Healthy Dining**. Leave a "Thank You" card (page 207).

2. Request the **Healthy Dining** menus at participating restaurants and use the discount coupons at the back of the book (if available).

3. Tell friends, family and business associates about **Healthy Dining**.

4. Tell other restaurants about **Healthy Dining** and recommend that they participate. Leave a "Please Join" note (page 209).

5. Give **Healthy Dining** books as gifts for birthdays, holidays, incentives, client or staff appreciation, or use for fundraisers. Call (858) 541-2049 to order or to inquire about wholesale rates.

6. Use **Healthy Dining** restaurants for your catering and party needs.

7. Invite **Healthy Dining** authors to speak for your organization or conference (see page xv).

8. Visit our website (www.healthy-dining.com) to stay up-to-date on health and restaurant news and events.

9. Subscribe to our **free** e-newsletter, *Cuisine Connection* at www.healthy-dining.com. You will receive "secret recipes" from local chefs, cooking tips, information about **Healthy Dining** restaurants, and much more!

10. Please call or e-mail us with suggestions and feedback: (858) 541-2049 or books@healthy-dining.com.

Thanks! Together we can make San Diego a healthier place to live and dine.

About Healthy Dining

Healthy Dining's mission is to enhance the health of Americans by propelling a shift toward healthier restaurant cuisine. **Healthy Dining's** culinary nutrition experts guide and inspire chefs and restaurateurs to create and serve dishes that emphasize lean proteins, fruits and vegetables, and whole grains. We provide consumers with nutrition information and specific "how to order healthier" guidelines for meals at popular restaurants. The team has worked with hundreds of restaurants throughout Southern California and has analyzed over 10,000 menu items for nutrition content — no other company in the U.S. matches this expertise.

Healthy Dining is earning respect from all corners — health professionals, the media, the restaurant industry, and tens of thousands of consumers, many of whom write and call, expressing appreciation for the impact that **Healthy Dining** continues to make in Southern California. **Healthy Dining** has received grants from the California Department of Health Services and the Centers for Disease Control and Prevention (CDC), and an award from the California Dietetic Association.

Anita Jones-Mueller, M.P.H. – Director

Anita earned her Master's Degree in Public Health from San Diego State University. Her background includes extensive work in the health and nutrition fields, both with individuals and with community group education and support sessions. Anita is one of the founders of the **Healthy Dining** program and the lead author of the book series. She has directed the **Healthy Dining** project from its inception into a growing community program. Anita oversees the nutrition analysis, directs marketing and public relations, and speaks to health professionals and community groups.

Esther Hill, Ph.D. – Editor/Publisher

Esther Hill, a physiologist with a Ph.D. in Biomathematics, worked for over 15 years in medical research at the University of California at San Diego. Dr. Hill's motivation for being involved in this project comes largely from dealing with her son's unstable diabetes. Her family found traveling and restaurant dining difficult, and she understands why nutrition information is so important to those with dietary restrictions. Dr. Hill is one of the founders of the **Healthy Dining** program. Currently she edits and publishes the **Healthy Dining** books.

Erica Bohm, M.S. – San Diego Regional Director

Erica Bohm earned her Master's Degree in Community Health Sciences from New York City's Hunter College. Her experience includes nutrition education, cholesterol reduction, weight control and smoking cessation. During her 20+ years in the health field, Erica has worked for the American Red Cross, the American Health Foundation, and other health organizations, research projects and businesses. Her roles in **Healthy Dining** include seminars, program promotion, and networking with restaurants, health professionals and organizations, community groups, businesses and the media.

Nicole Quartuccio, R.D. – Nutrition & Communications Manager

Nicole Quartuccio earned her Bachelor of Science Degree in Foods and Nutrition from San Diego State University and is a Board Member of the San Diego Dietetic Association. Nicole has recently been nominated as "Recognized Young Dietitian of the Year." She coordinates the nutrition analysis for the books, which includes working with the restaurant chefs and managers. Nicole also provides nutrition education for restaurant staff and members of the community, assists with publishing and book distribution, and manages **Healthy Dining's** e-mail newsletter and website, www.healthy-dining.com.

Susan Goldstein – Orange County Regional Director

Susan Goldstein earned her Bachelor of Science Degree in Human Development from Cornell University. Her background and knowledge in nutrition, health promotion, and fundraising combine over 15 years' professional and volunteer experience. She is a Board Member of the Juvenile Diabetes Research Foundation, Orange County chapter. Susan works closely with the restaurants to develop the **Healthy Dining** books and expand participation in the community. She is involved in program promotion and projects with health professionals, local businesses, education and marketing, the media, and community events.

Karen Rapaport Busch – Publishing Coordinator

Karen Busch earned her Bachelor of Science Degree in Foods and Nutrition from San Diego State University and recently completed the Utah State University's Distance Dietetic Internship. Karen has 7-plus years working in the medical field and previously volunteered with the **Healthy Dining in San Diego** program. Currently she coordinates with the restaurants to analyze their recipes, publish their menu pages, home recipes, and coupons, and provides assistance with community events in the San Diego area.

Acknowledgments

Healthy Dining wishes to thank Amy Liss, R.D. and Tahara Chatham for assisting with the book preparation.

We also especially thank the participating restaurants and all health-conscious diners who support **Healthy Dining**. Thanks for your enthusiasm and best wishes for many years of healthy dining out!

Foreword by the American Cancer Society

1.800.ACS.2345
www.cancer.org

Hope.Progress.Answers.

For a majority of Americans who do not smoke, dietary choices and physical activity are the most important modifiable determinants of cancer risk. Evidence suggests that one third of all cancers deaths that occur in the United States each year can be attributed to poor diet and lack of physical activity.

The American Cancer Society publishes nutrition and physical activity guidelines to advise health care professionals and the general public about dietary and other lifestyle practices that can reduce cancer risk. Although no diet can guarantee full protection against any disease, these guidelines offer the best information currently available about how diet and physical activity can reduce the risk of cancer.

Studies have shown that populations whose diets are high in vegetables and fruits and low in animal fat, meat and/or calories have a reduced risk of some of the most common types of cancer. In addition to these individual actions, a recommendation for community action is also included in the guidelines. This recommendation underscores the importance of community measures to support healthy behaviors by increasing access to healthful food choices and opportunities to be physically active.

The Healthy Dining program educates people on how to make healthful choices and creates an environment that supports healthy food choices which is consistent with the American Cancer Society's Nutrition and Physical Activity Cancer Prevention Guidelines. Thank you to the restaurants participating in the program for providing healthy dining options.

Sincerely,

Georjean Stoodt, MD, MPH
President Elect & Chair
Mission Delivery Group
American Cancer Society

Diane J. Fink, MD
Chief Mission Delivery Officer
American Cancer Society
California Division, Inc.

1-800-ACS-2345 www.cancer.org

Preface by Donald Lyman, M.D.

Chief, Chronic Disease and Injury Control
California Department of Health Services

State of California—Health and Human Services Agency
Department of Health Services

ARNOLD SCHWARZENEGGER
Governor

Dear Fellow Californians,

We live in a great State! At the California Department of Health Services (CDHS), it is our mission to enhance the health of all Californians. In the past fifteen years, our State has realized a 66 percent decrease in the consumption of tobacco, translating into an impressive 10 percent decrease in cancer incidence, compared to a 1 percent decrease nationally. *That is a significant success for California.*

With this accomplishment, we are now transitioning the CDHS priorities and efforts to improving the nutritional status of Californians. An estimated 35,000 premature deaths and $24.6 billion in health care and related costs every year can be linked to poor diet and physical inactivity in our state. We are challenged to turn this situation around as we have with tobacco use.

With nutrition a priority, it is of utmost importance that Californians have access to healthy choices, whether at home, at work, or when eating out. I applaud the restaurants participating in *Healthy Dining*. These restaurants are leading the nation in providing healthier cuisine. Whenever I am in Southern California, I look forward to using this *Healthy Dining* book to guide me to restaurants that offer healthy menu choices. This book makes it easy to enjoy great-tasting meals at popular restaurants.

Congratulations and best wishes in your efforts to lead a healthier lifestyle!

Sincerely,

Donald O. Lyman, MD, Chief
Chronic Disease and Injury Control

Division of Chronic Disease and Injury Control, MS 7200, P.O. Box 997413,
Sacramento, CA 95899-7413
(916) 449-5700
Internet Address: www.dhs.ca.gov/cdic

PEOPLE ARE TALKING ABOUT HEALTHY DINING ...

"What you eat makes all the difference! Lots of fresh fruits and vegetables, whole grains and lean proteins will bring you health and vitality and add years to your life. Congratulations to the chefs and restaurants participating in the Healthy Dining Program. They truly have your health and tastebuds in mind."
- Marilu Henner, Nutrition Author and Television & Film Actress

"I always applaud any effort to bring nutritional information to the community. You've done an outstanding job."
- Jeanne Jones, cookbook author and internationally syndicated columnist

"It's so exciting that Healthy Dining is available! It helps people realize that they can enjoy eating out and being healthy. Having a good time while doing what's good for them is doubly reinforcing.! I love recommending it to my clients!"
- Ali Chambers, M.A., lifestyle educator, Kaiser Permanente

"Don't go out to eat without this book!"
- William Johansen, Healthy Dining customer

"Healthy Dining makes it possible for us to find restaurants serving a variety of styles, including our favorite ethnic foods, staying within the guidelines my diabetes requires. This is the best book on healthy dining I've read. Without it I'd never eat out!"
- Joan W. Derrick, Healthy Dining customer

"A road map gets you where you want to go when you travel. Healthy Dining does the same thing when you dine out and do not want to do yourself in."
- Annette Globitis, R.D., nutrition education and counseling

"I love this book! In the perpetual battle of the bulge, it arms me with the knowledge to finally win the war."
- Rieva Lesonsky, Senior Vice President, Entrepreneur Magazine

"Thank you for the Healthy Dining book. My husband is very conscious about his diet, and I haven't been able to pry the book out of his hands yet. All I have to do now is convince him that it's healthier to eat at these restaurants than it is for me to cook!"
- Kathleen C. Peleti, CPA and restaurant customer

RESTAURATEURS ARE TALKING
ABOUT HEALTHY DINING ...

"At a time when more and more people in our country are expressing a desire to build healthier lifestyles, yet don't want to compromise convenience, quality, and taste, Healthy Dining is most appropriate. Helping restaurateurs expand their healthy menu options without compromising creativity or eliminating food is a real solution that will benefit all... Partnerships are very important to the restaurant industry and we support you in your efforts. Thanks again for providing this great service to local restaurants."
- Sheila Cohn, R.D., Manager of Nutrition Policy, National Restaurant Association

"The California Restaurant Association fully supports the Healthy Dining program and encourages member-restaurants to do likewise. Healthy Dining is a wonderful opportunity for restaurateurs to gain credibility with the public by serving healthy food. "
- Jot Condie, President, CEO, California Restaurant Association

"We are proud and honored to be a part of Healthy Dining, which has been a terrific organization, as a conduit for Wahoo's. Healthy Dining enables us to get the word out to our guests, as well as educating the industry and many patrons about better-for-them dining choices. Thank you for filling such a huge void."
- Steve Karfaridis, Marketing, Wahoo's Fish Taco

"Anthony's Seafood Group is proud to be associated with Healthy Dining in San Diego County for the past 7 years. We've observed an increased interest in a healthy lifestyle by our restaurant guests, many who request our Healthy Dining menus. The team at Healthy Dining is dedicated, professional and hard working. We look forward to a long and profitable association with them."
- Beverly Mascari, co-owner, Anthony's Seafood Group

"Subway restaurants have been part of the Healthy Dining program since 1997. We highly value the association with your organization..."
- Patt Miller, Director of Marketing, Subway Development Corporation of San Diego

"Baja Fresh has been an enthusiastic participant in the Healthy Dining Program since 2001. We fully support your very positive approach to restaurant nutrition. You have assisted us in offering informed choices to our customers and understanding nutrition needs."
Gene Cameron, Vice President of Marketing (former), Fresh Enterprises

"This is something very near and dear to my heart. I think every restaurant should have a Healthy Dining section on their menu."
- Tom Feltenstein, Chairman & Founder, Neighborhood Marketing Institute

THANK YOU

The **Healthy Dining** team offers a sincere THANK YOU to so many people and organizations who have contributed to **Healthy Dining's** success:

Thank you to the restaurants –
for caring about your customers and participating in **Healthy Dining**.

Thank you to all "healthy diners" –
For purchasing the **Healthy Dining** books and using them to choose the restaurants they patronize; thank you for your appreciative letters and comments; thank you for telling others about **Healthy Dining**.

Thank you to all the organizations promoting **Healthy Dining** –
By promoting the books and/or hosting an Extravaganza, you have helped make Southern California the healthiest place in the nation to dine out!

Thank you to all the Southern California businesses, community and health organizations, and media outlets for enabling us to make the following honors and achievements possible:

♦ Inspiring over 250 chefs and restaurants to offer great-tasting **Healthy Dining** menu items – there is no other program of this magnitude throughout the U.S.!

♦ Being featured on over 300 television and radio news and talk shows and in close to 125 newspaper and magazine articles;

♦ Receiving the California Dietetic Association's Meritorious Service Award;

♦ Completing a research grant for the California Department of Health Services, Cancer Prevention Section to study approaches to improve restaurant nutrition;

♦ Obtaining a research grant from the Centers For Disease Control and Prevention, Division of Nutrition and Physical Activity, to expand **Healthy Dining** nationwide.

All of the above have strengthened **Healthy Dining's** mission: to encourage an ever-expanding choice of delicious and healthful menu items at popular restaurants and eateries.

Looking for a delicious event for your company, organization or conference? Call about a

HEALTHY DINING
EXTRAVAGANZA

The **Healthy Dining** Extravaganza is a delicious, enlightening, fun and educational event. The Extravaganzas are held throughout Southern California at businesses, hospitals, weight and fitness centers, and other community organizations. Let us coordinate an Extravaganza for your group!

The Extravaganza includes:

- **Seminar**: *"The Fat & Skinny Facts on Restaurant Dining"* provides guests with valuable strategies and practical advice for healthful restaurant dining. An informative quiz gives real life examples of how calories and fat add up in restaurant meals. After this seminar, attendees are very motivated to enjoy healthful cuisine when eating out.

- **Chef Demonstration**: A popular chef demonstrates a recipe with health _and_ taste buds in mind. The chef will share secrets for healthful preparation. People love to watch a chef in action!

- **Lunch or Dinner**: The **Healthy Dining Tasting** features generous samples of healthy menu items from several local restaurants participating in **Healthy Dining**. Your guests will rave about this unique opportunity to taste sensational and healthy cuisine from a variety of restaurants. There is more than enough food to please everyone.

- **Healthy Dining Book**: Each guest receives the **Healthy Dining** book to guide them to restaurants that offer great-tasting, healthy cuisine.

Call us to start planning your Extravaganza! 858-541-2049.

Free e-newsletter!

Subscribe to our **free** e-newsletter, *Cuisine Connection*. You will receive "secret recipes" from local chefs, cooking tips, information about **Healthy Dining** restaurants, contests and much more!

Sign up at www.healthy-dining.com/newsletter.htm.

Sample e-newsletter:

Part I

Healthy Dining Tips

Realistic Guidelines and Practical Information

Healthy Dining menus are available at participating
restaurants for customer convenience.

The **Healthy Dining** menus illustrated above are condensed versions of the menu pages in this book. We encourage all participating restaurants to pass out their **Healthy Dining** menus along with their regular menus. Some restaurants, however, don't automatically provide them - **you need to request these special Healthy Dining menus.** And please do! The more that restaurants hear customers asking for specific nutrition information and ordering "Special Requests," the more they will recognize how important healthy dining is to so many people.

If nutrition information is important to you, if you want to have the choice to "order healthy," please request **Healthy Dining** menus in the restaurants and let them know that you appreciate the healthy menu choices.

INTRODUCTION

How to Use This Book

This introduction summarizes how to interpret the nutrition information for the featured menu items. Part I provides more in-depth information to help you become better informed about health and restaurant dining. Part II features nutrition profiles for specific entrées at participating restaurants at over 400 locations in San Diego. Part III presents a wonderful selection of chefs' recipes, and Part IV includes a Health Resource Guide. Part V lists **Healthy Dining's** Advisory Board. Part VI contains a list of other **Healthy Dining** books, Questionnaire & Book Order Form, and "Thank You" and "Please Join" notes to give to restaurants. Part VII contains over $150 in restaurant discount coupons, and finally, Part VIII contains three restaurant indexes for quick reference.

The Check Mark System – An easy way to find entrées to fit your goals

The nutrition profiles of restaurant meals vary widely. For this book, we strive to feature dishes that are low in fat, cholesterol, calories and sodium and contain two or more servings of fruits and/or vegetables. Not all of the dishes included in the book, however, meet **all** of these criteria. The check mark system described below will help you easily and quickly identify which entrées best fit your individual dietary goals. Also, be sure to look for the ♥ and ♉ symbols, which identify items that contain primarily unsaturated fat and at least two servings of fruits and/or vegetables, respectively.

Nutrition guidelines are difficult to set because each individual has different nutritional needs. For example, caloric needs vary according to age, gender, activity level, body weight and health goals (e.g., reducing body fat, weight maintenance, etc.). Nevertheless, the following are general guidelines to make the menu information easy to interpret. These guidelines are based on recommendations by the U.S. Surgeon General's Office and the American Heart Association; more details are included in Chapters 3 through 6. The following is a quick summary of the guidelines and check mark system:

ENTRÉE GUIDELINES

Calories	✓✓	Excellent Choice = 0 to 450 calories/entrée
	✓	Good Choice = 451 to 750 calories/entrée
Fat	✓✓	Excellent Choice = 0 to 15 grams (g)/entrée
	✓	Good Choice = 16 to 25 grams (g)/entrée
Cholesterol	✓✓	Excellent Choice = 0 to 75 milligrams (mg)/entrée
	✓	Good Choice = 76 to 150 milligrams (mg)/entrée
Sodium	✓✓	Excellent Choice = 0 to 300 milligrams (mg)/entrée
	✓	Good Choice = 301 to 600 milligrams (mg)/entrée

Healthy Dining in San Diego 3

It's important to note...

The **Healthy Dining** guidelines represent fairly high standards for restaurant entrées and are realistic goals for most diners, as discussed in Chapters 3 through 6.

We sometimes include a menu item that is described as "Moderate" or "High" in one of the nutrient categories because it does not fit within our "Excellent Choice" or "Good Choice" guidelines. "High" indicates that the nutrient contains more than double the amount of a "Good Choice" (or for sodium, over 1,000 mg). For example, an item that is considered "High" in cholesterol would have to contain over 300 mg. of cholesterol, since a "Good Choice" can contain 76 to 150 mg. Finally, "Moderate" means the nutrient value falls somewhere between a "Good Choice" and "High."

The **Healthy Dining** guidelines are general guidelines developed for the general public. You, your physician and your dietitian are responsible for setting individual nutritional guidelines according to your particular health needs. **Please note also that the numerical values for the nutrition information are approximations only, based on recipes supplied by the restaurants.**

If you are health-conscious and looking for better ways to eat and enhance your overall health, this book will provide an easy way to choose entrées that don't have the hidden calories, fat, cholesterol and sodium you'd rather avoid.

- If you want to lose weight, select items listed as Excellent Choice (✓✓) or Good Choice (✓) in the calorie and fat categories. For more information, see Chapters 3 and 4.

- If you want to reduce your blood cholesterol level, choose from items that are listed as Excellent Choice (✓✓) or Good Choice (✓) for both cholesterol and fat (see Chapter 5).

- To reduce dietary sodium, select those menu items that are shown as Excellent Choice (✓✓) or Good Choice (✓) in sodium, and request no added salt (see Chapter 6).

If your physician or dietitian has given you daily limits in terms of sodium, cholesterol, etc., by all means note the numerical values as well as the check marks, and be sure they fit your restrictions. You may need to ask for additional modifications to your meal.

We've included brief entrée descriptions, but they are not complete ingredient lists. Therefore, if you have food allergies or sensitivities, be sure to emphasize this to the restaurant personnel so they will understand how important it is to prepare your meal according to your specifications.

Comments about serving sizes, dressings and sauces, and side dishes

The nutrition information published in this book is based on the **full serving** (unless stated otherwise). Restaurant portions are frequently large, so you may not want to eat the full serving. If you eat only ⅔ of the entrée, you're only consuming ⅔ of the calories, fat, cholesterol, sodium, etc.

In some cases, the nutrition analysis includes dressings or sauces, and in other cases, it does not. We generally recommend that you order sauces and dressings on the side and use them sparingly. Dressings and sauces usually contain 5 to 10 grams of fat (45 to 90 calories) per tablespoon. Depending on your goals, you may choose to completely avoid them, or order them on the side and limit the amount you use. You will likely be served more than one tablespoon, so don't assume you can pour it all on your meal. You can measure out the amount you want using your teaspoon, keeping in mind that 3 teaspoons (tsp.) are equivalent to one tablespoon (Tbs.) or ½ ounce (oz).

The check mark system and guidelines listed on the previous page apply to entrées only. The calorie, fat, cholesterol and sodium guidelines for side dishes, appetizers, and desserts are equal to ⅓ of the entrée guidelines. (Other items, such as breads, are not generally shown.)

GUIDELINES for SIDE DISHES, APPETIZERS & DESSERTS †

Calories	✓✓ Excellent Choice = 0 to 150 calories/serving
	✓ Good Choice = 151 to 250 calories/serving
Fat	✓✓ Excellent Choice = 0 to 5 grams (g)/serving
	✓ Good Choice = 6 to 8 grams (g)/serving
Cholesterol	✓✓ Excellent Choice = 0 to 25 milligrams (mg)/serving
	✓ Good Choice = 26 to 50 milligrams (mg)/serving
Sodium	✓✓ Excellent Choice = 0 to 100 milligrams (mg)/serving
	✓ Good Choice = 101 to 200 milligrams (mg)/serving

Footnotes and other symbols

† Side dish guidelines are ⅓ of entree guidelines
♥ Primarily unsaturated fat (see Chapter 4)
* If you request no added salt (see Chapter 6)
🍎 at least 2 fruit/vegetable servings (see Chapter 8)

At the end of each restaurant's descriptive paragraph, a **price range** symbol appears:

$	Entrées generally under $10
$$	Entrées generally $10 to $20
$$$	Entrées generally over $20

How are restaurants selected to be included in Healthy Dining?

Our goal is to include a wide variety of restaurants. We do not specifically look for restaurants that specialize in serving "health food," but for a selection of popular restaurants that have an interest in providing healthful options and nutrition information. If you want organic, natural foods and vegetarian dishes, we include restaurants that cater to these preferences as well. A good clue for identifying vegetarian dishes (at more conventional restaurants) is to look for items with no cholesterol (no animal products) or very low values, which may indicate small quantities of cheese or dairy products. You may, of course, double check with the restaurant personnel before ordering.

Restaurants participating in this book have a genuine interest in offering healthy choices. They pay a fee for the nutrition analysis, and they have signed an agreement with Accents On Health to prepare the selected entrées in accordance with the recipes they submitted or clearly notify customers otherwise. We highly respect the restaurants included in this book for their interest and commitment to serving healthy entrées. We purposely include many different types of cuisines with a wide range of prices and believe this will have the greatest impact in encouraging all restaurants to offer healthy, delicious choices.

How are entrées selected?

When a restaurant participates in the **Healthy Dining** Program, our staff of culinary nutrition experts consults with the chef to identify a selection of menu items that meet the **Healthy Dining** guidelines. Our first choice is to find items already on the menu, without making any modifications to the original recipe. This would be the easiest for you as well as for the restaurant. However, in some cases the recipes don't meet the **Healthy Dining** guidelines, so we work with the chef to develop a "Special Request" version that is lower in calories, fat, cholesterol and/or sodium than the original dish (see Chapter 2). The analyses listed in this book for the "Special Request" items correspond to the lower calorie, fat, etc., content that you will be served **if and only if you make the "Special Request."** Otherwise you will be served a meal with higher fat and calorie values.

You can make a difference!

The restaurants in this book devote time, money and effort to participate in **Healthy Dining**. In many cases, the restaurants have modified recipes to meet your needs. Now they need to hear that this nutrition information is important to you and that you appreciate their participation in this unique program.

We encourage restaurants to pass out **Healthy Dining** menus along with their regular menus. These menus are condensed versions of the book pages. Some restaurants, however, do not automatically provide them — **you must request the Healthy Dining menu**s. And please do! The more that restaurants hear customers asking for specific nutrition information and ordering "Special Requests," the more they will recognize how important **Healthy Dining** is to so many people.

So, if this information is important to you, if you want to have the choice to "order healthy," **please tell the Healthy Dining restaurants!** Please tell other restaurants that you'd like them to participate. This will enable us to include more restaurants and an even greater variety of healthy choices in the next edition of **Healthy Dining.**

> Please ask for the **Healthy Dining** menus at participating restaurants.

We welcome your ideas

This program is growing, and we welcome your ideas on how to enhance it. Please write or e-mail us with your comments. We update this publication periodically and will continue to add more restaurants, more healthy entrées, and more nutrition information.

CHAPTER 1

Health:
Every Day Makes a Difference

Every day makes a difference...

A large body of medical research shows that **lifestyle** greatly influences health status. It is well recognized that **daily** health habits — what we eat and drink, whether or not we smoke, how much exercise we get and how effectively we manage stress — contribute to **how well and how long** we live. If you don't smoke, what you eat is probably the most important predictor of your health. That is powerful! What we eat today directly affects how we feel today, tomorrow and years from now. Think about what you've eaten today. If you include plenty of fruits, vegetables, whole grains and lean proteins in your diet, you will be at your best each day. By improving your diet, you can enjoy peak performance, energy, vitality, optimal well-being and longevity.

We've come a long way

Yes, we have come a long way in the last 100 years. In the early 1900s, our country suffered from problems of **malnutrition and underconsumption.** Rickets, pellagra, scurvy, beriberi and goiter plagued our nation, primarily due to a lack of essential nutrients. Fortunately, these vicious diseases are now virtually non-existent in the United States due to advances in medicine, fortification of foods, and successful cures.

However, during the past few decades, we have reached the opposite extreme. In 1988, the U.S. Surgeon General's Report on Nutrition and Health outlined the substantial impact of dietary practices on health. The main conclusion of the 1988 report was:

"**Overconsumption** of certain dietary components is now a major concern for Americans. While many food factors are involved, chief among them is the disproportionate consumption of foods high in fats, often at the expense of foods high in complex carbohydrates and fiber that may be more conducive to health."
– 1988 Surgeon General's Report on Nutrition and Health

Time Magazine summarized America's food evolution with the following statement:

> "If you had a craving for cookies a century ago, you had to fire up the wood stove and make the dough from scratch. If you wanted butter, you had to churn it. If you wanted a steak, you had to butcher the cow. Now you jump into the car and head for the nearest convenience store (*or fast food restaurant!*) — or if that is too much effort, you pick up a phone or log on to the Internet and have the stuff delivered to your door."
>
> — *Time Magazine*, June 7, 2004 (italic phrase added)

Unfortunate facts

Poor nutrition contributes substantially to four of the ten leading causes of death in the US: heart disease, cancer, stroke and diabetes. These nutrition-related diseases cost an estimated **$200 billion** each year. Approximately one-third of all cancer cases are due to diet-related risk factors, including an inadequate intake of fruits and vegetables and high calorie and fat intake.

Research by the Produce For Better Health Foundation shows that by age 45, almost half of all adults suffer from a medical condition in which nutrition is the focal point. Only 6% of all individuals are considered to have "good" diets as defined by the U.S. Department of Agriculture's (USDA) Healthy Eating Index.

An alarming prediction

> "Today's kids may be the first generation in history whose life expectancy is projected to be less than that of their parents."
>
> — David Katz, MD, Yale Prevention Research Center

That is sad! The lifestyle that Americans have created is reducing the lifespan for our children. In fact, some researchers have reported that today's children may have heart disease in their 20s — **if lifestyle habits are not immediately improved**.

A big problem

> "Having a culture bombarded with rushed lifestyles, fast foods, and physical inactivity has caught up with us — so we find ourselves grappling with the most serious health crisis since tobacco."
>
> — Carmen Nevarez, MD, MPH, Public Health Institute

Nutrition guidelines for Americans

It is of utmost importance that good nutrition and physical activity become priorities for Americans. Clearly, it is essential that Americans reduce intake of calories, fat, saturated fat, and refined carbohydrates because of the relationship between excess consumption of these nutrients and the development of many chronic diseases. The following guidelines are based on recommendations by leading health organizations, including the USDA, the U.S. Surgeon General's Office, the American Heart Association, the American Cancer Society, and the 5 A Day For Better Health Program. These guidelines offer consistent, simple and reliable advice for improving health:

1. Achieve and maintain a desirable body weight. To do so, choose a **balanced diet** in which energy (calorie) intake is consistent with energy expenditure. To reduce caloric intake, limit consumption of foods relatively high in calories, fat, and sugar, and minimize alcohol consumption. Increase energy expenditure through regular **exercise**.

2. **Reduce overall consumption of fat** (especially saturated fat and trans fat) **and cholesterol**. Choose foods low in fat such as vegetables, fruits, whole grain foods, fish, skinless poultry, lean meats and low/non-fat dairy products. Use food preparation methods that add little or no fat. Avoid or limit whole milk products, fatty meats, tropical oils, and partially hydrogenated vegetable oils (usually found in processed and packaged foods and commercial baked goods).

3. Eat a wide **variety of fruits and vegetables**. Choose at least 4½ cups per day (more for men). Include an assortment of colors, including **blue/purple** (blueberries, eggplant, plums, grapes, etc.), **green** (asparagus, broccoli, spinach, grapes, etc.), **white/tan/brown** (cauliflower, mushrooms, potatoes, onions, etc.), **yellow/orange** (peaches, oranges, bell peppers, lemons, etc.), and **red** (tomatoes, cherries, strawberries, watermelon, etc.). Fruits and vegetables contain important nutrients, dietary fiber, phytochemicals and antioxidants. Phytochemicals and antioxidants are powerful disease-fighting compounds found naturally in fruits and vegetables. They have been shown to protect against cancer, cardiovascular disease, diabetes and other medical conditions.

4. Eat a wide variety of **complex carbohydrates**. Include **whole grain** breads, cereals and pastas, brown rice, legumes, lentils, and beans. These complex carbohydrates provide fiber and important vitamins and minerals. Avoid foods that are low in nutritional value, such as candy, cookies, cakes, pies, chips, sodas, etc., as well as refined white rice, pasta and bread.

5. **Reduce intake of sodium** by choosing foods relatively low in sodium and limiting the amount of salt used in food preparation and at the table.

6. **Drink water**. Avoid or limit all colas, juices sweetened with high fructose corn syrup, and caffeinated beverages. Limit consumption of alcoholic beverages.

For more information, visit www.mypyramid.gov

YOU can make a difference!

The solution to our devastating (and rapidly growing!) nutrition-related health crisis depends on **each one of us taking a personal role in adopting and promoting good nutrition**. Start with yourself – be a role model. Make sure **you** are eating healthy as often as possible. After reviewing the nutrition guidelines listed above, answer the following questions:

♦ What are your strengths? What healthy foods do you regularly include in your diet?
♦ What foods do you need to eat more of?
♦ What foods do you need to limit or avoid?

You can do it!

Make a list of the healthy foods you want to eat more of and take that list to the grocery store with you. Make sure your home is well-stocked with lots of powerful, nutrient-filled foods. Choose foods that vitalize and energize your body, foods high in nutrients and disease-fighting compounds. Avoid the "junk" that produces fatigue, excess body fat and disease. Your body will love you for it!

As you continue to eat healthy, you will gain enhanced energy and vitality. You'll look and feel great. You'll be a role model for others and be a positive force in helping your spouse, children, grandchildren, co-workers, and others to eat healthier. So, plan ahead, be prepared and eat healthy as often as possible.

Now, what about eating away from home?

What's healthy and what's not when eating in restaurants? That's what **Healthy Dining** is all about. Never before has so much nutrition information been available for restaurant menu items — all in one easy-to-use resource. Each restaurant has its own unique recipes, prepared in its own special way. So nutrition information must be compiled restaurant-by-restaurant, recipe-by-recipe, by a qualified nutrition professional. There are books and other materials that give general information for dining out. They list common entrées to avoid and those that are probably best to order. However, as restaurants become more specialized and creative, "common" entrées are not so common, and general guidelines are not always accurate or useful.

As you read on about **Healthy Dining's** research, you will discover that the menu description does not provide an accurate indication of the healthfulness of a restaurant meal. The description may portray a healthy item, but many times there are additional ingredients that are not listed. In addition, the method of preparation may not be specified and the **amount of added oil and butter** is not disclosed. Without complete nutrition information, you don't know what you're getting, and over the long run, that can pose health risks. **Healthy Dining** makes the process of ordering healthy at restaurants easy, fun, delicious and full of flavor!

Goals of Healthy Dining in San Diego:

1. To guide you to restaurants that care about your health.

2. To give you all the information you need to order delicious restaurant meals that honor your health.

3. To provide you with easy-to-read nutrition profiles for featured entrées.

4. To give you useful, practical guidelines and advice for healthier restaurant dining.

5. To encourage restaurants to serve a wide variety of great-tasting, healthy choices.

Dining Out Challenges

How many times did you eat out last week? Four...five...maybe more? If you're like many Americans, you're eating out a lot these days. But that doesn't mean you can't enjoy a meal that's healthy and delicious, whether it's a casual lunch on the go or a special occasion.

Health-conscious diners face unknown challenges. **Restaurant meals often have 1,000 - 2,000 calories and 50 - 100 grams of fat.** The sodium and cholesterol content of many restaurant meals is also higher than you'd think. Portion sizes tend to be large. And butter, oil, cream, cheese, and salt are frequently added to achieve the taste and texture that many Americans expect. Diners often add "extras" such as sour cream, butter, and cheese, which push up the calorie, fat, and sodium counts even more. One example:

Chicken Breast
Topped with a Creamy Parmesan Sauce
Served with Dinner Salad, Baked Potato and Sautéed Vegetables

	Calories	Fat (g)	Cholest. (mg)	Sodium (mg)
Dinner Salad	30	0	0	55
Blue Cheese Dressing (2 Tbs.)	155	16	20	335
Chicken Breast (8 oz. fried)	440	13	205	185
Creamy Parmesan Sauce (5 Tbs.)	470	31	60	1160
Baked Potato	220	0	0	15
Butter (1 Tbs.)	100	13	30	115
Sour Cream (2 Tbs.)	60	6	10	15
Sautéed Vegetables	115	11	0	205
Meal Total	1590	90	325	2085

This example doesn't include drinks, an appetizer, bread or dessert, and it still contains:

- **close to the maximum** recommended calories and sodium for a **whole day** for most people

- **well over the maximum** recommended fat and cholesterol for a **whole day**

If dining out were only for special occasions, such large, rich meals could be wonderful treats; after all, there's nothing wrong with an occasional splurge. But busy schedules, travel, two-career families, socializing, celebration, relaxation, and convenience have made dining out a way of life today. So many people are looking for healthier choices when eating out.

Other fat-filled favorites:

	Calories	Fat (g)	Cholest. (mg)	Sodium (mg)
Salad bar - with potato & tuna salad, dressing, and muffins with butter	1715	89	310	2955
Ultimate cheeseburger with fries & shake	1625	96	165	1710
Lasagna with garlic bread & salad	1540	77	195	2805
Beef & cheese enchiladas, rice & refried beans	1510	88	210	3515
Italian manicotti with garlic bread	1395	79	410	2330
Pizza - sausage & mushroom	1290	48	85	1655
Chicken sandwich with onion rings & shake	1280	68	80	2290
Stir-fry chicken with rice & egg rolls	1215	62	100	2905
Seafood platter - fried - with tarter sauce	1195	70	95	1780
Fried chicken - with potato salad & cole slaw	1125	71	240	2550
Chicken fried steak with fries	1120	77	205	1895
Salmon - smothered in a cream sauce	1025	76	285	1015
Chimichanga with sour cream & cheese	920	68	205	2125
Omelet with hashbrowns	850	53	890	850

Does dining out have to be so destructive to our health?

Some say, "Order grilled fish, salads or vegetarian dishes. By avoiding red meat, fried foods and creamy sauces, you can dine out and eat healthy."

Be careful! We've analyzed hundreds of apparently "healthy" entrées and found that many were diet disasters. The menu descriptions portrayed healthy items, but when we looked into the preparation methods, we found the items contained excessive amounts of ingredients that should be consumed sparingly or avoided altogether.

Surprising nutrition information about seemingly "healthy" meals:

Grilled Swordfish - *Marinated in herbs and olive oil.*

885	Calories
71	Fat (g)
115	Cholesterol (mg)
845	Sodium (mg)

Nearly a full day's recommended fat intake. Too much olive oil used in the preparation!

Vegetarian Pasta Primavera - *Fresh vegetables and garlic sautéed in a vegetable broth. Served over fettucini noodles and tossed with Parmesan cheese.*

815	Calories
45	Fat (g)
140	Cholesterol (mg)
890	Sodium (mg)

The menu description doesn't mention that the pasta was heavily tossed with oil, and the vegetables were sautéed in both broth *and butter*. This brings the fat total to 75% of a FULL day's recommended fat intake.

The "Healthy" Sandwich - *Avocado, tomato & cheese on whole wheat bread.*

745	Calories
50	Fat (g)
65	Cholesterol (mg)
960	Sodium (mg)

May be healthy ingredients, but too much avocado, cheese, and mayonnaise add up to too much fat and sodium for a healthy meal.

Cobb Salad - *Crispy greens topped with chicken, avocado, bacon, tomato, hard-boiled egg and blue cheese crumbles. Served with a generous portion of your favorite dressing.*

1295	Calories
102	Fat (g)
645	Cholesterol (mg)
2555	Sodium (mg)

Salads can be good sources of vegetables, but with several high fat ingredients, this one is much too high in fat, cholesterol, sodium and calories.

Shrimp Stir-fry - *Shrimp and assorted vegetables with chow mein noodles.*

865	Calories
64	Fat (g)
390	Cholesterol (mg)
670	Sodium (mg)

Too much fat, calories, cholesterol and sodium. 1 oz. oil to sauté (27 g fat), butter/cream sauce (25 g fat), and the chow mein noodles (9 g fat) quickly add up.

Tostada - *Mexican beans, guacamole, lettuce, tomato and cheese.*

1415	Calories
77	Fat (g)
290	Cholesterol (mg)
2010	Sodium (mg)

The cheese alone contributes 520 calories, 43 grams of fat, 135 mg cholesterol and 800 mg sodium.

Healthy Dining has found other items labeled "Light" or "Light-Fare" that included potato skins (deep fried), vegetables with cheese sauce, a hamburger patty with cottage cheese (too much saturated fat), cheese quesadillas (saturated fat in the cheese) and deep fried fish tacos.

Even many entrées with a ♥ next to them were too high in fat. Here are a few examples:

??? Heart Healthy Entrées ???

♥ Eggplant Salad	34 grams fat - 86% of calories from fat
♥ Pasta with Tomatoes & Garlic	42 grams fat - 50% of calories from fat
♥ Grilled Halibut	64 grams fat - 75% of calories from fat

How can items be designated as "healthy" or "light" when, in fact, they aren't? Restaurants might designate meals as healthy simply because they are vegetarian or fish or contain no butter. The heart symbol used on restaurant menus has no standardized meaning, and often no explanation is offered about the meaning of the heart designation.

Uncertainties and unknowns faced by restaurant diners

Consumers usually have no way of knowing the nutrition content of restaurant meals. Restaurant meals are not required to have "nutrition facts labels" like those that appear on packaged foods in markets.

Ingredients, food preparation techniques and portion size – for identically named and described dishes – vary widely from restaurant to restaurant. For example, a stir-fry is generally considered a healthy choice, but in many cases, the preparation includes considerable amounts of fat.

Since each restaurant has its own unique recipes, prepared in its own special way, nutrition information must be compiled restaurant-by-restaurant, recipe-by-recipe, ideally by a qualified nutrition professional.

As demonstrated in the previous examples, however, many dishes described as "healthy" actually are not. A restaurant may designate a meal as healthy simply because it is vegetarian or contains no butter, but in most cases, dishes with health claims have never been analyzed for nutrition content. The hearts used on most restaurant menus have no standardized meaning, and often there is no explanation of the meaning that the restaurant is attributing to their heart designation. In this **Healthy Dining** book, we use the heart symbol to identify meals that contain primarily unsaturated fat (see Chapter 4), and this book clearly identifies its meaning (page 41).

Restaurant regulations

In an attempt to protect consumers from vague, incorrect, or misleading information, the Food and Drug Administration (FDA) implemented regulations for restaurants that make health and nutrition claims about their food. The regulations require that dishes with descriptions such as "low fat" or "low calorie" meet specified criteria and that restaurants provide nutrition information to substantiate any health claims made.

Unfortunately, however, the large majority of restaurants don't provide healthful menu items with corresponding nutrition information. In such cases, diners are at a loss for determining the nutritional content of restaurant meals.

The menu items featured in this book represent meals created with an eye on nutrition **and** taste, substantiated by credible nutrition data. These dishes are great for your health **and** your tastebuds.

Some scrumptious and healthy examples: (see page 43 for key to symbols)

RUTH'S POT ROAST
from Susan's Healthy Gourmet (Home delivery or pick-up)
A family recipe served with garlic mashed potatoes, gravy, green beans and squash.
✓✓ CALORIES: Excellent Choice (380) ✓✓ CHOLESTEROL: Excellent Choice (70 mg)
✓✓ FAT: Excellent Choice (7 g) ✓ SODIUM: Good Choice (440 mg)

ANTHONY'S SEAFOOD KABOB
at Anthony's Fish Grotto (San Diego Bay, Chula Vista & La Mesa)
Shrimp, scallop & swordfish kabob, basted with teriyaki sauce & served over citrus rice.
✓✓ CALORIES: Excellent Choice (380) ✓ CHOLESTEROL: Good Choice (145 mg)
✓✓ FAT: Excellent Choice (6 g)♥ ✓ SODIUM: Good Choice (590 mg)*

BROCCOLI–EGGPLANT–MUSHROOM PIZZA – 9-INCH (½ PIZZA) ☼

at Leucadia Pizzeria (Encinitas, La Jolla/UTC, Rancho Santa Fe, Carmel Mountain Ranch)

Grilled eggplant, red onions, broccoli, mushrooms, sun-dried tomatoes, fresh basil, mozzarella cheese, and tomato sauce. Analysis is for ½ of a 9-inch pizza.

✓ CALORIES: Good Choice (580)　　✓✓ CHOLESTEROL: Excellent Choice (20 mg)

✓✓ FAT: Excellent Choice (15 g)　　✓ SODIUM: Good Choice (360 mg)*

CHARBROILED FISH TACO

at Wahoo's Fish Taco (La Jolla, Encinitas, Point Loma & Mission Valley)

✓✓ CALORIES: Excellent Choice (235)　　✓✓ CHOLESTEROL: Excellent Choice (55 mg)

✓✓ FAT: Excellent Choice (4 g)　　✓ SODIUM: Good Choice (325 mg)*

HEALTH SALAD (½ POUND) ☼

at Jimbo's...Naturally! (Del Mar, Carlsbad, Escondido)

Medley of fresh vegetables tossed in a dill vinaigrette. A great summer salad!

✓✓ CALORIES: Excellent Choice (205)　　✓✓ CHOLESTEROL: Excellent Choice (0 mg)

✓ FAT: Good Choice (18 g)♥　　✓✓ SODIUM: Excellent Choice (135 mg)*

THREE INGREDIENT TASTE ☼

at Chin's Szechwan Cuisine (10 locations in San Diego County)

A combination of tender chicken, beef, and shrimp stir-fried with broccoli and Chinese peas in a Chef's special brown sauce.

✓✓ CALORIES: Excellent Choice (275)　　✓ CHOLESTEROL: Good Choice (110 mg)

✓✓ FAT: Excellent Choice (13 g)　　✓ SODIUM: Good Choice (505 mg)*

FRESH HAWAIIAN AHI WITH PAPAYA CILANTRO SALSA

at Café Pacifica (Old Town)

Simply grilled and served with fresh seasonal vegetables.

✓✓ CALORIES: Excellent Choice (395)　　✓ CHOLESTEROL: Good Choice (100 mg)

✓✓ FAT: Excellent Choice (15 g)♥　　✓✓ SODIUM: Excellent Choice (105 mg)*

The menu items here and in the following chapters are just a taste of the wonderful entrées served at the restaurants participating in **Healthy Dining in San Diego**. We invite you to visit the restaurants featured in this book. You'll discover a whole new world of menu items that are marvelously delicious and good for you!

"Special Requests"

In some cases, after analyzing the restaurant recipes, we found dishes that contained too many calories and/or too much fat, cholesterol or sodium. So we recommended that the chef modify the dishes to meet the **Healthy Dining** guidelines. We note these dishes as "Special Requests," or in some cases "**Healthy Dining** versions." These "Special Requests" may be prepared with less oil or butter, salad dressing or sauce served on the side, less cheese, etc. When you order, **you must ask for the "Special Request" or "Healthy Dining Preparation"** for your meal to correspond to the published nutrition information. See the examples below to find out how many calories and grams of fat you save by ordering some of these special versions.

Examples of "Special Requests:"

RISOTTO PREGO – SPECIAL REQUEST
at Prego (Mission Valley)
Arborio rice, grilled chicken, asparagus, and saffron. Parmigiano not included in analysis.
<u>*Request no butter and less oil*</u> *(½ Tbs. oil).*
This request saves 180 calories and 20 grams of fat.

MAHI TACOS – SPECIAL REQUEST 🍎
at Fred's Mexican Café (Old Town, Gaslamp and Pacific Beach)
A house specialty…marinated mahi filets with cabbage and two grilled flour tortillas, tomatillo sauce and pico de gallo, served with our classic Mexican rice and wholesome black beans.
<u>*Request no jack or cheddar cheese, less margarine*</u> *(½ Tbs.)* <u>*and tomatillo sauce on the side.*</u>
Tomatillo sauce not included in analysis; 70 cal, 8 g fat per Tbs..
This request saves 495 calories and 47 grams of fat if you use only 1 Tbs. of the tomatillo sauce.

GRILLED VEGGIE SANDWICH – SPECIAL REQUEST 🍎
at Crest Café (Hillcrest)
Fresh and crunchy cucumbers, mushrooms, tomatoes and avocado layered on our grilled onion roll and topped with melted cheese. Served with fresh fruit. <u>*Request no butter.*</u>
This request saves 165 calories and 19 grams of fat.

> Remember: For items marked as **"Special Request"** – you must order that dish as recommended in order to receive the published nutritional values.

CHAPTER 3

Do Your Calories Have a Purpose?

Calories sometimes have a bad reputation in our society. We're counting calories and cutting calories, often overlooking the fact that calories keep us alive and produce the energy needed to function properly. It's important to consider both the quantity and quality of the calories we consume.

What are you getting from your calories?

Calories are derived from the carbohydrates, protein and fat in foods. Recommendations vary according to individual needs, but generally 45% to 65% of total daily calories should come from carbohydrates, 10% to 35% from protein, and 20% to 30% from fat. The discussion later in this chapter shows how to calculate these percentages. In brief:

Protein helps to build and restore many parts of the body, including muscles, skin, hair, red blood cells, enzymes, hormones, and disease-fighting antibodies. You probably don't need as much protein as you think. Many nutrition experts suggest limiting the size of your protein (meat, fish, etc.) serving in a meal to 3-4 oz., i.e., the size of a deck of cards.

Fat of certain types is essential for proper nerve and hormone function, as well as for building membranes such as skin, blood vessels, and organs. For an "average" person consuming 2000 calories per day, the recommendation of less than 30% of calories from fat corresponds to under 66 grams of fat per day, or about 22 grams of fat per meal (< 2 Tablespoons of fat). This means only small amounts of salad dressings, butter for flavoring vegetables, oil for sautéing, toppings such as sour cream or cheese, and desserts.

Carbohydrates are the body's main energy source. Most carbohydrates should come from high quality sources such as vegetables, fruits, whole grains, and legumes. These foods contain lots of nutrients like vitamins, minerals, phytochemicals and fiber.

It's important to make your calories work for you. They should give you as much nutrition and energy as possible. Avoid foods that have primarily "empty" calories. Sugar (including corn syrup and most other sweeteners), refined grain products, such as white flour, and many fats contribute calories without giving you much nutrition. Most "enriched" flours and grains used in cereals and baking restore only part of the nutrients you need. It's much better to eat whole grains and other unprocessed or minimally-processed foods to get the nutrients you need.

How many calories do you need?

Calorie needs vary among individuals. Many meal plans assume 2000 calories per day, but if you are an active male who gets lots of exercise, you probably need more than that. If you are a sedentary female, especially if you are trying to lose weight, you probably need fewer than 2000 calories per day.

Many people eat too many calories and need to cut back. It is the number of calories (of any kind) you eat compared to the energy used in daily activities and exercise that determines whether you gain, lose, or maintain your weight. If you don't know what your calorie intake should be, ask your doctor or dietitian, or visit www.wvda.org/calcs or www.mypyramid.gov for more information.

You probably do not need to measure and count everything you eat once you know how large your portions sizes should be and which foods to emphasize and which to restrict. Including a wide variety of the healthier foods will help you avoid filling up on the not-so-healthy ones. Of course, it's best to avoid (or use sparingly) foods that have a high percentage of fat (e.g., butter, margarine, oils, sour cream, cheese, cream cheese, etc.).

In terms of restaurant dining, be aware that portion sizes tend to be very large. When you dine out, be careful to choose items that fit the **Healthy Dining Guidelines,** or plan to share the meal or take some home with you.

In summary, calories do count! Either too many or too few can cause problems, and so can the wrong kind of calories. A balanced diet is important for keeping up your energy and overall health.

How to calculate % calories from fat, protein and carbohydrates:

Many experts recommend limiting fat to less than 30% of total calories, and the example below shows how to make those calculations, and includes additional information about how to balance your meals.

Example:

Grilled Salmon
Seven ounces of grilled, herb-seasoned salmon, served with veggies and baked potato.

Analysis for salmon alone:

Total Calories:	275
Protein:	38 grams
Carbohydrates:	0 grams
Fat:	12 grams

To calculate the percentage of calories from fat:

1. Each gram of fat has nine calories. So multiply grams of fat by 9 calories per gram:
   12 grams x 9 cals/gram = 108 calories from fat

2. Divide the calories from fat by total calories and multiply by 100 to get a percentage:
   108 calories/275 calories x 100 = 39%

39% of calories from this dish come from fat, which is above the recommended maximum of 20% to 30% of calories from fat. However, the recommendation of 20% to 30% of calories from fat is the suggested average for the whole day. Some foods will add little, if any, fat to your diet, while other foods may supply a big chunk of the fat for the day.

By themselves, many meats and fish contain 30% to 50% fat. Even soybeans contain about 40% of their calories from fat. Entrées that are made up largely of carbohydrates (such as pasta or rice dishes) generally have a lower percentage of calories from fat.

Generally, high-protein entrées are not eaten by themselves. If you choose quality carbohydrate side dishes such as vegetables, grains, breads, and fruits, the percentage of fat for the overall meal is significantly less. As an example of how the side dishes change the overall percentage fat, let's include the side dishes that are served with this entrée:

Analysis for salmon meal:	Calories	Fat (g)
Salmon	275	12
Vegetables	32	1
Plain Baked Potato	375	1
Butter (1 tsp)	33	4
Totals	715	18

To calculate percentage of calories from fat:

1. Multiply grams of fat by 9 calories per gram:
   18 grams of fat x 9 cals/gram = 162 calories from fat

2. Divide by total calories and multiply by 100 to get a percentage:
   162 calories from fat/715 total calories x 100 = 23%

Only 23% of total calories from this meal come from fat, which is within the recommended guidelines and significantly less than the percentage of fat calculated for the salmon alone.

This example demonstrates how a meal can be a good choice even when the protein-rich part of the meal by itself (the salmon, in this case) exceeds 30% of calories from fat. Also, remember that a meal like this one will probably be the largest of your day, and your choices for the remainder of the day can also bring the overall percentage of fat down. Finally, note that salmon contains essential omega-3 oils and is primarily unsaturated fat (see Chapter 4 for more about types of fat).

How the check mark guidelines for calories are set

The **Healthy Dining** guidelines assume an average intake of 2,000 calories per day. Next, we assume that the restaurant meal accounts for the largest of the day's meals, up to 40% of the daily calorie allotment, or 800 calories. So 750 calories for the main entrée would fit into the calorie budget. Thus, an upper limit of 750 calories is considered as a "Good Choice" for calories. The "Excellent Choice" value of 450 calories represents a proportionately lower level, corresponding to about 1200 to 1500 calories per day:

✓✓ Excellent Choice = 0 to 450 calories/entrée
✓ Good Choice = 451 to 750 calories/entrée

> Glance through the restaurant pages and use the quick, easy check mark system to see the wide variety of entrées which contain high-quality, nutritious calories and are "Excellent Choice" (✓✓) or "Good Choice" (✓) for calories.

Some delicious examples of "Excellent" and "Good" calorie choices:

DAILY'S SPICY GRILLED CHICKEN PIZZA ♨
at Daily's (La Jolla/UTC)
Grilled chicken & red onions, peppers, spicy tomato marinade with skim milk mozzarella cheese on our whole wheat pizza crust.
✓ CALORIES: Good Choice (465)

POLLO BOWL
at El Pollo Loco (many locations)
Flame-broiled boneless skinless breast with pinto beans, Spanish rice, tomato, onion & cilantro.
✓ CALORIES: Good Choice (545)

FRESH MAHI MAHI ENSALADA ♨
at Baja Fresh (many locations in San Diego County)
Charbroiled Mahi Mahi, romaine lettuce, Pico de Gallo salsa, avocado, tomato & shaved cheese.
✓✓ CALORIES: Excellent Choice (360)

VEGGIE WRAP ♨
at Brockton Villa (La Jolla)
Crunchy veggies with hummus wrapped in a colorful tortilla. Analysis for Veggie Wrap only.
✓ CALORIES: Good Choice (580)

GUILTLESS GRILL® SALMON
at Chili's Grill & Bar (12 locations in San Diego area)
*8 oz. salmon fillet lightly seasoned & seared to perfection!
Served with steamed fresh veggies & black beans.*
✓ CALORIES: Good Choice (480)

CHAPTER 4

Fat — the Good, the Bad, & the Stuff Your Mother Didn't Warn You About

Fat is necessary in a healthy diet and comes in several forms. Together with protein, fats help to build muscles, nerves, blood vessels and other important structures in the body. However, not all fats are created equal, as discussed below.

The good

Unsaturated fats (monounsaturated and polyunsaturated) are considered "good" fats because they help lower blood cholesterol levels and reduce the risk of heart disease. These fats should be included in the diet in small to moderate amounts. Unsaturated fats are generally liquid at room temperature and mostly come from plant oils. Common examples of unsaturated fats are olive, peanut, corn, sunflower, safflower, and soybean oils. Some plant foods, such as olives and avocados, although solid, contain primarily unsaturated fat.

Even more than being "good," there are some fats that are "essential," such as Omega-3 and Omega-6 fatty acids. This means the body cannot make or convert them from any other components. You must get them directly from foods you eat. Omega-3 fatty acids are found primarily in fish (especially high in salmon, albacore tuna, mackerel, herring, and rainbow trout). Omega-6 fatty acids are found primarily in nuts and seeds (especially high in flax seed and relatively high in walnuts and some other nuts). These foods provide essential fat and are good in small to moderate quantities.

Even "good" fats should not be consumed in large amounts because they are a concentrated source of calories and can easily lead to weight gain. A diet low in total fat, with the majority of that fat coming from unsaturated sources, tends to lower blood cholesterol levels and heart disease risk.

The bad

Saturated fats are often referred to as "bad" fats because they raise cholesterol and triglyceride levels in the body, thereby increasing the risk of cardiovascular disease. Saturated fats are generally solid at room temperature and mostly come from animal products. Some examples of saturated fat are butter, lard, shortening, cheese, cream (including ice cream) and fats from meat. Palm oil and coconut oil, although from plant sources, are also high in saturated fat.

The Stuff Your Mother Didn't Warn You About

Trans-fats have taken the media spotlight as they are considered **particularly** "bad" fats. These fats mostly come from vegetable oils that have been turned into solids though a chemical process known as "hydrogenation." Food manufacturers have perfected the hydrogenation process by adding hydrogen molecules to the liquid vegetable oils. The new unnatural form of the fat has a more rigid structure than natural fats do, which allows food products to have a longer shelf life.

These hydrogenated products are found in most margarines, many other spreads, and in many packaged and processed foods (cookies, pastries, chips, boxed meals, pudding, etc.). In addition, trans-fats are found in foods fried in partially hydrogenated oils, such as French fries, fried chicken and fried fish.

Many scientists believe that these trans-fats are harmful because they cannot be used properly by the body, and they block the important functions of the "good" types of fat.

Fortunately, legislation requires manufacturers to list the amount of trans-fat in their products as of 2006. Regardless, it is wise to opt for unprocessed foods and avoid (or limit) foods that contain "hydrogenated" or "partially hydrogenated" oils.

How much fat is too much?

Leading health organizations have set guidelines for fat intake at no more than 20% – 30% of total calories. For a daily intake of 2,000 calories, no more than 400 – 600 calories per day should come from fat. With each gram of fat contributing 9 calories, approximately 66 grams of fat is the upper limit of fat recommended per day. If you're not careful, it's easy to exceed that with just one meal!

The recommended limit of 66 grams of fat per day corresponds to an average of 22 grams of fat per meal. To put this into perspective, one tablespoon of oil contains 13 grams of fat, so the total fat should be **under 2 tablespoons** per meal.

In addition to total fat intake, it is recommended that no more than 10% of the total calories consumed in a day should come from **saturated fat** sources. Assuming 2,000 calories per day, fewer than 200 calories (22 grams) should be from saturated fat. This averages about 7 grams of fat or about ½ **tablespoon of saturated fat** per meal.

How the check mark guidelines for fat are set

What is a reasonable limit per meal or per entrée? Keeping in mind the average 22 grams of fat per meal discussed above, assuming the restaurant meal is the largest meal of the day, and assuming you're careful about side dishes, we set entrée guidelines of:

✓✓ Excellent Choice = 0 to 15 grams of fat/entrée
 ✓ Good Choice = 16 to 25 grams of fat/entrée

If you're very active and take in more calories, then a higher limit would be appropriate. If you're on a **weight loss diet** or **very low fat diet,** then the "Excellent Choice" guideline of up to 15 grams of fat per entrée is probably more appropriate.

Notice that these recommended guidelines represent an average intake for an average meal. Don't be overly concerned about the cutoff between our designations of "Good Choice" and "Excellent Choice." Unless you're on a very restricted diet, the difference between an entrée with 16 grams of fat (which would receive one check mark) and one with 15 grams of fat (two check marks) is probably not worth worrying about. You can compensate for an occasional meal with somewhat more fat (but don't overdo it!) by reducing fat intake during other meals.

A summary of fat

When assessing the fat content of food, it is important to look at:
1. The **number of grams** of fat
2. The **percentage of calories** from fat
3. The **type** of fat - minimize or avoid saturated and hydrogenated fats

> On the restaurant menu pages of this book, the heart symbol (♥) next to the grams of fat indicates that the fat is primarily unsaturated (the "good" type). Look for it!

Some delicious examples of "Excellent" and "Good" choices for fat:

Notice that many contain primarily unsaturated fat (designated with the ♥).

ALL CRAB COMBO ☺
at SandCrab Café (Escondido)
Snow crab, blue crab, stone crab claws, king crab leg, new potatoes and corn on the cob. Sausage and bread not included in analysis.
✓✓ FAT: Excellent Choice (3 g)♥

CHICKEN WITH VEGETABLES ☺
at Pick Up Stix (many locations)
Steamed white meat chicken with broccoli, carrots, zucchini, mushrooms and water chestnuts in a sauce of white wine, garlic and soy. Analysis does not include rice (separate analysis).
✓✓ FAT: Excellent Choice (10 g)

LINGUINE CON GAMBERI E CARCIOFI
at Harry's American Bar & Grill (La Jolla/UTC)
Thin flat pasta, prawns, baby artichokes, garlic, white wine, and olive oil.
✓ FAT: Good Choice (16 g)♥

GRILLED ATLANTIC SALMON – HEALTHY DINING PREPARATION ☺
at 150 Grand Café (Escondido)
with mixed berry coulis, berries, roasted fingerling potatoes, and watercress.
✓✓ FAT: Good Choice (18 g)♥

BEEF VEGGIE BOWL
at Flame Broiler (La Jolla)
Teriyaki beef with broccoli, cabbage & carrots served over steamed rice & topped with teriyaki sauce.
✓✓ FAT: Excellent Choice (10 g)

HONEY MUSTARD HAM SANDWICH
at Subway (many San Diego area locations)
✓✓ FAT: Excellent Choice (5 g)

Now – how well are YOU doing?

If you're not careful, all the "extras" in your meal can add too much fat to your diet very quickly. Consider the following high-fat culprits:

	Calories	Fat (g)	Cholest.(mg)	Sodium (mg)
Salad Dressings: (3 Tbs.)				
Blue Cheese	230	24	25	500
Oil & Vinegar	215	24	0	0
Italian	205	21	0	350
French	200	19	5	640
Thousand Island	175	17	15	325
Ranch	160	17	10	290
Toppings: (2 Tbs.)				
Margarine	200	23	0	265
Butter	200	23	60	235
Mayonnaise	200	22	15	155
Tarter Sauce	150	16	20	195
Cream Cheese	100	10	30	85
Cheese (1 oz. cheddar)	115	9	30	175
Sour Cream	65	6	15	15
Desserts:				
Cheesecake	385	24	80	285
Ice Cream (1 cup)	350	24	90	110
Chocolate Cake	405	17	5	300
Apple Pie	325	14	30	205

Instead try:

- Fat-free or low-fat salad dressings
- Salsa, low-fat cottage cheese, or plain yogurt as salad dressing or topping for potatoes
- Only very small amounts of regular or high-fat salad dressings
- Fruit, low-fat frozen yogurt, sorbet, or sherbet for dessert

CHAPTER 5

Cholesterol—Where, What and How?

Where does cholesterol come from?

Most of the cholesterol in your blood is manufactured by your liver and is carried in the blood in protein packages called lipoproteins. The form of these lipoproteins determines whether the cholesterol is categorized as "good" (HDL) or "bad" (LDL) cholesterol.

The body uses cholesterol to form hormones and cell membranes, producing about 1,000 milligrams (mg) of cholesterol each day. In addition, the average American consumes 400 to 600 mg daily from food. The U.S. Surgeon General's office and the American Heart Association recommend a maximum of 300 mg of cholesterol per day from food.

The cholesterol derived from dietary sources is essentially the same as the cholesterol the body manufactures. Although dietary cholesterol is found only in animal products, excess fat in the diet (especially saturated and trans-fat) increases the amount of cholesterol the body produces.

A high-fat/high-cholesterol diet can cause the buildup of cholesterol in the bloodstream. Excess cholesterol in the blood accumulates in the walls of the blood vessels. Over time the arteries become narrowed, and eventually the flow of blood is reduced, resulting in a heart attack or stroke.

What determines blood cholesterol levels?

1. **Genetics**. Some individuals, no matter how prudent their diet or how regularly they exercise, can't achieve a low cholesterol level without the use of blood cholesterol-lowering medications.

2. **Diet**. Foods high in saturated fat or trans-fat **increase** blood cholesterol levels. These include butter, whole milk products, palm and coconut oils, cheese, beef, pork, and egg yolks. In addition, many packaged and processed foods are high in saturated fat and/or trans-fat, which also have a cholesterol-raising effect.

A diet **low in total fat**, with fat intake primarily from unsaturated fat sources, **reduces** cholesterol levels. **High fiber foods**, especially oat bran, apples, carrots, oranges, and legumes (beans, peas and lentils) **decrease** cholesterol levels by inhibiting the absorption of cholesterol into the bloodstream. **Fish and fish oils**, which contain omega-3 fatty acids, also **decrease** "bad" LDL cholesterol levels.

3. **Smoking, stress and some medications** also raise cholesterol levels.

How should blood cholesterol be measured?

For an accurate and complete cholesterol measure, a tube of blood should be drawn from the arm by a qualified health professional. You should not eat or drink anything (except water) for 12 hours before the blood draw. The laboratory which analyzes the blood sample should follow the reference methods set by the U. S. Centers for Disease Control and Prevention. The fingertip method often used at shopping malls and health fairs or the recently introduced home tests may not provide results that are as accurate or thorough (many do not give adequate information about the types of cholesterol).

Summary on dietary cholesterol and fat

- Consuming **too much of any fat** (even unsaturated oils) can increase body weight, which may increase blood cholesterol levels. Oils, margarine, and butter all have approximately the same number of calories and fat grams per ounce, and so all have the same potential to contribute to excess weight. Therefore, it's important to limit your total intake of all types of fat.

- Even though oils, margarine, and butter have about the same calorie and fat counts, there is a big difference in the chemical make-up of these fats. Butter is high in saturated fat, and **saturated fats increase blood cholesterol** levels. Saturated fats stimulate the production of LDLs ("bad cholesterol"), resulting in increased blood cholesterol levels. Therefore, if you avoid only dietary cholesterol in the food you eat, without reducing the amount of saturated fat, you may not lower your blood cholesterol level at all.

- **Avoid hydrogenated fats,** too, because they are also saturated. Many margarines, although cholesterol-free, are partially hydrogenated and contain **trans-fatty acids,** which have been shown to have a cholesterol-raising effect.

- Vegetable oils are generally **unsaturated fats.** In small amounts, liquid oils (such as olive, corn, canola, etc.) may help to decrease cholesterol levels. Remember, though, that all oils are 100% fat and high in calories, so use only small amounts.

- The **amount of cholesterol** found in foods is not as important as the **amount of saturated fat**. Nevertheless, you should minimize intake of very concentrated sources of cholesterol. Shellfish is very low in saturated fat but moderately high in cholesterol. Most medical experts agree that shellfish, in moderate quantities, is a healthy choice.

- Cholesterol is found only in animal products. Don't be misled, though — just because foods don't contain cholesterol doesn't mean they are also low in fat! In fact, many "no-cholesterol" foods are loaded with fat. Be sure to check the number of fat grams on nutrition labels.

How the check mark guidelines for cholesterol are set

The Surgeon General's Office and the American Heart Association recommend that cholesterol consumption be limited to 300 mg per day. If the day's total were evenly divided in thirds, this would suggest a limit of 100 mg per meal. We set our guidelines for cholesterol as follows:

✓✓ Excellent Choice = 0 to 75 mg cholesterol/entrée
✓ Good Choice = 76 to 150 mg cholesterol/entrée

If every meal in your day were at the "Good Choice" limit of 150 mg, you would exceed the recommended amount. But since a restaurant meal usually contains a larger portion of meat or other cholesterol-containing foods than side dishes or other meals of the day, you can easily compensate for this cholesterol intake by choosing foods with little or no cholesterol for the remaining selections.

If you are watching your blood cholesterol level, select items that are:

1. "Excellent Choice" or "Good Choice" for fat
2. Primarily unsaturated (designated with the ♥)
3. "Excellent Choice" or "Good Choice" for cholesterol

Flavorful examples of "Excellent" and "Good" choices for cholesterol:

GRILLED EGGPLANT ꚛ
at Rice Jones (Hillcrest)
with zucchini, red pepper, green onion, garlic, served with Jones rice.
✓✓ FAT: Excellent Choice (15 g)♥   ✓✓ CHOLESTEROL: Excellent Choice (0 mg)

HEALTHMEX CHICKEN BURRRITO
at Rubio's Fresh Mexican Grill (multiple locations)
Grilled all-white meat chicken with rice, black beans, roasted chipotle salsa and salsa fresca in a warm whole wheat tortilla. Served with rice (see separate analysis below) instead of chips.
✓✓ FAT: Excellent Choice (10 g)   ✓✓ CHOLESTEROL: Excellent Choice (70 mg)

BARBEQUE CHICKEN PIZZA (2 SLICES)
at Pat & Oscar's (multiple locations)
BBQ chicken, red onions, cilantro & BBQ sauce. Analysis is for 2 slices (⅓ pizza).
✓✓ FAT: Excellent Choice (14 g)   ✓✓ CHOLESTEROL: Excellent Choice (50 mg)

OAK ROASTED SALMON ON PONZU SALAD ꚛ
at Sammy's Woodfired Pizza (Carlsbad, Del Mar, La Jolla,
Mission Valley, Costa Verde, Downtown & Scripps Ranch)
Shredded cabbage, cucumber, edamame and ponzu sauce.
✓ FAT: Good Choice (19 g)♥   ✓ CHOLESTEROL: Good Choice (110 mg)

CHAPTER 6

Sodium — To Salt or Not to Salt?

Sodium is an essential nutrient. It helps to maintain blood volume, regulate the balance of water in the cells, and transmit nerve impulses. The kidneys control sodium balance by increasing or decreasing sodium in the urine.

Americans generally consume more sodium than needed. The American Heart Association recommends a maximum intake of 2,400 mg of sodium per day. That's the amount in about 1 tsp. of salt. However, sodium occurs in other forms than salt, as well.

Many foods contain sodium naturally, and it is often added to foods during preparation or processing in the form of salt or other additives and flavorings. Sodium is common in seasoning salts (1620 - 1850 mg per teaspoon), monosodium glutamate (MSG, 492 mg per teaspoon), soy sauce (343 mg per teaspoon), and meat tenderizer (1750 mg per teaspoon) and is often found in prescription drugs and over-the-counter medications.

In the United States, nearly one in three adults has elevated blood pressure. Sodium intake is only one of the factors known to affect blood pressure, and not everyone is equally susceptible. The sensitivity to sodium seems to be very individualized. At present, there is not a good method to predict who is salt-sensitive or who will develop high blood pressure. Low-sodium diets may help some people avoid high blood pressure and some people with high blood pressure to control their blood pressure. In some individuals, a low-sodium diet will not affect blood pressure at all.

Since most Americans consume more sodium than needed, consider reducing your sodium intake, especially if your physician has recommended doing so. Use less table salt, read labels carefully, and eat sparingly those foods that have large amounts of sodium. Remember that a substantial amount of the sodium you eat may be "hidden" - either occurring naturally in foods or as part of a preservative or flavoring agent that has been added.

To avoid too much sodium:

- Cook without salt or with only small amounts of added salt.
- Flavor foods with herbs, spices, and lemon juice.
- Add little or no salt to food at the table.
- Discover the natural flavors of foods prepared without high sodium ingredients.
- Limit intake of salty foods such as potato chips, pretzels, salted nuts & popcorn, cured meats, condiments (soy sauce, steak sauce, garlic salt), pickled foods, cheese and canned foods.

- Read food labels carefully to determine the amounts of sodium.
- Use lower sodium products to replace those with higher sodium content when possible.

To avoid too much sodium when dining out:

1. Order entrées listed as "Excellent Choice" or "Good Choice" for sodium levels, and
2. Request no added salt whenever possible.

The sodium content for dishes featured in this book reflects three sources: (1) sodium that occurs naturally in foods that are part of the recipe, (2) sodium in the form of salt that is included in a prepared sauce, marinade or other recipe in which salt cannot be reduced for an individual portion (for example, soups, which are typically made in advance in large quantities), and (3) soy sauce, teriyaki sauce, and other ingredients containing high concentrations of sodium (see below).

There are two circumstances in which the amount of salt in your restaurant meal can be reduced: (1) Often, the restaurant's standard recipe includes salt that can be omitted when the chef prepares your order, and (2) Some chefs cook with salt "to taste," which means they may add a pinch of salt here and there throughout the preparation. In both cases, if you want to minimize the amount of sodium consumed, it's important to **specify very clearly** that you want "no added salt."

Often items with high sodium values contain soy sauce, teriyaki sauce, fish sauce, or other high sodium ingredients (see Chapter 9). These ingredients are included in the analyses unless specifically stated otherwise. You may request less (or none) of these ingredients to reduce the sodium content. However, you should be aware that the taste will probably be altered.

Many items included in this book are listed as "Moderate" (meaning 600 to 1000 mg sodium per entrée) or "High" in sodium (meaning above 1000 mg sodium per entrée) and are **not recommended** for those watching sodium intake.

> The asterisk (*) next to the sodium values reminds you to specify "no added salt" when ordering your meal to get the values as published.

How the check mark guidelines for sodium are set

Since no more than 2,400 mg of sodium is recommended per day, we consider 960 mg (40% of maximum recommended daily intake) to be a reasonable maximum for an entire meal and 600 mg to be a reasonable maximum for an entrée. Therefore, the guidelines are:

✓✓ Excellent Choice = 0 to 300 mg sodium/entrée
✓ Good Choice = 301 to 600 mg sodium/entrée

Examples of "Excellent" and "Good" choices for sodium:

CHICKEN TIKKA KABAB
at Star of India (Pacific Beach, Del Mar & Downtown)
Tandoori-prepared boneless chicken marinated with fresh herbs and spices.
✓✓ SODIUM: Excellent Choice (295 mg)*

GRILLED SWORDFISH WITH CILANTRO PESTO
at The Fish Market (Del Mar and Harbor Drive)
Grilled swordfish served with cilantro pesto sauce.
✓✓ SODIUM: Excellent Choice (255 mg)*

CEDAR PLANKED SALMON ON JICAMA ORANGE SALAD 🍎
at Pacific Coast Grill
with a wildflower honey drizzle.
✓✓ SODIUM: Excellent Choice (120 mg)*

CHAPTER **7**

Protein, Carbohydrates & Fiber

Protein: the building blocks

Protein is very important for a healthy body. Protein provides materials for growth, helps to maintain and repair tissues, manufactures the lipoproteins to carry fat and cholesterol, and assists in the maintenance of proper fluid levels. Generally, it's easy to get protein in your diet, and most Americans consume 2 - 3 times more than necessary. Excess protein does not create muscle, as many hope, but is stored as fat. Excess protein puts a strain on the liver and kidneys. In addition, some protein sources are also high in fat, saturated fat, calories and cholesterol, such as beef, whole milk products, eggs, poultry skin, and cheese.

The best sources of protein are low-fat foods, including fish, poultry without skin, skim or low-fat milk products and tofu. Whole grains, vegetables and especially legumes (dried beans, peas and lentils) also contain some protein. Unless you are a very strict vegetarian, you probably get adequate protein with a balanced diet. If you are a strict vegetarian, a dietitian can analyze your diet to make sure you're getting adequate amounts of protein.

Carbohydrates: energy

Contrary to what you may be hearing in the media, carbohydrates **are** very healthy for you and necessary in performing every day functions. Carbohydrates support your muscles and brain, making this nutrient vital for health and survival.

According to leading health organizations, about 45-65% of your calories should be coming from carbohydrates. In other words, about half of what you eat during the day should come from "healthy" carbohydrate sources such as:

- ◆ whole grains
- ◆ fruits
- ◆ vegetables
- ◆ beans and other legumes
- ◆ low or non-fat dairy products

These foods are considered healthy sources of carbohydrates because they provide more nutrients such as vitamins, minerals, phytochemicals (see Chapter 8) and fiber than the "not-so-healthy" carbs such as cookies, cakes, pies, potato chips and refined grain products like white rice, white bread and white pasta. Whole grains, vegetables, and legumes are particularly high in fiber and "complex carbohydrates," which take longer to digest than refined carbohydrates, and thus help stabilize blood sugar levels.

Even the much-maligned potato can be a valuable source of vitamins and minerals, especially when eaten baked or boiled with the skin. Just avoid the fatty, fried versions such as potato chips, French fries and hash browns. Similarly, corn is a good source of carbohydrates, as opposed to refined products coming from this vegetable, such as corn syrup and deep-fried, over-salted corn chips.

Studies have shown that healthy carbohydrates are beneficial in lowering blood cholesterol, controlling body weight, and reducing the risk of many diseases, so it is important to recognize the difference between "healthy" and "not-so-healthy" carbohydrates.

According to Jeffrey Prince of the American Institute for Cancer Research, "Eating vegetables, fruits, whole grains and beans, which are predominantly carbohydrate, is linked to a reduced risk of cancer, heart disease, stroke, diabetes and a range of other chronic diseases." Furthermore, low-carb diets that promote increased intake of animal proteins and fat are, according to Prince, "increasing the risk of developing cancer, heart disease, stroke, type-2 diabetes and other chronic diseases."

Low-Carb Diets (and the Theories Behind Them)

So, you may be asking yourself, "If carbohydrates are so good for me, then what is all the hype about low-carb diets?" The theory behind these fad diets is that by eating carbohydrates (even the healthy ones), insulin function becomes impaired, making it difficult to convert the carbohydrates into energy. Instead, the carbohydrates are stored as fat and cause weight gain.

Some people **may** have a problem with insulin balance, especially when eating the faster-absorbing, "not-so-healthy" carbohydrates (sugary "junk foods" and **refined** grain products such as white rice, white bread, white pasta, corn chips, pastries, and most crackers and snack foods). However, the "healthy" carbohydrates listed on the previous page are digested more slowly, especially when eaten as part of a balanced meal containing lean proteins and small amounts of fat. A "**lower-carb**" approach is good if it means you are reducing the amount of "empty" calories coming from the "not-so-healthy" carbohydrates, while maintaining a reasonable level of "healthy" carbohydrates.

Most medical and nutrition experts agree that the long-term safety and effectiveness of low-carb diets have not been proven. Health professionals are concerned with the low-carb diets because they usually add more fat (especially saturated fat) and protein to compensate for the decrease in carbs. Adding excessive amounts of these nutrients to the diet increases the risk for heart, kidney and other diseases (not to mention constipation due to lack of fiber).

It is very important to understand that only by eating **excess** carbohydrates, or any food group for that matter, will you gain weight. Overindulging in the "not-so-healthy" carbohydrates will cause weight gain, but the "healthy carbs" listed on the previous page help satisfy appetite better than the refined products do, so overindulgence is less likely.

What About Fiber?

We can't forget about this powerful nutrient! Dietary fiber is a term used to describe parts of plant foods that usually aren't digestible by humans. Its role is to move food through the body for digestion as well as help the body absorb nutrients from the food.

The typical American diet is much too low in fiber. The American Cancer Society recommends 20-38 grams per day (depending on age and gender), while the average American only eats 7-8 grams per day. By increasing your intake of "healthy" carbohydrates, you can easily add more fiber to your diet. It is important to remember that as you increase fiber in your diet, you also need to drink more water to avoid feeling bloated and gassy.

There are two main types of fiber: soluble and insoluble. **Soluble fiber,** which may help lower blood cholesterol and control blood sugar, is found in oats, beans, carrots, apples and oranges. **Insoluble fiber** helps to move food quickly through the body and protect against colorectal cancer, and is found in wheat bran and whole grains. Because both types of fiber have different functions for improving health, a variety of foods containing fiber should be included in your diet.

Healthy Carbohydrates at San Diego Restaurants

The following are a few examples of wonderfully tasty dishes served by **Healthy Dining** restaurants in the San Diego area. Each provides an excellent source of "healthy" carbohydrates:

MUSHROOM RANCHERO – SPECIAL REQUEST ☙
at Ranchos Cocina (Ocean Beach & Northpark)
Fresh mushrooms, corn tortillas, pico de gallo, and ranchero sauce. Request brown rice and black beans.

MEDITERRANEAN-STYLE CHICKEN SAUSAGE ☙
at The French Gourmet (Pacific Beach)
Chicken sausage with lots of Italian flavor - sun-dried tomatoes, pine nuts, basil, parsley, bell peppers and white wine, served with rosemary potatoes and steamed seasonal vegetables.

CHICKEN FAJITAS ☙
at Acapulco (Old Town, Escondido, Rancho Bernardo & San Marcos)
Juicy chicken breast in our own special marinade on a sizzling skillet with sautéed onions & bell peppers. Served with rice, beans, pico de gallo, guacamole & warm corn or flour tortillas.

WARM QUINOA SALAD WITH SHRIMP AND ASPARAGUS (8 oz.)
at Whole Foods Market (La Jolla and Hillcrest)
High-protein, nutty quinoa combines well with lively flavors for this elegant dish.

CHAPTER 8

Fruits & Vegetables — Nutrition Heavyweights

Fruits and vegetables deserve a special chapter in this book because of their importance in a healthy diet, and because their contributions overlap those of the other chapters so much. In addition to providing carbohydrates and high quality calories, they are packed full of other essentials — vitamins, minerals, fiber, antioxidants, and the more-recently discovered classes of compounds called phytochemicals (discussed in more detail below). Although numerical values are generally not available for these other substances, they are important and deserve special consideration as you make your food selections.

The Centers for Diseases Control and Prevention (CDC), the World Health Organization, the National Cancer Institute, and the American Cancer Society, along with many other health agencies and organizations, emphasize the strong relationship between fruit and vegetable consumption and health. The latest guidelines issued by the Departments of Health and Human Services and Agriculture encourage Americans to eat at least **2 cups of fruits (4 servings) and 2½ cups of vegetables (5 servings) each day** (based on an average intake of 2000 calories per day).

Research shows that people who eat even 2½ cups of fruits and vegetables a day have only half the cancer risk of those who eat less than one cup a day. Hundreds of studies show that increased fruit and vegetable consumption may also help prevent heart disease, stroke, hypertension, birth defects, cataracts, diabetes, obesity and other serious conditions.

Fruits and vegetables are nutritional powerhouses which:
- are excellent sources of vitamins and minerals
- contain antioxidants and phytochemicals
- contain fiber
- are virtually fat-free (exceptions: coconut, olives & avocado) and cholesterol-free
- are particularly helpful in weight management, due to their high-fiber, high-water, and low-fat content

Vitamins and minerals

Vitamins and minerals are essential in maintaining the health of the brain, heart, bones, teeth and nerves; making and repairing red blood cells; regulating the body's balance of fluids; and in other vital functions.

Many fruits and vegetables are particularly good sources of vitamins A, C, E and K, some B vitamins, and many important minerals needed for healthy bodies.

Beta-carotene and related compounds called carotenoids are converted by the body to vitamin A. Carotenoids (from the word "carrot") are found in high concentrations in carrots and other orange and yellow vegetables and fruits such as winter squash and cantaloupes. Dark green, leafy vegetables, such as spinach, kale, broccoli, and other members of the cabbage family, also contain high concentrations of carotenoids.

Dark green vegetables are also excellent sources of folic acid (a B vitamin needed during pregnancy to reduce the risk of neural defects in the fetus), vitamins E and K, and minerals such as calcium, magnesium, manganese, iron, and potassium. Many fruits are also a good source of minerals, such as chromium (grapes), iron (cherries), manganese (pineapple), and potassium (apricots, bananas, orange juice, peaces and prunes).

Citrus fruits are good sources of vitamin C, as is the family of plants that includes tomatoes, red and green peppers, potatoes, and eggplant. Other good sources of vitamin C include papayas, strawberries, kiwis, cantaloupe, and the cabbage family, including broccoli, cauliflower and Brussels sprouts.

While there is some overlap in the vitamins and minerals supplied by the fruits and vegetables listed above, you need **a wide variety of colorful fruits and vegetables** to fully benefit from the various nutrients they contain.

Antioxidants

Antioxidants are disease-fighting compounds found in many foods, especially fruits and vegetables. Antioxidants neutralize free radicals, compounds that damage cells and lead to cardiovascular disease, cancer, cataracts, premature aging, and impaired immunity.

Antioxidants include some vitamins (A, C, and E), beta carotene, some minerals (for example, selenium, copper, zinc, and manganese) and some of the phytochemicals.

Phytochemicals

Found in plant foods, phytochemicals ("plant chemicals") are substances that are recognized as powerful disease-fighting compounds.

Fruits and vegetables contain hundreds of thousands of different phytochemical compounds. Many are categorized as carotenoids, flavenoids (compounds that give flavor and colors to fruits and vegetables), and other compounds, such as allicin, indoles, lycopenes, lutein, and phenols. Scientists studying phytochemicals are finding an impressive range of health benefits. But you don't need to be an expert in science or nutrition to reap the benefits for yourself!

The 5 A Day Program and Produce for Better Health Foundation suggest eating a wide variety of fruits and vegetables from different color groups to get an assortment of phytochemicals, vitamins and minerals.

Color & examples	Phytochemical examples	Potential benefits
Red: apples, cherries, strawberries, watermelon, beets, red peppers, radicchio, tomatoes	Lycopene, anthocyanins	Maintain memory function, heart health, and urinary tract health; reduce blood pressure, fight infections, and reduce risk of some cancers
Orange/yellow: apricots, mangos, oranges, peaches, pineapple, cantaloupe, carrots, corn, winter squash	Carotenoids, bioflavonoids,	Maintain health of heart, eyes, and immune system, slow aging, and reduce risk of some cancers
Green: leafy greens, asparagus, broccoli, green beans, peas, spinach, honeydew, kiwi, avocados,	Lutein, indoles, carotenoids	Improve vision, strengthen bones and teeth, and reduce risk of some cancers
Blue/purple: blueberries, blackberries, purple grapes, plums, eggplant, purple cabbage	Anthocyanins, phenolics, resveratrol	Facilitate healthier aging, enhance memory function, urinary tract health and cardiovascular health, and reduce risk of some cancers
White/tan/brown: onions, garlic, cauliflower, turnips, mushrooms, potatoes, bananas, pears, dates	Allicin, quercetin, sulphoraphane	Improve heart health, maintain healthy cholesterol levels, and reduce risk of some cancers

Not all foods listed above, even within the same group, have the same health benefits. Foods with the same phytochemicals may contain different concentrations of the phytochemicals, and the compounds may be absorbed differently. Even different varieties of foods within the same category (such as different varieties of apples or lettuce) may contain widely varying concentrations and kinds of phytochemicals. However, those darker in color usually contain higher concentrations. So think "more color and more variety" in making your selections!

What is considered one serving?

Fruits	Vegetables
1 medium whole fruit (apple, banana)	1 cup of raw, leafy vegetables
½ cup of fresh, frozen or canned fruit	½ cup cut up fresh, frozen or canned vegetables
6 oz. (¾ cup) 100% fruit juice	6 oz. (¾ cup) 100% vegetable juice
¼ cup of dried fruit	½ cup cooked beans, peas, or lentils

How can I get more fruits and vegetables in my diet?

At home:
- Top your hot or cold cereal with fresh fruit.
- Enjoy a glass of 100% juice with breakfast.
- Make smoothies with fresh or frozen fruits and juices for a great breakfast or lunch.
- Choose 100% fruit and vegetable juices as delicious alternatives to soft drinks.

- At dinner, include a salad or raw vegetables, and use low-fat or non-fat dressing to reduce fat and calories.
- Steamed vegetables are always a good side dish.
- Add vegetables to your favorite entrées, like tacos, lasagna, casseroles and pasta dishes.
- Add pureed vegetables to sauces to fortify them.
- Try more vegetarian meals, like tofu, rice or pasta with vegetables, and stir-fry dishes.
- For dessert, bake apples, peaches, pears, or bananas, or make fruit cobblers.
- Experiment with new recipes that emphasize fruits and vegetables. Discover some of the many cookbooks that specialize in fruits and vegetables.

For a snack or when you're on the go:
- Choose fruits and vegetables that can be eaten out of hand, like apple wedges, baby carrots, broccoli spears, or cherry tomatoes, grapes, bananas, and seasonal items like peaches and plums.
- In place of candy, choose dried fruit, which you can easily pack in a bag and take on the road or eat at your office.

When dining out:
- Order a dinner salad to begin your meal.
- Request an extra serving of vegetables as a side dish.
- Order meals that include vegetables or fruits as a major component. To keep fat and calories in check, request vegetables steamed without the butter, oil or cream sauce.
- Ask for extra lettuce and tomato (or other vegetables) on sandwiches and burgers.
- Choose lower fat/lower calorie desserts such as fresh fruit, sherbet or sorbet, or angel food cake with fruit topping.
- Choose dishes listed in the book that have at least 1 cup of fruits/vegetables.

For more information, visit: www.cdc.gov/5aday , www.5aday.org , or www.5aday.gov

> Look for the ♻ symbol next to the dish title. The ♻ indicates an entrée provides at least 1 cup of fruits or vegetables (or ½ cup for a side dish).

Examples of restaurant meals with 2 or more fruit/vegetable servings:

POLLO ALA DIAVOLA ♻
at Prego (Mission Valley)
Mesquite grilled chicken breast marinated in spicy mustard greens, and served with fresh steamed vegetables and roasted potatoes.

SONORA BURRITO LITE ♻
at El Torito (8 San Diego area locations)
Grilled chicken breast, fresh pico de gallo, mild chiles, reduced-fat jack cheese & roasted tomatillo sauce. Served with fresh fruit relish (included in analysis) & frijoles de la olla (separate analysis).

CHAPTER **9**

Additional Tips for Healthy Dining

Here are some additional dining tips, adapted from "Eating Better When Eating Out," from the USDA Human Nutrition Information Service:

Appetizers: Enjoy raw vegetables dipped in salsa or low-calorie dressing, fruit or steamed seafood. Limit rich sauces, dips and batter-fried foods.

Soups: Choose broth or tomato-based soups rather than creamed soups. Lentil, bean and split pea soups are high in fiber. Most soups are high in sodium.

Breads: Whole grain bread is the best source of complex carbohydrates, vitamins, minerals, and fiber. Watch out for breads with added fat or sugar such as croissants, biscuits, cornbread, muffins (e.g., bran, corn, blueberry) and sweet rolls. Use toppings (butter, cream cheese and margarine) very sparingly.

Vegetables and Salads: Plain vegetables are high in fiber and nutrients and very low in calories, fat and sodium. However, butter, margarine and sauces increase the amount of calories, fat, cholesterol and sodium considerably. Look for vegetables seasoned with lemon, herbs or spices rather than fat and salt. Remember – salad dressings and toppings can add a lot of calories, fat and sodium.

Watch out for prepared salads that contain mayonnaise, salad dressing or oil, such as macaroni salad, potato salad, creamy coleslaw, tuna and chicken salad, and marinated vegetables. Some pasta salads are made with large amounts of oily dressing.

Main Entrées: Ask how meals are prepared and what ingredients are used. Is the fish or chicken broiled with butter or other fat? Is it served with a sauce? How large is the portion? Are vegetables fresh or canned, buttered or creamed?

Fish or poultry that is broiled, grilled, baked, steamed or poached is a good choice. However, entrées are often basted with large amounts of fat. Ask to have your entrée prepared without added fat, and that chicken be prepared without skin (or remove the skin before eating). Request that lemon juice, wine or only a small amount of fat be used and that no salt be added.

Watch out for menu selections termed "light fare" or "light." "Light" may or may not mean lower in fat and calories. We have found restaurants in which "On the Light Side" means anything from smaller portions to lower prices!

Choose dishes flavored with herbs and spices rather than rich sauces, gravies, or dressings, or ask for gravies, sour cream, sauces, and other toppings to be served on the side and use sparingly. Limit your use of soy sauce, steak sauce, catsup, mustard, pickles and other condiments to help control sodium.

Portions are often very large. Ask for a take-home bag and eat the remaining portion the next day. Or share an entrée with a friend and get an extra appetizer.

Many stir-fried entrées are prepared with very little oil, while some are prepared with too much. Request that yours be prepared with very little.

Pizza can be a low-fat, nutritious choice if you order yours with half the cheese and only vegetable toppings.

Sandwiches can be an excellent choice if you choose lean deli meats such as turkey or ham (but watch portion size!) instead of higher fat cold cuts, such as bologna or salami. Choose whole grain breads and go easy on or avoid oil, butter, avocado, and mayonnaise.

Desserts: Fruits are great! Sherbet, sorbet and low-fat frozen yogurt are much lower in fat than ice cream. If temptation gets to you, share the dessert with a dinner partner.

Words that signal **high fat** include:

buttered or buttery	creamed or creamy	rich
scalloped	fried	breaded
fritters	tempura	croquettes
crispy	with gravy	in cheese sauce
Hollandaise	au gratin	à la king
Béarnaise	Alfredo	Newburg

Words that signal **high sodium** include:

smoked	barbecued	pickled
broth	soy sauce	teriyaki
Creole sauce	marinated	cocktail sauce
tomato base	Parmesan	mustard sauce
fish sauce	hoisin sauce	chili paste

Analysis Methods, Accuracy & Disclaimer

How is the nutrition analysis done?

Using recipes supplied by the restaurant, a computerized nutritional analysis is performed with the Nutritionist IV or ESHA Food Processor computer programs. The programs use the U.S. Department of Agriculture (USDA) database, and we update with new data when it becomes available. When values for recipe ingredients are not available from the USDA database, we contact the manufacturer for nutrition information. If the manufacturer does not have nutritional information, we match ingredients as closely as possible to a similar product that does have nutrition information.

The data coming from the USDA database and the computer analysis imply a high degree of accuracy. In reality, the USDA found that nutritional values of foods can vary between similar food samples by as much as 20%, and the numbers coming from their measurements represent their average data. As recommended by the FDA, we round the data as follows: for calories, cholesterol and sodium, to the nearest 5 mg; for fat, protein, carbohydrates and fiber to the nearest whole number. It is important to note that the numerical values for the selected menu items published in this book are *approximations only*.

Notes about accuracy

One method to obtain nutritional information is a chemical analysis performed in a professional laboratory. That is, in fact, how the USDA obtained the information for its database. It is very expensive and time-consuming, and therefore not feasible for this project. Every effort was made to ensure accurate information from the computerized analysis and the USDA database.

Two main challenges were encountered with the computerized analysis. First, how much marinade do meats actually absorb? Second, how much oil is absorbed in flash-frying (a method commonly used in Chinese foods)? After numerous conversations with experts throughout the U.S., we found that there has been very little research in these areas. As recommended by nutritionists at the USDA and the Human Nutrition Information Service, we calculate that one gram per one ounce of marinade is absorbed, and that one teaspoon per six ounces of meat is absorbed with flash-frying.

Disclaimer:

The purpose of this book is to provide nutrition information for selected menu items from restaurants that have chosen to participate in the **Healthy Dining** program. Please note that the items listed in this book are not necessarily appropriate or healthful for all individuals. Some people need to be more careful about certain items such as salt or sugar, or have food allergies which put additional restrictions on their food choices. Each individual is responsible, in cooperation with his or her physician, dietitian or other health consultant, for making personal dietary decisions. We have not included all the restaurants that serve healthy food, nor are we recommending all entrées from restaurants that are included in this book.

It is also important to note that the numerical values for the nutrition information included in this book are approximations only, and that the categories "Good Choice" and "Excellent Choice" give a better overall indication of the nutrition content of the menu items.

All information contained in this book has been carefully compiled and reviewed by qualified health professionals. Nutrition information is based on recipes supplied by the restaurants. Participating restaurants have agreed to prepare food according to the recipes submitted for a period of one year, or to clearly notify customers otherwise. The authors are not responsible for maintaining quality control over the food that is prepared by the restaurants. The restaurants are ultimately responsible for the quality of the food they serve.

Remember to request the **Healthy Dining** menus!

Part II
Healthy Dining Menus
Arranged alphabetically
Also see indexes at back, arranged by cuisine, location, and alphabetically.

Summary of check mark system:

ENTRÉE GUIDELINES †

Calories
   ✓✓ Excellent Choice = 0 to 450 calories/entrée
   ✓ Good Choice = 451 to 750 calories/entrée

Fat
   ✓✓ Excellent Choice = 0 to 15 grams (g)/entrée
   ✓ Good Choice = 16 to 25 grams (g)/entrée

Cholesterol
   ✓✓ Excellent Choice = 0 to 75 milligrams (mg)/entrée
   ✓ Good Choice = 76 to 150 milligrams (mg)/entrée

Sodium
   ✓✓ Excellent Choice = 0 to 300 milligrams (mg)/entrée
   ✓ Good Choice = 301 to 600 milligrams (mg)/entrée

FOOTNOTES
♥   Primarily unsaturated fat
*   If you request no added salt
†   Side dish guidelines are 1/3 of entrée guidelines (see page 5)
🍎   at least 2 fruit/vegetable servings for entrées, 1 for side dishes

PRICE RANGE SYMBOLS
$ Average entrée under $10
$$ Average entrée $10 to $20
$$$ Average entrée over $20

Special Request – modification of the usual restaurant recipe or preparation method. You must ask for the "Special Request" for the nutrient composition of the dish to correspond to the published nutrition information.

Menus

Relax with the Mera family at Andrés. Just imagine that you are in Cuba in the 1950s where the rumba, warm tropical beaches and fine Caribbean cuisine are a part of every day. Savor the natural resources of the island: simmered black beans, delicious yuca, popular plantains and pork, and seafood from surrounding waters. Here, in our little piece of Cuba, the Mera family prepares and serves each meal true to authentic style. The foods, spices and meats are the best, and ingredients are individually chosen without restraint of cost, to prepare the finest Cuban meal for you. Savor the experience! $$

Andrés Cuban Restaurant 1235 Morena Blvd., San Diego 92110   (619) 275-4114

CAMERONES ENCHILADAS – SPECIAL REQUEST
Tender shrimp in our tomato sauce with onions, garlic, green peppers and spices. Some like it hot and spicy. If you do, let us know! Served with yellow rice and Cuban style black beans (see analyses below). Request less oil (½ oz).
✓✓ CALORIES: Excellent Choice (380) CHOLESTEROL: High (390 mg)
✓ FAT: Good Choice (20 g)♥ SODIUM: Moderate (940 mg)*
PROTEIN: 42 g, CARBOHYDRATE: 4 g, FIBER: 1 g

PESCADO AL MOJO – SPECIAL REQUEST
Fish of the day sautéed in olive oil, garlic and spices. Served with yellow rice and Cuban style black beans (see analyses below). Request less oil (½ oz).
✓✓ CALORIES: Excellent Choice (355) ✓✓ CHOLESTEROL: Excellent Choice (65 mg)
✓ FAT: Good Choice (18 g)♥ ✓✓ SODIUM: Excellent Choice (110 mg)*
PROTEIN: 42 g, CARBOHYDRATE: 5 g, FIBER: 0 g

POLLO A LA PLANCHA
Boneless chicken breast marinated in lemon and garlic, grilled and smothered with onions. Served with rice and Cuban style black bean (see analyses below).
✓✓ CALORIES: Excellent Choice (445) ✓ CHOLESTEROL: Good Choice (150 mg)
✓ FAT: Good Choice (20 g) ✓✓ SODIUM: Excellent Choice (135 mg)*
PROTEIN: 56 g, CARBOHYDRATE: 7 g, FIBER: 1 g

CAMERONES AL AJILLO – SPECIAL REQUEST
Succulent shrimp, sautéed in olive oil, garlic, wine and spices. Served with a side of yellow rice and Cuban style black bean (see analyses below). Request less oil (½ oz).
✓✓ CALORIES: Excellent Choice (335) CHOLESTEROL: High (390 mg)
✓ FAT: Good Choice (16 g)♥ ✓ SODIUM: Good Choice (445 mg)*
PROTEIN: 42 g, CARBOHYDRATE: 2 g, FIBER: 0 g

PESCADO EN SALSA ROJA – SPECIAL REQUEST
Fish of the day with tomato sauce, onions, garlic, green peppers and spices. Served with a side of yellow rice and Cuban style black bean (see analyses below). Request less oil (½ oz).
✓✓ CALORIES: Excellent Choice (395) ✓✓ CHOLESTEROL: Excellent Choice (65 mg)
✓ FAT: Good Choice (21 g)♥ ✓ SODIUM: Good Choice (440 mg)*
PROTEIN: 42 g, CARBOHYDRATE: 8 g, FIBER: 1 g

BLACK BEANS - CAL: 270, FAT: 6 g♥, CHOL: 0 mg, SOD: <5 mg, PROT: 15 g, CARB: 42 g; FIBER: 7 g
YELLOW RICE - CAL: 245, FAT: 3 g♥, CHOL: 0 mg, SOD: 390 mg, PROT: 5 g, CARB: 49 g; FIBER: 1 g

Welcome to Anthony's. Established in 1946, Anthony's Fish Grotto continues to provide the finest seafood dining our city has to offer. We are confident you will enjoy every aspect of your meal, from our vast selection of healthy, fresh seafood to the service provided by our friendly team members. $

Anthony's Fish Grotto

San Diego Bay: Harbor Dr. at Ash Street   (619) 232-5103
Chula Vista: I-5 at "E" Street   (619) 425-4200
La Mesa: I-8 at Severin Drive   (619) 463-0368

ANTHONY'S SEAFOOD KABOB

Shrimp, scallop and swordfish kabob, basted with teriyaki sauce and served over citrus rice pilaf.

✓✓ CALORIES: Excellent Choice (380)   ✓ CHOLESTEROL: Good Choice (145 mg)
✓✓ FAT: Excellent Choice (6 g)♥   ✓ SODIUM: Good Choice (590 mg)*
PROTEIN: 42 g, CARBOHYDRATE: 37 g, FIBER: 1 g

FRESH SEABASS WITH POMODORO SAUCE

Charbroiled sea bass brushed with olive oil, topped with a flavorful pomodoro sauce and served with citrus rice pilaf.

✓✓ CALORIES: Excellent Choice (410)   ✓✓ CHOLESTEROL: Excellent Choice (70 mg)
✓✓ FAT: Excellent Choice (14 g)♥   ✓✓ SODIUM: Excellent Choice (135 mg)*
PROTEIN: 35 g, CARBOHYDRATE: 37 g, FIBER: 2 g

HALIBUT WITH ORANGE MINT BASIL BUTTER

Mild and tender halibut with orange mint basil butter sauce, served with citrus rice pilaf.

✓ CALORIES: Good Choice (475)   ✓ CHOLESTEROL: Good Choice (95 mg)
✓ FAT: Good Choice (22 g)   ✓ SODIUM: Good Choice (330 mg)*
PROTEIN: 38 g, CARBOHYDRATE: 30 g, FIBER: 1 g

GRILLED SWORDFISH GREEK SALAD – SPECIAL REQUEST ☺

Romaine, olives, cucumber, beets, tomato, red onion and feta cheese with marinated grilled swordfish. <u>Request dressing on the side</u> (60 cal, 6 g fat per Tbs.)
(Dressing and crispy pita not included in analysis.)

✓✓ CALORIES: Excellent Choice (400)   ✓ CHOLESTEROL: Good Choice (95 mg)
✓ FAT: Good Choice (21 g)   SODIUM: Moderate (995 mg)*
PROTEIN: 35 g, CARBOHYDRATE: 19 g, FIBER: 6 g

GRILLED FISH TACOS – SPECIAL REQUEST

Two grilled fish tacos with guacamole and beans.
<u>Request taco sauce on the side</u> (not included in analysis).

✓ CALORIES: Good Choice (615)   ✓✓ CHOLESTEROL: Excellent Choice (75 mg)
✓ FAT: Good Choice (21 g)♥   SODIUM: High (1990 mg)
PROTEIN: 46 g, CARBOHYDRATE: 56 g, FIBER: 7 g

GRILLED SHRIMP WITH HONEY MUSTARD

Served with citrus rice pilaf.

✓✓ CALORIES: Excellent Choice (320)   CHOLESTEROL: Moderate (250 mg)
✓✓ FAT: Excellent Choice (3 g)♥   ✓ SODIUM: Good Choice (375 mg)*
PROTEIN: 30 g, CARBOHYDRATE: 43 g, FIBER: 1 g

Antonio's Hacienda Mexican Restaurant
700 N. Johnson Ave. #A, El Cajon, CA 92020 (619) 442-9827
www.antonioshacienda.com

Tierrasanta Mexican Restaurant
5950 Santo Rd. San Diego, CA 92124   (858) 277-3412
www.tierrasantamexicanrestaurant.com

Family owned and operated since 1988, Tierrasanta Mexican Restaurant and Antonio's Hacienda Restaurant serve authentic Mexican food prepared with the highest quality fresh ingredients. Owner Francisco Sifuentes started working in the restaurant business as a busboy back in 1980 and worked his way up to waiter, bartender, manager and owner of a Mexican restaurant called Café Vallarta. Since then he has owned five restaurants, four of which are still within the family. Please visit our friendly family restaurants, which offer great customer service, very nice atmospheres, and the best margaritas in town! $

VEGETABLE FAJITAS – SPECIAL REQUEST ☺

Prepared with green peppers, onions, and tomatoes. Served with rice, beans, and tortillas.
Request less oil (1 Tbs). Analysis does not include rice or tortillas (1 tortilla = 115 cal, 3½ g fat).
- ✓ CALORIES: Good Choice (565)   ✓✓ CHOLESTEROL: Excellent Choice (0 mg)
- ✓ FAT: Good Choice (21 g)♥   SODIUM: High (2145 mg)
- PROTEIN: 21 g, CARBOHYDRATE: 82 g, FIBER: 26 g

GARDEN FRESH BURRITO – SPECIAL REQUEST ☺

Grilled vegetables with rice, mushrooms and whole beans wrapped in a flour tortilla.
Request less oil (½ Tbs.)
- ✓ CALORIES: Good Choice (565)   ✓✓ CHOLESTEROL: Excellent Choice (<5 mg)
- ✓ FAT: Good Choice (21 g)♥   SODIUM: High (1785 mg)
- PROTEIN: 17 g, CARBOHYDRATE: 83 g, FIBER: 11 g

ARROZ CON POLLO – SPECIAL REQUEST

Sliced chicken breast prepared with onions, mushrooms, and green peppers. Served on a bed of rice with jack cheese, garnished with avocados and tomatoes. Request less cheese (½ oz).
- ✓ CALORIES: Good Choice (530)   ✓✓ CHOLESTEROL: Excellent Choice (60 mg)
- FAT: Moderate (27 g)   SODIUM: High (2090 mg)
- PROTEIN: 27 g, CARBOHYDRATE: 45 g, FIBER: 5 g

CAMARONES FAJITAS – SPECIAL REQUEST ☺

Marinated shrimp grilled with fresh peppers, tomatoes, onions, and special spices.
Served with rice, beans, guacamole and three tortillas. Request less oil (1 Tbs) and whole beans instead of refried beans. Analysis does not include rice or tortillas (1 tortilla = 115 cal, 3½ g fat).
- ✓ CALORIES: Good Choice (615)   CHOLESTEROL: Moderate (295 mg)
- ✓ FAT: Good Choice (22 g)♥   SODIUM: High (2470 mg)
- PROTEIN: 49 g, CARBOHYDRATE: 58 g, FIBER: 20 g

The first Arby's opened in Boardman, Ohio in 1964, featuring the now famous roast beef sandwiches. Forrest and Leroy Raffel established Raffel Brothers, a food consulting business, in the 1950s, and then expanded into a fast food concept. The owners chose the name Arby's to stand for the initials of Raffel Brothers, R.B., although some think it stands for "roast beef." The chain now operates more than 3400 restaurants worldwide. For the best-tasting roast beef sandwiches or any of a wide variety of other choices, visit Arby's soon! $

Arby's San Diego area locations:

(For a complete list of all locations, please visit www.arbys.com)

Chula Vista: 2244 Otay Lakes Rd.	(619) 482-0265	Oceanside: 1863 Mission Ave.	(760) 722-8467
El Cajon: 325 N. 2nd St.	(619) 579-5162	San Diego: 7110 Clairemont Mesa Bl.	(858) 292-1174
El Cajon: 709 Parkway Plaza	(619) 440-0331	San Diego: 3777 Midway Dr.	(619) 226-8174
Escondido: 350 W. El Norte Pkwy.	(760) 739-8488	San Diego: 9089 Mira Mesa Bl.	(858) 271-6289
Escondido: North County Fair	(760) 747-1905	San Diego: 6225 Mission Gorge Rd.	(619) 282-9970
La Mesa: 5341 Jackson Dr.	(619) 462-3471	San Diego: 1770 Rosecrans St.	(619) 223-1784
Lakeside: 12136 Woodside Ave.	(619) 390-0369	San Marcos: 1280 W. San Marcos Bl.	(760) 471-8771

REGULAR ROAST BEEF SANDWICH

✓✓ CALORIES: Excellent Choice (320)   ✓✓ CHOLESTEROL: Excellent Choice (45 mg)
✓✓ FAT: Excellent Choice (13 g)   SODIUM: Moderate (950 mg)
PROTEIN: 21 g, CARBOHYDRATE: 34 g, FIBER: 2 g

SUPER ROAST BEEF SANDWICH

Roast beef, red ranch sauce, tomato, and leaf lettuce on a sesame seed bun.
✓✓ CALORIES: Excellent Choice (440)   ✓✓ CHOLESTEROL: Excellent Choice (45 mg)
✓ FAT: Good Choice (19 g)   SODIUM: High (1130 mg)
PROTEIN: 22 g, CARBOHYDRATE: 48 g, FIBER: 3 g

CHICKEN BREAST FILLET SANDWICH

Breaded chicken breast fillet, leaf lettuce, tomatoes and mayonnaise on a sesame seed bun.
✓ CALORIES: Good Choice (500)   ✓✓ CHOLESTEROL: Excellent Choice (55 mg)
✓ FAT: Good Choice (25 g)   SODIUM: High (1220 mg)
PROTEIN: 25 g, CARBOHYDRATE: 48 g, FIBER: 3 g

MARTHA'S VINEYARD™ SALAD ⌣

A combination of iceberg, Romaine, and spring mix, diced grilled chicken, diced apples, dried cranberries, grape tomatoes and shredded cheddar cheese.
(Almonds and vinaigrette not included in analysis); analysis below.
✓✓ CALORIES: Excellent Choice (250)   ✓✓ CHOLESTEROL: Excellent Choice (60 mg)
✓✓ FAT: Excellent Choice (8 g)   ✓ SODIUM: Good Choice (490 mg)
PROTEIN: 26 g, CARBOHYDRATE: 23 g, FIBER: 4 g
SLICED ALMONDS: CAL: 81, FAT: 7 g, CHOL: 0, SODIUM: 0, PROT: 4 g, CARB: 2 g, FIBER: 1 g
RASPBERRY VINAIGRETTE DRESSING: CAL: 190, FAT: 14 g, CHOL: 0, SODIUM: 390 mg, PROT: 0, CARB: 18 g, FIBER: 0

MARKET FRESH® ROAST TURKEY & SWISS SANDWICH

Roast turkey, mayonnaise, spicy brown honey mustard, red onion rings, tomato, lettuce, & big eye Swiss cheese on honey wheat bread.
✓ CALORIES: Good Choice (720)   ✓ CHOLESTEROL: Good Choice (90 mg)
FAT: Moderate (27 g)   SODIUM: High (1790 mg)
PROTEIN: 45 g, CARBOHYDRATE: 74 g, FIBER: 5 g

Nutrition analysis supplied by Arby's.

Baja Fresh is not your ordinary Mexican restaurant. All of our food is prepared fresh at each location. This ensures the FRESH, quality difference that you taste in our food. We believe we have developed recipes that provide you with the fullest and most pleasing FLAVORS for each of our offerings. While we have worked to develop products that reflect the best FLAVORS and quality for each of our items, many of our customers modify their orders to satisfy their individual taste or dietary needs (i.e., no onions, no sour cream, etc.). $

Baja Fresh San Diego Locations:

Aero Dr.: 3737 Murphy Canyon Rd. (858) 277-5700
Downtown: 145 Broadway (619) 702-2252
Encinitas: 194 El Camino Real (760) 633-2262
Escondido: 890 W. Valley Pky. #400 (760) 480-9997
Hillcrest: 120 W. Washington St. (619) 497-1000

Mira Mesa: 9015 Mira Mesa Blvd. (858) 577-0590
Mission V: 845 Cam. De La Reina (619) 295-1122
Point Loma: 3369 Rosecrans St. (619) 222-3399
R. Bernardo: 11980 Brndo Plz. Dr. (858) 592-7788
Vista: 620 Hacienda Dr. (760) 643-0110

For a complete list of all locations, visit www.bajafresh.com

TORTILLA SOUP (WITHOUT CHICKEN) AND SIDE SALAD

A warm and savory soup garnished with ripe avocado slices, crispy tortilla strips & Jack Cheese, & a touch of onion and fresh cilantro. Analysis includes side salad with romaine, tortilla strips, & shaved cheese and soup without chicken. Chicken adds 40 cals, 25 mg chol. and 9 g protein.

✓✓ CALORIES: Excellent Choice (290)   ✓✓ CHOLESTEROL: Excellent Choice (20 mg)
✓✓ FAT: Excellent Choice (15 g)   SODIUM: High (1950 mg)
PROTEIN: 11 g, CARBOHYDRATE: 31 g, FIBER: 6 g
FAT FREE SALSA VERDE: CAL: 15, FAT: 0 g, CHOL: 0, SODIUM: 370 mg, PROT: 0 g, CARB: 3 g, FIBER: 1 g

CHIPOTLE GLAZED CHARBROILED CHICKEN SALAD ☺

Warm chicken tenders, Chipotle glazed, roasted corn, poblano and red peppers, grilled sweet pineapple, sliced avocado, cotija cheese and cilantro. Served with a tangy Chipotle pineapple vinaigrette (see analysis below) & a savory flauta filled with cheese & roasted corn & chiles (incl. in analysis).

✓ CALORIES: Good Choice (600)   ✓ CHOLESTEROL: Good Choice (105 mg)
✓ FAT: Good Choice (22 g)   SODIUM: High (1120 mg)
PROTEIN: 47 g, CARBOHYDRATE: 56 g, FIBER: 11 g
CHIPOTLE VINAIGRETTE: CAL: 110, FAT: 9 g, CHOL: 0, SODIUM: 490 mg, PROT: 0 g, CARB: 8 g, FIBER: 0 g

CHILE LIME CHICKEN SALAD ☺

Warm chicken tenders topped with cotija cheese, black beans, roasted corn, poblano and red peppers, grilled roma tomatoes, sweet tomato chutney and cilantro. Normally served with seasoned flour tortilla chips & chile lime dressing (analysis for dressing below).

✓ CALORIES: Good Choice (640)   ✓ CHOLESTEROL: Good Choice (90 mg)
✓ FAT: Good Choice (16 g)   SODIUM: High (1390 mg)
PROTEIN: 51 g, CARBOHYDRATE: 75 g, FIBER: 22 g
CHILE LIME DRESSING: CAL: 170, FAT: 16 g, CHOL: 10 mg, SODIUM: 450 mg, PROT: 0 g, CARB: 5 g, FIBER: 0 g

FRESH MAHI MAHI ENSALADA ☺

Charbroiled Mahi Mahi, romaine lettuce, Pico de Gallo salsa, avocado, tomato slices and shaved cheese.

✓✓ CALORIES: Excellent Choice (360)   ✓✓ CHOLESTEROL: Excellent Choice (70 mg)
✓✓ FAT: Excellent Choice (14 g)   SODIUM: High (1020 mg)
PROTEIN: 35 g, CARBOHYDRATE: 27 g, FIBER: 11 g
FAT FREE SALSA VERDE: CAL: 15, FAT: 0 g, CHOL: 0, SODIUM: 370 mg, PROT: 0 g, CARB: 3 g, FIBER: 1 g

"BAJA STYLE" CHARBROILED CHICKEN TACO

Mini soft corn tortillas with chopped onion and cilantro, hot or mild salsa, and charbroiled chicken. Analysis for one taco without side of corn tortilla chips.

✓✓ CALORIES: Excellent Choice (180)   ✓✓ CHOLESTEROL: Excellent Choice (25 mg)
✓✓ FAT: Excellent Choice (4 g)   ✓✓ SODIUM: Excellent Choice (230 mg)
PROTEIN: 12 g, CARBOHYDRATE: 25 g, FIBER: 3 g

Nutrition information provided by Baja Fresh.

See page 43 for key to symbols: * ♥ † ☺ and $

FINE PERSIAN CUISINE

Bandar awarded the finest Persian cuisine in San Diego since 1996. We invite you to experience a unique world of award-winning distinction. Please visit our website at www.bandarrestaurant.com. $$

Bandar

825 4th Avenue, San Diego, CA 92101   (619) 238-0101

SHISH KABOB (½ SERVING) ☺

Juicy marinated chunks of filet mignon, skewered and charbroiled to perfection with charbroiled vegetables. Served with basmati rice (not included, see analysis below). (Analysis is for ½ of a full serving).

✓✓ CALORIES: Excellent Choice (365)   ✓ CHOLESTEROL: Good Choice (130 mg)
✓✓ FAT: Excellent Choice (15 g)   ✓✓ SODIUM: Excellent Choice (185 mg)*
PROTEIN: 45 g, CARBOHYDRATE: 11 g, FIBER: 3 g

ADAS POLO (½ SERVING)

Juicy chunks of charbroiled boneless chicken tenders marinated in a special sauce (saffron, onion, fresh lemon juice). Served with basmati rice mixed with lentils, black currant raisins, fresh dates and saffron (not included, see analysis below). (Analysis is for ½ of a full serving.)

✓✓ CALORIES: Excellent Choice (275)   ✓ CHOLESTEROL: Good Choice (130 mg)
✓✓ FAT: Excellent Choice (7 g)   ✓✓ SODIUM: Excellent Choice (165 mg)*
PROTEIN: 48 g, CARBOHYDRATE: 3 g, FIBER: 1 g

FISH KABOB (½ SERVING) ☺

Salmon charbroiled with vegetables. Served with basmati rice (not included, see analysis below). (Analysis is for ½ of a full serving).

✓ CALORIES: Good Choice (460)   CHOLESTEROL: Moderate (175 mg)
✓ FAT: Good Choice (19 g)♥   ✓✓ SODIUM: Excellent Choice (135 mg)*
PROTEIN: 59 g, CARBOHYDRATE: 11 g, FIBER: 3 g

GHEIMEH BADEMJAN (½ SERVING) ☺

A savory medley of eggplant, yellow split peas and a special tomato base, lightly spiced to perfection. Served with basmati rice (not included, see analysis below). (Analysis is for ½ of a full serving).

✓✓ CALORIES: Excellent Choice (345)   ✓✓ CHOLESTEROL: Excellent Choice (0 mg)
✓✓ FAT: Excellent Choice (8 g)♥   SODIUM: High (1470 mg)
PROTEIN: 17 g, CARBOHYDRATE: 58 g, FIBER: 8 g

BASMATI RICE (1 CUP)†

✓ CALORIES: Good Choice (215)   ✓✓ CHOLESTEROL: Excellent Choice (0 mg)
✓✓ FAT: Excellent Choice (2 g)♥   ✓✓ SODIUM: Excellent Choice (0 mg)
PROTEIN: 4 g, CARBOHYDRATE: 43 g, FIBER: 1 g

BLUE POiNT
COASTAL CUISINE

A traditional oyster bar defines Blue Point as an authentic seafood restaurant - the first seafood restaurant and oyster bar in San Diego's Historic Gaslamp Quarter. Blue Point has been awarded the "Best Customer Service 2004," "Best Seafood 2004" and "Favorite Place to Dine 2004" by The Gaslamp Quarter Association, and "Best Seafood Restaurant 2000, 2001, 2002, 2003" by the San Diego Restaurant Association and the "Gold Medallion Award 1998, 1999."

Blue Point exudes elegance with rich cherry wood interior, complemented by polished brass railings and pillowy black leather booths. Sophistication emanates from this San Francisco-style supper club. Blue Point extends a first class dining experience in everything from the top-notch menu and professional staff to the best 40s big band swing music and magnificent atmosphere. $$$

Blue Point Coastal Cuisine
565 Fifth Avenue, San Diego, CA 92101   (619) 233-6623

FRESH CIOPPINO
Crab leg, oyster, mussels, clams, shrimp, and fish in saffron tomato fumet.
✓✓ CALORIES: Excellent Choice (330)   CHOLESTEROL: Moderate (180 mg)
✓✓ FAT: Excellent Choice (10 g)♥   ✓ SODIUM: Good Choice (545 mg)*
PROTEIN: 41 g, CARBOHYDRATE: 16 g, FIBER: 2 g

CITRUS MARINATED SWORDFISH – SPECIAL REQUEST
Grilled with black Thai rice and shiitake mushrooms. Request Citrus Emulsion on the side (not included in analysis) and less oil (1 tsp. for rice and 1 tsp. for mushrooms).
✓ CALORIES: Good Choice (555)   ✓ CHOLESTEROL: Good Choice (90 mg)
✓ FAT: Good Choice (24 g)♥   ✓✓ SODIUM: Excellent Choice (220 mg)*
PROTEIN: 52 g, CARBOHYDRATE: 38 g, FIBER: 4 g

SAUTÉED SHRIMP AND PAPPERDELLE PASTA – SPECIAL REQUEST ♨
Heirloom tomatoes, baby spinach and caramelized shallots. Request less oil for shrimp (½ Tbs).
✓ CALORIES: Good Choice (700)   CHOLESTEROL: Moderate (275 mg)
✓ FAT: Good Choice (25 g)   SODIUM: High (1020 mg)*
PROTEIN: 48 g, CARBOHYDRATE: 70 g, FIBER: 5 g

ROASTED CORN AND POBLANO SOUP † ♨
✓✓ CALORIES: Excellent Choice (100)   ✓ CHOLESTEROL: Good Choice (35 mg)
✓✓ FAT: Excellent Choice (5 g)   ✓ SODIUM: Good Choice (105 mg)*
PROTEIN: 10 g, CARBOHYDRATE: 13 g, FIBER: 2 g

SHRIMP AND LOBSTER POTSTICKERS WITH LEMONGRASS PONZU GLAZE †
Five potstickers per order. (Analysis for 1 potsticker and 1 Tbs. Lemongrass Ponzu Glaze).
CALORIES: 70, FAT: 2 g♥, CHOLESTEROL: 30 mg, SODIUM: 475 mg, PROTEIN: 6 g, CARBOHYDRATE: 6 g, FIBER: 0

When the first Brigantine opened, we were best known for our fresh swordfish. We bought the fish directly from the boats. Throughout the years, we've added to our menu more seafood, many signature items and numerous fresh catches of the day. We serve fish from all over the world, using many different preparation methods. $$-$$$

The Brigantine

Pt. Loma: 2725 Shelter Island Dr. (619) 224-2871 La Mesa: 9350 Fuerte Dr. (619) 465-1935
Coronado: 1333 Orange Ave.   (619) 435-4166 Escondido: 421 W. Felicita (760) 743-4718
Del Mar: 3263 Camino del Mar (858) 481-1166 Poway: 13455 Poway Rd.   (858) 486-3066

WOK TOSSED ASIAN NOODLES – SPECIAL REQUEST ♘

With crisp vegetables and shiitake mushroom sauce. Vegetarian. Request less oil (1 Tbs).
✓ CALORIES: Good Choice (470)   ✓✓ CHOLESTEROL: Excellent Choice (0 mg)
✓✓ FAT: Excellent Choice (15 g)♥   SODIUM: High (1345 mg)*
PROTEIN: 10 g, CARBOHYDRATE: 71 g, FIBER: 4 g

WOK CHARRED AHI WITH VEGETABLES – SPECIAL REQUEST ♘

*Stacked with Asian vegetables and jasmine rice. Request wasabi soy butter on the side,
(not included in analysis: 1 Tbs. = 5 calories, 8 g fat).*
✓ CALORIES: Good Choice (455)   ✓ CHOLESTEROL: Good Choice (100 mg)
✓✓ FAT: Excellent Choice (5 g)♥   SODIUM: High (1425 mg)*
PROTEIN: 59 g, CARBOHYDRATE: 40 g, FIBER: 4 g

MEDITERRANEAN VEGETABLE SALAD ♘

*Roasted Portobello mushrooms and eggplant paired with grilled carrots, asparagus, sweet bell peppers
and marinated Tunisian artichoke hearts. Served with Meyer lemon hummus (included in analysis).*
✓ CALORIES: Good Choice (575)   ✓✓ CHOLESTEROL: Excellent Choice (0 mg)
FAT: Moderate (27 g)♥   SODIUM: High (1590 mg)*
PROTEIN: 17 g, CARBOHYDRATE: 74 g, FIBER: 16 g

CALIFORNIA SUMMER SALAD – SPECIAL REQUEST ♘

*Tender spinach and romaine lettuces tossed with candied pecans, tart apples and sweet red crab.
Request dressing on the side (dressing not included in analysis: 1 Tbs. = 50 calories, 5 g fat).*
✓✓ CALORIES: Excellent Choice (385)   ✓ CHOLESTEROL: Good Choice (95 mg)
✓ FAT: Good Choice (20 g)   ✓ SODIUM: Good Choice (450 mg)*
PROTEIN: 31 g, CARBOHYDRATE: 23 g, FIBER: 6 g

SHRIMP LETTUCE WRAPS – SPECIAL REQUEST † ♘

*Jumbo wild Mexican shrimp tossed with Asian vegetables and shiitake mushroom sauce, served over
crispy rice noodles with lettuce cups. Request less oil (1 Tbs). (Crispy rice noodles not included
in analysis; analysis is for 1 lettuce cup and ½ Tbs. Red Ginger Dipping sauce.)*
CALORIES: 140, FAT: 6 g♥, CHOLESTEROL: 55 mg, SODIUM: 705 mg*, PROTEIN: 8 g, CARB: 13 g, FIBER: 1 g

"The Dr. Rodes/Brockton Villa House"
~ *The La Jolla Historical Society ~ circa 1894*

The Brockton Villa Restaurant is located in one of La Jolla's few remaining historic beach cottages (circa 1894), overlooking the world-famous La Jolla Cove. The restaurant has won many awards, including six prestigious Silver Fork Awards. Breakfast, lunch and dinner are served daily. The menu, the view and the friendly service make Brockton Villa equally popular among locals and tourists, so reservations are highly recommended! $-$$

Brockton Villa Restaurant
1235 Coast Blvd., La Jolla, CA 92037   (858) 454-7393

EGGS IPANEMA – SPECIAL REQUEST
Canadian bacon, sliced tomato, poached eggs and an English muffin.
Topped with a spicy tomato coconut sauce. <u>Request fresh fruit instead of breakfast potatoes</u>.
(Analysis for Eggs Ipanema and fruit only.)

✓ CALORIES: Good Choice (555)   CHOLESTEROL: High (435 mg)
✓ FAT: Good Choice (20 g)   SODIUM: Moderate (780 mg)*
PROTEIN: 24 g, CARBOHYDRATE: 41 g, FIBER: 4 g

GREEK STEAMERS – SPECIAL REQUEST ♨
Three steam-scrambled eggs (NO butter or oil used) with tomato, basil and feta.
<u>Request fresh fruit instead of breakfast potatoes</u>. (Analysis for Greek Steamers and fruit only.)

✓✓ CALORIES: Excellent Choice (360)   CHOLESTEROL: High (755 mg)
✓ FAT: Good Choice (22 g)   ✓ SODIUM: Good Choice (555 mg)*
PROTEIN: 26 g, CARBOHYDRATE: 12 g, FIBER: 2 g

SKINNY DIP SALAD ♨
Grilled shrimp and chicken with gazpacho salsa and citrus vinaigrette.

✓✓ CALORIES: Excellent Choice (365)   CHOLESTEROL: High (340 mg)
✓✓ FAT: Excellent Choice (11 g)   ✓ SODIUM: Good Choice (405 mg)*
PROTEIN: 57 g, CARBOHYDRATE: 7 g, FIBER: 3 g

VEGGIE WRAP ♨
Crunchy veggies with hummus wrapped in a colorful tortilla. (Analysis for wrap only.)

✓ CALORIES: Good Choice (580)   ✓✓ CHOLESTEROL: Excellent Choice (0 mg)
✓ FAT: Good Choice (25 g)♥   SODIUM: Moderate (935 mg)*
PROTEIN: 16 g, CARBOHYDRATE: 75 g, FIBER: 10 g

FISH PAPILLOTE
Baked and served "en parchment" with seasonal vegetables
and rice pilaf (rice pilaf not included in analysis).

✓✓ CALORIES: Excellent Choice (415)   ✓ CHOLESTEROL: Good Choice (130 mg)
✓ FAT: Good Choice (25 g)♥   ✓ SODIUM: Good Choice (305 mg)*
PROTEIN: 42 g, CARBOHYDRATE: 5 g, FIBER: 2 g

Cafe India

Fine Indian Cuisine

Cafe India offers healthy Indian cuisine in a peaceful and cozy atmosphere. We offer oven-baked breads, a large selection of vegetarian entrées and traditional chicken and lamb dishes. The vegetarian lunch buffet is served from 11 am to 3 pm (noon to 4 pm on Sunday), while open 11 am to 10 pm Tuesday – Saturday and noon to 10 pm on Sunday. $

Cafe India 3760-5 Sports Arena Boulevard, San Diego   (619) 224-7500

BHINDI SABZI ᕫ

Okra curry.

✓✓ CALORIES: Excellent Choice (150)   ✓✓ CHOLESTEROL: Excellent Choice (0 mg)

✓✓ FAT: Excellent Choice (10 g)♥   ✓ SODIUM: Good Choice (590 mg)*

PROTEIN: 4 g, CARBOHYDRATE: 14 g, FIBER: 6 g

CHANA MASALA ᕫ

Garbanzo bean curry topped with onions and tomatoes.

✓✓ CALORIES: Excellent Choice (350)   ✓✓ CHOLESTEROL: Excellent Choice (0 mg)

✓✓ FAT: Excellent Choice (10 g)♥   ✓✓ SODIUM: Excellent Choice (105 mg)*

PROTEIN: 16 g, CARBOHYDRATE: 54 g, FIBER: 15 g

BENGAN BHARTA ᕫ

Tandoori (clay) oven baked eggplant sautéed with onions, garlic, tomatoes and peas.

✓✓ CALORIES: Excellent Choice (210)   ✓✓ CHOLESTEROL: Excellent Choice (0 mg)

✓✓ FAT: Excellent Choice (6 g)♥   ✓✓ SODIUM: Excellent Choice (40 mg)*

PROTEIN: 6 g, CARBOHYDRATE: 38 g, FIBER: 11 g

ALOO SABZI ᕫ

Potato curry.

✓✓ CALORIES: Excellent Choice (255)   ✓✓ CHOLESTEROL: Excellent Choice (0 mg)

✓✓ FAT: Excellent Choice (7 g)♥   ✓✓ SODIUM: Excellent Choice (10 mg)*

PROTEIN: 5 g, CARBOHYDRATE: 45 g, FIBER: 4 g

Cafe
PACIFICA

Conveniently located in the heart of San Diego's historic Old Town, Cafe Pacifica features contemporary, fresh seafood cuisine with a distinct California dash of the day's locally-grown herbs and produce. Cafe Pacifica serves only the very freshest fish, as well as a variety of seafood and delicious pasta dishes. The readers of San Diego Magazine continually name Cafe Pacifica as the city's "Best Seafood Restaurant" in their readers' poll. $$-$$$

Cafe Pacifica

2414 San Diego Avenue, San Diego, CA 92110
(619) 291-6666   www.cafepacifica.com

FRESH HAWAIIAN AHI WITH PAPAYA CILANTRO SALSA ♂

Simply grilled and served with fresh seasonal vegetables.
✓✓ CALORIES: Excellent Choice (395)   ✓ CHOLESTEROL: Good Choice (100 mg)
✓✓ FAT: Excellent Choice (15 g)♥   ✓✓ SODIUM: Excellent Choice (105 mg)*
PROTEIN: 56 g, CARBOHYDRATE: 9 g, FIBER: 3 g

FRESH SWORDFISH WITH SPICY BLACK BEAN SAUCE

Simply grilled and served with fresh seasonal vegetables.
✓✓ CALORIES: Excellent Choice (440)   ✓ CHOLESTEROL: Good Choice (90 mg)
✓ FAT: Good Choice (22 g)♥   SODIUM: Moderate (735 mg)*
PROTEIN: 49 g, CARBOHYDRATE: 11 g, FIBER: 4 g

FRESH SALMON WITH SWEET MANGO SAUCE ♂

Simply grilled and served with fresh seasonal vegetables.
✓ CALORIES: Good Choice (555)   ✓ CHOLESTEROL: Good Choice (120 mg)
FAT: Moderate (27 g)♥   ✓✓ SODIUM: Excellent Choice (125 mg)*
PROTEIN: 47 g, CARBOHYDRATE: 30 g, FIBER: 4 g

FRESH SEA BASS WITH TOMATO BASIL SALSA ♂

Simply grilled and served with fresh seasonal vegetables.
✓✓ CALORIES: Excellent Choice (430)   ✓ CHOLESTEROL: Good Choice (95 mg)
✓ FAT: Good Choice (24 g)♥   ✓✓ SODIUM: Excellent Choice (260 mg)*
PROTEIN: 45 g, CARBOHYDRATE: 9 g, FIBER: 4 g

JUMBO SHRIMP WITH SWEET MANGO SAUCE ♂

Simply grilled and served with fresh seasonal vegetables.
✓ CALORIES: Good Choice (465)   CHOLESTEROL: High (445 mg)
✓ FAT: Good Choice (16 g)♥   ✓ SODIUM: Good Choice (535 mg)*
PROTEIN: 50 g, CARBOHYDRATE: 30 g, FIBER: 4 g

See page 43 for key to symbols: * ♥ † ♂ and $ *Healthy Dining in San Diego* **55**

Chile Peppers Mexican Eatery serves delicious Mexican food at affordable prices for breakfast, lunch, and dinner. We cater parties, corporate events, and special occasions. Check out our catering menu! We deliver. Please call for delivery hours. Our online menu makes it easy for you and can save you time when planning your special event. It's easy to call and order from our online menu! We'll have your order ready for you to pickup! Visit our website at www.chilepeppersmexeat.com. $

Chile Peppers Mexican Eatery

10299 Scripps Trail, Scripps Ranch, CA 92131   (858) 578-4210
10425 Tierrasanta Blvd., Tierrasanta, CA 92124   (858) 503-6750
COMING SOON: Hwy. 79 South, Temecula, CA 92592

CHICKEN FAJITA BURRITO – SPECIAL REQUEST

Chicken, vegetables and guacamole. Request guacamole on the side.
(Guacamole not included in analysis: 1Tbs.=20 calories, 2 g fat.)

✓ CALORIES: Good Choice (685)   ✓ CHOLESTEROL: Good Choice (130 mg)
✓ FAT: Good Choice (24 g)   SODIUM: High (1655 mg)*
PROTEIN: 44 g, CARBOHYDRATE: 75 g, FIBER: 5 g

VEGGIE BURRITO – SPECIAL REQUEST 🍎

Green peppers, tomatoes, onions and beans.
Request whole beans instead of refried beans and no rice.

✓✓ CALORIES: Excellent Choice (445)   ✓✓ CHOLESTEROL: Excellent Choice (30 mg)
✓ FAT: Good Choice (17 g)   SODIUM: Moderate (950 mg)*
PROTEIN: 13 g, CARBOHYDRATE: 66 g, FIBER: 11 g

CHEESE QUESADILLA (WITHOUT CHICKEN) – SPECIAL REQUEST

From the Light Menu: Whole-wheat tortilla with cheese and salsa fresca. Request no chicken.

✓ CALORIES: Good Choice (455)   ✓✓ CHOLESTEROL: Excellent Choice (50 mg)
✓ FAT: Good Choice (23 g)   SODIUM: Moderate (985 mg)*
PROTEIN: 19 g, CARBOHYDRATE: 46 g, FIBER: 5 g

CHICKEN BURRITO

From the Light Menu: Grilled skinless chicken breast, iceberg lettuce,
salsa, and cheese in a whole-wheat tortilla.

✓ CALORIES: Good Choice (455)   ✓✓ CHOLESTEROL: Excellent Choice (75 mg)
✓ FAT: Good Choice (16 g)   SODIUM: High (1290 mg)*
PROTEIN: 32 g, CARBOHYDRATE: 48 g, FIBER: 6 g

BEAN AND CHEESE BURRITO – SPECIAL REQUEST

Beans, Jack and cheddar cheese. Request whole beans instead of refried and less cheese (1½ oz).

✓ CALORIES: Good Choice (665)   ✓✓ CHOLESTEROL: Excellent Choice (40 mg)
✓ FAT: Good Choice (22 g)   SODIUM: High (1810 mg)*
PROTEIN: 25 g, CARBOHYDRATE: 93 g, FIBER: 12 g

Chili's Grill & Bar offers a fun, energetic atmosphere and a distinct, fresh mix of grilled American favorites. Chili's features several "Guiltless Grill" menu items, which include low-fat and low-calorie versions of some of the restaurant's popular offerings. Chili's serves several delicious low-fat salad dressings as well as a kids menu with healthy choices, such as the Grilled Chicken Sandwich and Chicken Platter. Healthy side items are also available with Chili's entrées, including Steamed Broccoli, Black Beans, Fresh Veggies and Corn on the Cob. All items are available to go. $

Chili's San Diego area locations: (Please visit www.chilis.com for complete location information)

Clairemont Mesa: 4060 Clairemont Mesa Blvd. (Clairemont Square)	(858) 273-3058
Escondido: 1105 W. Valley Parkway (off 15 Freeway, 1½ miles south of 78 Freeway)	(760) 737-5101
Encinitas: 1004 N. El Camino Real (at Olivenhain in Encinitas Ranch Shopping Center)	(760) 634-5488
La Mesa: 8285 Fletcher Parkway (1½ miles north of 8 Freeway at Jackson)	(619) 589-9890
Mission Valley: 4252 Camino del Rio N. (off 8 Freeway and Mission Gorge Rd.)	(619) 280-7996
Oceanside: 2627 Vista Way (off Hwy. 78, 1 block west of El Camino Real)	(760) 967-1064
Rancho del Rey: 800 Paseo del Rey (1½ miles east of 805 Freeway on H St.)	(619) 656-2910
Sorrento Valley/Mira Mesa: 5969 Lusk Blvd. (1 mile off 805 Freeway & Mira Mesa Blvd.)	(858) 457-5962
Scripps/Poway: 10184 Scripps Poway Pkwy. (off 15 Freeway & Scripps Poway Pkwy)	(858) 566-2096
Santee: 9804 Mission Gorge Rd. (Mission Gorge & Cuyamaca in Santee Trolley Center)	(619) 258-5811
Sports Arena: 3494 Sports Arena Blvd. (across from the Sports Arena)	(619) 223-1107
Temecula: 27645 Ynez Rd. (off the 15 Freeway and Rancho California Rd. exit)	(909) 694-0099

GUILTLESS CHICKEN SANDWICH

Grilled chicken sandwich with no-fat honey-mustard dressing, lettuce, pickle and tomato. Served with black beans & steamed fresh veggies with Parmesan cheese.
✓ CALORIES: Good Choice (490)   ✓✓ FAT: Excellent Choice (8 g)
PROTEIN: 39 g, CARBOHYDRATE: 63 g, FIBER: 11 g

GUILTLESS CHICKEN PLATTER

Grilled chicken breast with rice, sweet corn on the cob and steamed fresh veggies with Parmesan cheese.
✓ CALORIES: Good Choice (580)   ✓✓ FAT: Excellent Choice (9 g)
PROTEIN: 39 g, CARBOHYDRATE: 85 g, FIBER: 5 g

GUILTLESS GRILL® SALMON

8 oz. salmon fillet lightly seasoned & seared to perfection! Served with steamed fresh veggies and black beans.
✓ CALORIES: Good Choice (480)   ✓✓ FAT: Excellent Choice (14 g)♥
PROTEIN: 54 g, CARBOHYDRATE: 31 g, FIBER: 10 g

GUILTLESS BLACK BEAN BURGER

Our meatless black bean patty topped with low-fat ranch, shredded lettuce, tomato, pickle & onion.
✓ CALORIES: Good Choice (650)   ✓✓ FAT: Excellent Choice (12 g)♥
PROTEIN: 38 g, CARBOHYDRATE: 96 g, FIBER: 26 g

Nutrition information supplied by Chili's represents an approximate analysis of each product.
At time of press, cholesterol and sodium values were not available.

Chin's Restaurants have been voted "Best Chinese" for eighteen consecutive years and are honored by the public recognition and patronage. Our goal is to provide you with exceptional Chinese cuisine along with friendly service while surrounded by the unique ambiance of Chin's. Using only the freshest ingredients, all dishes are prepared to order to ensure quality. We are here to serve you. $-$$

Chin's Szechwan Cuisine

Carlsbad: 2958 Madison St.   (760) 434-7115
Encinitas: 625 Encinitas Bl.   (760) 753-3903
Escondido: 445 N. Escondido Bl. (760) 480-4115
Miramar: 9355 Kearny Mesa Rd. (858) 536-2300
Oceanside: 4140 Oceanside Bl. (760) 631-4808

Oceanside: 2241 El Camino Real   (760) 439-3600
Rancho Bernardo: 15721A Bernardo Ht. Pky. (858) 676 0166
San Marcos: 631 S. Rancho Santa Fe Rd. (760) 591-9648
Scripps Ranch: 9978 Scripps Ranch Bl.   (858) 566-0031
Vista: 600 E. Vista Way   (760) 732-3880

Each analysis below is for the dinner-sized portion.

HUNAN CHICKEN STRIPS

Sliced chicken breast sautéed with green peppers and onions in a black bean sauce.

✓✓ CALORIES: Excellent Choice (385)   ✓ CHOLESTEROL: Good Choice (135 mg)
✓✓ FAT: Excellent Choice (14 g)   SODIUM: High (1040 mg)*
PROTEIN: 51 g, CARBOHYDRATE: 13 g, FIBER: 3 g

IMPERIAL SHRIMP ☺

✓✓ CALORIES: Excellent Choice (270)   CHOLESTEROL: Moderate (285 mg)
✓✓ FAT: Excellent Choice (10 g)♥   SODIUM: High (1100 mg)*
PROTEIN: 36 g, CARBOHYDRATE: 12 g, FIBER: 4 g

SAUTÉED ASSORTED MIXED VEGETABLES ☺

Assorted farm fresh vegetables stir-fried in a Chef's special white sauce.

✓✓ CALORIES: Excellent Choice (180)   ✓✓ CHOLESTEROL: Excellent Choice (5 mg)
✓✓ FAT: Excellent Choice (8 g)♥   ✓✓ SODIUM: Excellent Choice (245 mg)*
PROTEIN: 8 g, CARBOHYDRATE: 24 g, FIBER: 7 g

SZECHWAN BRAISED STRING BEANS ☺

A famous Szechwan dish! A fresh selection of string beans, dry braised with imported Chinese preserved cabbage in a Chef's spicy garlic sauce and stir-fried with or without ground pork. Analysis does not include ground pork.

✓✓ CALORIES: Excellent Choice (200)   ✓✓ CHOLESTEROL: Excellent Choice (0 mg)
✓✓ FAT: Excellent Choice (10 g)♥   ✓✓ SODIUM: Excellent Choice (265 mg)*
PROTEIN: 9 g, CARBOHYDRATE: 18 g, FIBER: 6 g

THREE INGREDIENT TASTE ☺

A combination of tender chicken, beef, and shrimp stir-fried with broccoli and Chinese peas in a Chef's special brown sauce.

✓✓ CALORIES: Excellent Choice (275)   ✓ CHOLESTEROL: Good Choice (110 mg)
✓✓ FAT: Excellent Choice (13 g)   ✓ SODIUM: Good Choice (505 mg)*
PROTEIN: 31 g, CARBOHYDRATE: 10 g, FIBER: 3 g

Welcome to San Diego County's first organic, vegan, and raw restaurant. All food at Cilantro Live is prepared with natural and organic ingredients, without the use of any heat over 112 degrees. This process is in harmony with the way nature maintains the vitality of the enzymes and nutrients present in our food. We at Cilantro Live are committed to educate and enlighten our society to the power of great nutrition. We are very pleased to bring this healthful way of living to you and in a beautiful, comfortable, and convenient atmosphere. $

Cilantro Live!

315½ 3rd Avenue, Chula Vista, CA 91910   (619) 827-7401
300 Carlsbad Village Dr., Ste. 106, Carlsbad, CA 92008   (760) 585-0136

CILANTRO BURGER ☼

Sun-dried tomatoes, flax seeds, red peppers, garlic and mushroom, with lettuce, tomato & organic ketchup.

✓✓ CALORIES: Excellent Choice (105)   ✓✓ CHOLESTEROL: Excellent Choice (0 mg)
✓✓ FAT: Excellent Choice (5 g)♥   ✓✓ SODIUM: Excellent Choice (200 mg)*
PROTEIN: 4 g, CARBOHYDRATE: 14 g, FIBER: 7 g

CILANTRO SPRING ROLLS WITH HOISIN SAUCE ☼

Broccoli sprouts, red and yellow peppers, cilantro, mint, red and green cabbage, avocado, and jicama wrapped in a fine rice paper.

✓✓ CALORIES: Excellent Choice (315)   ✓✓ CHOLESTEROL: Excellent Choice (0 mg)
✓✓ FAT: Excellent Choice (1 g)♥   ✓✓ SODIUM: Excellent Choice (80 mg)*
PROTEIN: 9 g, CARBOHYDRATE: 69 g, FIBER: 5 g

CILANTRO LIVE! SOUP

Chicken flavored soup with jalapeno, garlic and miso, garnished with chopped avocado and tomatoes.

✓✓ CALORIES: Excellent Choice (205)   ✓✓ CHOLESTEROL: Excellent Choice (0 mg)
✓✓ FAT: Excellent Choice (13 g)♥   SODIUM: Moderate (750 mg)*
PROTEIN: 5 g, CARBOHYDRATE: 15 g, FIBER: 5 g

PIZZZZZZAZA! ☼

Crispy multi-grain crust topped with a sun-dried tomato sauce, miso cheese, tri-colored onions, red peppers, and kalamata olives.

✓✓ CALORIES: Excellent Choice (385)   ✓✓ CHOLESTEROL: Excellent Choice (0 mg)
✓ FAT: Good Choice (22 g)♥   SODIUM: Moderate (645 mg)*
PROTEIN: 14 g, CARBOHYDRATE: 41 g, FIBER: 9 g

ROMA RAW-VIOLI ☼

Thinly sliced roma tomatoes delicately stuffed with a pine nut-basil cheese and topped with a pesto sauce.

✓✓ CALORIES: Excellent Choice (400)   ✓✓ CHOLESTEROL: Excellent Choice (0 mg)
FAT: Moderate (32 g)♥   ✓✓ SODIUM: Excellent Choice (105 mg)*
PROTEIN: 16 g, CARBOHYDRATE: 21 g, FIBER: 6 g

CLAIM JUMPER
RESTAURANTS

Open daily for lunch and dinner, Claim Jumper Restaurants offer a large selection of freshly prepared items using the finest and freshest ingredients available. The friendly staff is very accommodating regarding special menu requests. Portions are generous. Many guests share appetizers, entrées or desserts (there is never a charge for an extra plate), and leftovers are conveniently packaged to take home. For more information visit www.claimjumper.com $$

Claim Jumper

Carlsbad: 5958 Avenida Encinas	(760) 431-0889
Carmel Mountain Ranch: 12384 Carmel Mountain Rd.	(858) 485-8370
La Mesa: 5500 Grossmont Center Dr.	(619) 469-3927
Temecula: 29540 Rancho California Rd.	(951) 694-6887

VEGETABLE SOUP (6 oz. cup) † ☺

✓✓ CALORIES: Excellent Choice (105) ✓✓ CHOLESTEROL: Excellent Choice (5 mg)
✓ FAT: Good Choice (6 g)♥ SODIUM: High (745 mg)*
PROTEIN: 3 g, CARBOHYDRATE: 11 g, FIBER: 2 g

BLACK BEAN STEAK CHILI

Prime top sirloin, black beans, tomatoes, onions and spices topped with sour cream and salsa. Served in a sourdough loaf (sourdough loaf and cheese toast not included in analysis).
✓ CALORIES: Good Choice (525) ✓ CHOLESTEROL: Good Choice (130 mg)
✓ FAT: Good Choice (22 g) SODIUM: High (1625 mg)*
PROTEIN: 48 g, CARBOHYDRATE: 34 g, FIBER: 9 g

CALIFORNIA CITRUS CHICKEN SALAD – SPECIAL REQUEST ☺

Fresh chicken breast, iceberg, romaine hearts, avocado, green apples, golden raisins, mandarin wedges, dried cranberries, bleu cheese crumbles and green onions. Request dressing and pecan brittle on the side (not included in analysis). (Garlic bread not included in analysis.)
✓ CALORIES: Good Choice (585) ✓ CHOLESTEROL: Good Choice (125 mg)
✓ FAT: Good Choice (21 g) ✓ SODIUM: Good Choice (405 mg)*
PROTEIN: 49 g, CARBOHYDRATE: 54 g, FIBER: 13 g

OAXACAN SEABASS (LUNCH PORTION) – SPECIAL REQUEST

Request less oil (1 Tbs).
✓ CALORIES: Good Choice (695) ✓ CHOLESTEROL: Good Choice (80 mg)
✓ FAT: Good Choice (24 g)♥ SODIUM: High (1400 mg)*
PROTEIN: 44 g, CARBOHYDRATE: 71 g, FIBER: 4 g

CALIFORNIA ROLL ☺

Avocado, snow crab and cucumber rolled in a soybean-sesame sheet. This item can be shared; nutrition analysis is for full order. (Analysis for wasabi pepper and ponzu sauces shown separately below.)
✓✓ CALORIES: Excellent Choice (430) ✓✓ CHOLESTEROL: Excellent Choice (55 mg)
✓✓ FAT: Excellent Choice (11 g)♥ SODIUM: High (1150 mg)*
PROTEIN: 20 g, CARBOHYDRATE: 65 g, FIBER: 9 g

WASABI PEPPER SAUCE (1 Tbs.): 35 CAL, 4 g FAT, 2 mg CHOL, 200 mg SOD, 1 g PROTEIN, 2 g CARB, 0 FIBER
SWEET PONZU SAUCE (1 Tbs.): 25 CAL, 0 FAT, 0 CHOL, 205 mg SOD, ½ g PROTEIN, 6 g CARB, 0 FIBER

For over 20 years in Hillcrest, the Crest Cafe has been a longstanding neighborhood favorite with its "Hearty Homemade Comfort Food," including gourmet burgers, salads, pasta, and home cookin' specialties. Open from 7 a.m. to midnight every day, this casual art deco cafe with church pew seating and friendly, knowledgeable staff will make each visit enjoyable. $

Crest Cafe

425 Robinson Avenue, San Diego, CA 92103   (619) 295-2510

SALMON BURGER – SPECIAL REQUEST ♻

Fresh salmon combined with capers, tarragon, horseradish and fresh lemon juice topped with avocado. Served with a side salad. Request less avocado (½ oz). (Analysis does not include side of Cajun mayo or salad dressing.)

✓ CALORIES: Good Choice (715)   ✓✓ CHOLESTEROL: Excellent Choice (75 mg)
✓ FAT: Good Choice (25 g)   SODIUM: High (1315 mg)*
PROTEIN: 39 g, CARBOHYDRATE: 84 g, FIBER: 10 g

CAROLENA'S TORTILLA ♻

A light breakfast of corn tortillas filled with scrambled eggs, salsa fresca, jalapeno jack cheese, and avocado. Served with chopped mango.

✓✓ CALORIES: Excellent Choice (435)   CHOLESTEROL: Moderate (240 mg)
✓ FAT: Good Choice (22 g)   ✓ SODIUM: Good Choice (590 mg)*
PROTEIN: 19 g, CARBOHYDRATE: 46 g, FIBER: 9 g

CREST BREASTWICH – SPECIAL REQUEST ♻

Broiled breast of chicken on an onion bun with sliced tomatoes, and avocado served with mini salad. Request less butter (1 tsp). (Analysis does not include dressing/chips/fries.)

CALORIES: Moderate (830)   CHOLESTEROL: Moderate (190 mg)
✓ FAT: Good Choice (22 g)   SODIUM: Moderate (925 mg)*
PROTEIN: 79 g, CARBOHYDRATE: 77 g, FIBER: 11 g

GRILLED VEGGIE SANDWICH – SPECIAL REQUEST ♻

Fresh and crunchy cucumbers, mushrooms, tomatoes and avocado layered on our grilled onion roll and topped with melted cheese. Served with fresh fruit. Request no butter.

✓ CALORIES: Good Choice (700)   ✓✓ CHOLESTEROL: Excellent Choice (25 mg)
✓ FAT: Good Choice (17 g)   SODIUM: Moderate (840 mg)*
PROTEIN: 24 g, CARBOHYDRATE: 119 g, FIBER: 13 g

CECELIA'S CHOPPED SALAD – SPECIAL REQUEST ♻

Chopped turkey, mangos, walnuts, Gorgonzola cheese, jicama, apples and spinach. Request less cheese (1½ oz.), less walnuts (2 Tbs.) and dressing on the side (not included in analysis).

✓ CALORIES: Good Choice (585)   CHOLESTEROL: Moderate (180 mg)
✓ FAT: Good Choice (24 g)   SODIUM: Moderate (855 mg)*
PROTEIN: 66 g, CARBOHYDRATE: 28 g, FIBER: 11 g

TURKEY ENCHILADAS – SPECIAL REQUEST ♻

Rolled in corn tortillas and topped with our homemade enchilada sauce. Served with refried beans and jicama slaw (jicama slaw not included in analysis). Request less cheese (1 Tbs.) and no sour cream (not included in analysis).

CALORIES: Moderate (785)   ✓ CHOLESTEROL: Good Choice (125 mg)
✓ FAT: Good Choice (23 g)   SODIUM: High (1370 mg)*
PROTEIN: 67 g, CARBOHYDRATE: 76 g, FIBER: 20 g

Restaurant

Where Nutritious is Delicious

When cardiac surgeon Pat Daily couldn't find a quick-service restaurant that prepared good-tasting, low-fat food – the way he likes to eat – he opened his own! All of Daily's menu items contain fewer than 10 grams of fat and/or less than 20% of the calories from fat. Voted <u>Best Healthy Restaurant</u> by Channel 8's Unknown Eater and the San Diego Reader, Daily's uses the freshest, highest quality ingredients and publishes the <u>nutritional content on all the menu items</u>. The menu includes an array of salads, fruit smoothies, sandwiches, hot pasta, grilled fish, and even low-fat desserts. Below are 6 of the most popular menu items. $

Daily's Restaurant
8915 Towne Centre Drive, San Diego, CA 92122
Phone (858) 453-1112   Fax (858) 453-1393

3-BEAN & CORN CHILI (VEGETARIAN) ☺
with brown rice, a dollop of yogurt, and green salad. (Dressing not included in analysis.)
✓✓ CALORIES: Excellent Choice (285)   ✓✓ CHOLESTEROL: Excellent Choice (0 mg)
✓✓ FAT: Excellent Choice (3½ g)♥   ✓ SODIUM: Good Choice (350 mg)
PROTEIN: 13 g, CARBOHYDRATE: 53 g, FIBER: 8 g

VEGGIE LASAGNA
Served with green salad or soup (not included in analysis).
✓✓ CALORIES: Excellent Choice (230)   ✓✓ CHOLESTEROL: Excellent Choice (30 mg)
✓✓ FAT: Excellent Choice (10 g)   SODIUM: Moderate (845 mg)
PROTEIN: 18 g, CARBOHYDRATE: 18 g, FIBER: 1 g

GRILLED CHICKEN PESTO WITH PENNE
Served with green salad or soup (not included in analysis).
✓✓ CALORIES: Excellent Choice (420)   ✓ CHOLESTEROL: Good Choice (130 mg)
✓✓ FAT: Excellent Choice (9 g)   ✓✓ SODIUM: Excellent Choice (140 mg)
PROTEIN: 37 g, CARBOHYDRATE: 46 g, FIBER: 4 g

DAILY'S SPICY GRILLED CHICKEN PIZZA ☺
Grilled chicken & red onions, peppers, spicy tomato marinade with skim milk mozzarella cheese on our whole wheat pizza crust.
✓ CALORIES: Good Choice (465)   ✓✓ CHOLESTEROL: Excellent Choice (60 mg)
✓✓ FAT: Excellent Choice (9 g)   ✓ SODIUM: Good Choice (445 mg)
PROTEIN: 38 g, CARBOHYDRATE: 53 g, FIBER: 5 g

CAJUN CATFISH ☺
with black beans, brown rice and green salad. (Dressing not included in analysis.)
✓✓ CALORIES: Excellent Choice (400)   ✓✓ CHOLESTEROL: Excellent Choice (70 mg)
✓✓ FAT: Excellent Choice (7 g)♥   ✓ SODIUM: Good Choice (430 mg)
PROTEIN: 33 g, CARBOHYDRATE: 47 g, FIBER: 4 g

DAILY'S FUDGY BROWNIE SUNDAE †
CALORIES: Moderate (260)   ✓✓ CHOLESTEROL: Excellent Choice (15 mg)
✓✓ FAT: Excellent Choice (2 g)♥   SODIUM: Moderate (290 mg)
PROTEIN: 10 g, CARBOHYDRATE: 60 g, FIBER: 1 g

Nutrition analysis supplied by Daily's except for Veggie Lasagna and Grilled Chicken Pesto with Penne.

In 1982, Dave Corriveau and Buster Corley brought an idea to life. Create a place where adults can enjoy great food, terrific drinks and the latest interactive games - all in one place. They discovered a winning formula. Over the past 18 years, Dave & Buster's has grown from one location in Dallas, Texas, to a nationwide organization. And with the help of our creative and dedicated employees, we're able to keep growing and providing our guests with a unique experience. Our Special Events Department will also help you plan meetings or business luncheons. Just call to see how easy and fun it can be! $-$$

Dave & Buster's

2931 Camino del Rio N., San Diego, CA 92108   (619) 280-7115

HULI HULI SALMON – SPECIAL REQUEST

*Chargrilled Atlantic salmon fillet glazed with Hawaiian ginger sesame sauce.
Served with green beans and citrus rice (see separate analysis for rice).
Request green beans steamed instead of sautéed.*

✓CALORIES: Good Choice (520)   ✓CHOLESTEROL: Good Choice (120 mg)
✓FAT: Good Choice (19 g)♥   SODIUM: Moderate (890 mg)*
PROTEIN: 47 g, CARBOHYDRATE: 41g, FIBER: 2 g

OONA'S GRILLED CHICKEN SALAD (½ SALAD) – SPECIAL REQUEST 🍎

*Lemon and herb seasoned grilled chicken breast over a salad of fresh lettuces tossed with
cavatappi pasta, roasted red peppers, artichokes, olives and basil pesto. Large salad;
analysis is for ½ of a whole salad. Request dressing on the side (not included in analysis).*

✓ CALORIES: Good Choice (495)   ✓✓ CHOLESTEROL: Excellent Choice (60 mg)
✓ FAT: Good Choice (19 g)   SODIUM: High (1320 mg)*
PROTEIN: 31 g, CARBOHYDRATE: 47 g, FIBER: 4 g

CHARGRILLED ATLANTIC SALMON – SPECIAL REQUEST

*Atlantic salmon fillet lightly seasoned with fresh herbs.
Served with green beans and citrus rice (see separate analysis for rice).
Request less garlic butter (½ tsp.) and green beans steamed instead of sautéed.*

✓✓ CALORIES: Excellent Choice (405)   ✓ CHOLESTEROL: Good Choice (125 mg)
✓ FAT: Good Choice (21 g)♥   SODIUM: Moderate (535 mg)*
PROTEIN: 46 g, CARBOHYDRATE: 8 g, FIBER: 2 g

CHICKEN MONTE CARLO – SPECIAL REQUEST

*Lemon herb grilled chicken breasts topped with Boursin cheese, roasted red peppers and fresh basil.
Served with green beans. Request green beans steamed instead of sautéed.*

✓ CALORIES: Good Choice (625)   CHOLESTEROL: Moderate (245 mg)
✓ FAT: Good Choice (25 g)   SODIUM: Moderate (790 mg)*
PROTEIN: 83g, CARBOHYDRATE: 11 g, FIBER: 2 g

CITRUS RICE *(1 cup)* †

✓ CALORIES: Good Choice (210)   ✓✓ CHOLESTEROL: Excellent Choice (10 mg)
✓ FAT: Good Choice (6 g)   SODIUM: High (790 mg)*
PROTEIN: 3 g, CARBOHYDRATE: 36 g, FIBER: 1 g

See page 43 for key to symbols: * ♥ † 🍎 and $ *Healthy Dining in San Diego* **63**

El Pollo Loco *offers a fresh, wholesome alternative to traditional fast food with real food you can feel good eating. Our fresh chicken is marinated in a special blend of herbs, spices and citrus juices and then flame-grilled right before your eyes for flavor you won't find anywhere else. We serve our chicken with warm tortillas, fresh salsas and a wide variety of healthful sides, from fresh vegetables and salads to our famous pinto beans and Spanish rice. Complimenting our meals are signature entrees such as our Original Pollo Bowl® and Chicken Tortilla Soup that enable you to satisfy your appetite without sacrifice. Treat yourself to the delicious taste of El Pollo Loco, any way you like it.*

El Pollo Loco has 20 San Diego area locations to serve you. For the one nearest you, please call 1-877-375-4968 or visit www.elpolloloco.com. $

FLAME-GRILLED SKINLESS CHICKEN BREAST – SPECIAL REQUEST
Request chicken skinless.

✓✓ CALORIES: Excellent Choice (155)   ✓ CHOLESTEROL: Good Choice (95 mg)
✓✓ FAT: Excellent Choice (4 g)   ✓ SODIUM: Good Choice (540 mg)
PROTEIN: 29 g, CARBOHYDRATE: 0 g, FIBER: 0 g

POLLO CHOICE SKINLESS BREAST MEAL – SPECIAL REQUEST ⏾
Flame-grilled skinless chicken breast with fresh vegetable blend, garden salad and house salsa. Salad dressing not included in analysis. Request chicken skinless.

✓✓ CALORIES: Excellent Choice (345)   ✓ CHOLESTEROL: Good Choice (110 mg)
✓ FAT: Good Choice (16 g)   SODIUM: High (1065 mg)
PROTEIN: 38 g, CARBOHYDRATE: 16 g, FIBER: 7 g

BRC BURRITO
Pinto beans, Spanish rice and cheese in a flour tortilla.

✓✓ CALORIES: Excellent Choice (425)   ✓✓ CHOLESTEROL: Excellent Choice (15 mg)
✓ FAT: Good Choice (17 g)   SODIUM: High (1135 mg)
PROTEIN: 18 g, CARBOHYDRATE: 62 g, FIBER: 6 g

ORIGINAL POLLO BOWL®
Flame-grilled boneless skinless chicken breast with pinto beans, Spanish rice, pico de gallo, onions and cilantro.

✓ CALORIES: Good Choice (545)   ✓✓ CHOLESTEROL: Excellent Choice (40 mg)
✓✓ FAT: Excellent Choice (10 g)   SODIUM: High (2170 mg)
PROTEIN: 32 g, CARBOHYDRATE: 83 g, FIBER: 13 g

CHICKEN TACO AL CARBON
Flame-grilled chicken, onions and cilantro in warm corn tortillas.

✓✓ CALORIES: Excellent Choice (150)   ✓✓ CHOLESTEROL: Excellent Choice (30 mg)
✓✓ FAT: Excellent Choice (4 g)   ✓✓ SODIUM: Excellent Choice (225 mg)
PROTEIN: 9 g, CARBOHYDRATE: 18 g, FIBER: 1 g

CHICKEN TORTILLA SOUP (SMALL 10 oz.)
Made fresh with plenty of flame-grilled chicken, carrots, celery, Cotija cheese, cilantro and tortilla strips.

✓✓ CALORIES: Excellent Choice (220)   ✓ CHOLESTEROL: Good Choice (80 mg)
✓✓ FAT: Excellent Choice (9 g)   SODIUM: High (1135 mg)
PROTEIN: 21 g, CARBOHYDRATE: 17 g, FIBER: 1 g

INDIVIDUAL SIDES:

⏾ **FRESH VEGETABLES:** CAL: 70, FAT: 4 g, CHOL: 0, SOD: 80 mg, PROTEIN: 3 g, CARB: 6 g, FIBER: 4 g

⏾ **PINTO BEANS:** CAL: 155, FAT: 4 g, CHOL: 0, SOD: 675 mg, PROTEIN: 7 g, CARB: 24 g, FIBER: 9 g

SPANISH RICE: CAL: 160, FAT: 1 g, CHOL: 0, SOD: 420 mg, PROTEIN: 3 g, CARB: 33 g, FIBER: 1 g

⏾ **GARDEN SALAD (SMALL):** CAL: 120, FAT: 12 g, CHOL: 15 mg, SOD: 280 mg, PRO: 10 g, CARB: 8 g, FIBER: 1 g

Established in 1954, everything on the El Torito menu is prepared fresh daily with ingredients indigenous to Mexico. In addition to El Torito's signature favorites like fresh Tableside Guacamole (customized to guest preferences), Handmade Tamales made fresh with stone-ground corn masa and Sizzling Enchiladas, our chefs have prepared a variety of healthy and delicious items prepared to meet your nutritional needs. Join us at El Torito where we offer fresh, authentic Mexican dishes served with warm and gracious hospitality. $

El Torito Restaurants

Chula Vista: 271 Bay Blvd.   (619) 425-6013
Encinitas: 1068 N. El Camino Real   (760) 479-0003
La Jolla: 8910 Villa La Jolla Dr.   (858) 453-4115
La Mesa: 5024 Baltimore Dr.   (619) 698-7404

Mira Mesa: 8223 Mira Mesa Blvd.   (858) 566-5792
Mission Valley: 445 Camino del Rio S. (619) 296-6154
Oceanside: 2693 Vista Way   (760) 439-5407
R. Bernardo: 16375 Bern. Ctr. Dr.   (858) 485-1905

Visit www.eltorito.com for a complete list of all El Torito locations.

POLLO FRESCO – SPECIAL REQUEST ○

Grilled chicken breast, seasoned with adobo sauce, atop sautéed fresh spinach with reduced-fat jack cheese. Served with fresh fruit relish (included in analysis) and frijoles de la olla (see separate analysis below). _Request no tortilla strips._

✓ CALORIES: Good Choice (560)   CHOLESTEROL: Moderate (170 mg)
✓ FAT: Good Choice (24 g)   SODIUM: High (2415 mg)*
PROTEIN: 62 g, CARBOHYDRATE: 23 g, FIBER: 5 g

GRILLED SOFT CHICKEN TACOS – SPECIAL REQUEST

Traditional rolled soft tacos: flour tortillas with grilled chicken breast, jack cheese, lettuce-cabbage mix, relleno sauce, pico de gallo and guacamole. Analysis is for 2 soft tacos (plate comes with 3 tacos). Served with frijoles de la olla, rice and sweet corn cake (see separate analyses below). _Request no tortilla strips._

✓ CALORIES: Good Choice (505)   ✓ CHOLESTEROL: Good Choice (85 mg)
✓ FAT: Good Choice (23 g)   SODIUM: High (1160 mg)*
PROTEIN: 35 g, CARBOHYDRATE: 40 g, FIBER: 5 g

SONORA BURRITO LITE ○

Grilled chicken breast, fresh pico de gallo, mild chiles, reduced-fat jack cheese and roasted tomatillo sauce. Served with fresh fruit relish (included in analysis) and frijoles de la olla (see analysis below).

✓ CALORIES: Good Choice (680)   ✓ CHOLESTEROL: Good Choice (150 mg)
✓ FAT: Good Choice (22 g)   SODIUM: High (2510 mg)*
PROTEIN: 65 g, CARBOHYDRATE: 56 g, FIBER: 8 g

GRILLED CHICKEN QUESADILLA LITE

Grilled chicken breast, reduced-fat jack cheese and roasted pasilla chiles wrapped in a grilled flour tortilla served with fresh fruit relish.

✓ CALORIES: Good Choice (525)   ✓ CHOLESTEROL: Good Choice (115 mg)
✓ FAT: Good Choice (19 g)   SODIUM: High (1280 mg)*
PROTEIN: 51 g, CARBOHYDRATE: 39 g, FIBER: 4 g

FRESH FISH TACOS

Seasonal fresh fish, chipotle sauce, lettuce, cabbage, fresh pico de gallo and cotija cheese. Analysis for 2 tacos. Served with frijoles de la olla, rice and sweet corn cake (see separate analyses below).

✓ CALORIES: Good Choice (540)   ✓✓ CHOLESTEROL: Excellent Choice (45 mg)
✓ FAT: Good Choice (24 g)   SODIUM: Moderate (915 mg)*
PROTEIN: 29 g, CARBOHYDRATE: 47 g, FIBER: 3 g

RICE (4 oz): CALORIES: 145, FAT: 2 g♥, CHOL: 0, SODIUM: 550 mg, PROTEIN: 3 g, CARB: 29 g, FIBER: 1 g

FRIJOLES DE LA OLLA (4 oz): CAL: 145, FAT: 1 g♥, CHOL: 0, SOD: 430 mg, PROT: 8 g, CARB: 27 g, FIB: 8 g

SWEET CORN CAKE (1½ oz): CAL: 115, FAT: 6 g, CHOL: 0, SOD: 145 mg, PROT: 1 g, CARB: 15 g, FIBER: 1 g

See page 43 for key to symbols: * ♥ † ○ and $ _Healthy Dining in San Diego_ **65**

The Fish Market - casual style dining in a clean and comfortable atmosphere. The freshness and quality of our fish speaks for itself. We also offer a retail market where you can select from our extensive variety of fresh fish and menu items for take out. Our entire staff is committed to providing you, our guest, with the utmost in courteous, attentive service and superior seafood knowledge. Your experience is our number one priority; you are the most important person in our restaurants! $$-$$$

The Fish Market

640 Via de la Valle, Del Mar, CA 92075   (858) 755-2277
750 N. Harbor Dr., San Diego, CA 92101   (619) 232-3474

PASTA ANGELICA WITH SEAFOOD – SPECIAL REQUEST ☝

Angel hair pasta tossed with scallops, pesto, garlic and tomatoes.
Request less oil (¼ oz.) and no cheese.

✓ CALORIES Good Choice (610)   ✓✓ CHOLESTEROL: Excellent Choice (40 mg)
✓ FAT: Good Choice (17 g)♥   ✓ SODIUM: Good Choice (540 mg)*
PROTEIN: 33 g, CARBOHYDRATE: 80 g, FIBER: 5 g

MAZATLAN PRAWNS – SPECIAL REQUEST ☝

Mesquite charbroiled shrimp with jalapeno peppers, onion, bell
pepper and tomato. Request less oil and butter (¼ oz. each).

✓✓ CALORIES: Excellent Choice (390)   CHOLESTEROL: High (350 mg)
✓✓ FAT: Excellent Choice (15 g)   SODIUM: Moderate (740 mg)*
PROTEIN: 38 g, CARBOHYDRATE: 15 g, FIBER: 4 g

FRESH BAJA HALIBUT – SPECIAL REQUEST

Mesquite charbroiled halibut with black beans, garlic, ginger and soy sauce.
Request less olive and sesame oil (½ Tbs. each).

✓ CALORIES: Good Choice (505)   ✓ CHOLESTEROL: Good Choice (90 mg)
✓ FAT: Good Choice (21 g)♥   SODIUM: High (1778 mg)
PROTEIN: 63 g, CARBOHYDRATE: 12 g, FIBER: 5 g

GRILLED SWORDFISH WITH CILANTRO PESTO

Grilled swordfish served with cilantro pesto sauce.

✓✓ CALORIES: Excellent Choice (420)   ✓ CHOLESTEROL: Good Choice (95 mg)
✓ FAT: Good Choice (24 g)♥   ✓✓ SODIUM: Excellent Choice (255 mg)*
PROTEIN: 47 g, CARBOHYDRATE: 1 g, FIBER: ½ g

WARM SPINACH SALAD WITH FETA CHEESE – SPECIAL REQUEST ☝

Request less oil (1 Tbs).

✓✓ CALORIES: Excellent Choice (305)   ✓✓ CHOLESTEROL: Excellent Choice (25 mg)
✓ FAT: Good Choice (20 g)   SODIUM: High (1325 mg)
PROTEIN: 8 g, CARBOHYDRATE: 24 g, FIBER: 4 g

SHELLFISH MARINARA (½ ORDER) ☝

Linguine with clams topped with marinara sauce and grated
romano cheese. (Analysis is for ½ of a full order.)

✓ CALORIES: Good Choice (485)   ✓✓ CHOLESTEROL: Excellent Choice (45 mg)
✓✓ FAT: Excellent Choice (13 g)   SODIUM: High (1440 mg)
PROTEIN: 26 g, CARBOHYDRATE: 63 g, FIBER: 7 g

Flame Broiler
The Rice Bowl King

Always Good, Always Guaranteed

At The Flame Broiler, you get delicious, low fat, no frying, no skin, no MSG, all served with one-of-a-kind sauce. We are a healthy quick service Asian-style restaurant, serving the public with health in mind. Please come and enjoy your meal! $

The Flame Broiler 8867 Villa La Jolla Drive, Suite 606, La Jolla, CA 92037
(in the Whole Foods Shopping Center, next to Rubio's)   (858) 587-8989

For location nearest you, go on www.fbroiler.com

"BOWLS"

CHICKEN
Flame Broiler chicken served over steamed rice & topped with Flame Broiler sauce & green onions.
✓✓ CALORIES: Excellent Choice (450)   ✓ CHOLESTEROL: Good Choice (115 mg)
✓✓ FAT: Excellent Choice (12 g)   SODIUM: Moderate (650 mg)*
PROTEIN: 37 g, CARBOHYDRATE: 46 g, FIBER: 1 g

BEEF
Flame Broiler beef served over steamed rice and topped with Flame Broiler sauce and green onions.
✓✓ CALORIES: Excellent Choice (435)   ✓✓ CHOLESTEROL: Excellent Choice (70 mg)
✓✓ FAT: Excellent Choice (10 g)   SODIUM: Moderate (705 mg)*
PROTEIN: 36 g, CARBOHYDRATE: 48 g, FIBER: 1 g

VEGGIE 🍎
Broccoli, cabbage & carrots served over steamed rice & topped with Flame Broiler sauce & green onions.
✓✓ CALORIES: Excellent Choice (175)   ✓✓ CHOLESTEROL: Excellent Choice (0 mg)
✓✓ FAT: Excellent Choice (1 g)♥   ✓ SODIUM: Good Choice (585 mg)*
PROTEIN: 6 g, CARBOHYDRATE: 39 g, FIBER: 5 g

CHICKEN VEGGIE 🍎
*Flame Broiler chicken with broccoli, cabbage and carrots served
over steamed rice and topped with Flame Broiler sauce.*
✓ CALORIES: Good Choice (485)   ✓ CHOLESTEROL: Good Choice (115 mg)
✓✓ FAT: Excellent Choice (12 g)   SODIUM: Moderate (675 mg)*
PROTEIN: 39 g, CARBOHYDRATE: 54 g, FIBER: 4 g

BEEF VEGGIE 🍎
*Flame Broiler beef with broccoli, cabbage and carrots served over
steamed rice and topped with Flame Broiler sauce.*
✓✓ CALORIES: Excellent Choice (390)   ✓✓ CHOLESTEROL: Excellent Choice (70 mg)
✓✓ FAT: Excellent Choice (10 g)   SODIUM: Moderate (735 mg)*
PROTEIN: 36 g, CARBOHYDRATE: 39 g, FIBER: 3 g

HALF & HALF
Flame Broiler chicken & beef served over steamed rice & topped with Flame Broiler sauce & green onions.
✓✓ CALORIES: Excellent Choice (445)   ✓ CHOLESTEROL: Good Choice (90 mg)
✓✓ FAT: Excellent Choice (11 g)   SODIUM: Moderate (675 mg)*
PROTEIN: 36 g, CARBOHYDRATE: 47 g, FIBER: 1 g

Fred's Mexican Cafe, with three convenient locations in San Diego, prides itself on using the freshest & highest quality ingredients available. As recipient of the 2004 Lamplighter Award for Best Mexican Cuisine, our distinction for delicious & healthy Mexican food is well founded. All of our San Diego locations include indoor & outdoor dining, lively music and a relaxed atmosphere. The menu is filled with familiar and reasonably priced Mexican selections as well as a few of Fred's Baja-inspired favorites. $

Fred's Mexican Cafe

Old Town: 2470 San Diego Ave.   (619) 858-TACO   Gaslamp: 527 5th Ave.   (619) 232-TACO
Pacific Beach: 1165 Garnet Ave.   (858) 483-TACO

CALIFORNIA BURRITO – SPECIAL REQUEST ☺

Black beans, lettuce, pico de gallo, guacamole and cheese. Request less cheese (1 Tbs).
(Analysis does not include the sour cream served on the side.)
✓ CALORIES: Good Choice (690)   ✓✓ CHOLESTEROL: Excellent Choice (5 mg)
✓ FAT: Good Choice (25 g)   SODIUM: High (1390 mg)*
PROTEIN: 22 g, CARBOHYDRATE: 96 g, FIBER: 17 g

CHICKEN TACOS – SPECIAL REQUEST ☺

Char-broiled chicken in our special marinade with shredded lettuce and two grilled flour tortillas, melted cheese, tomatillo sauce & pico de gallo...served with our classic Mexican rice and wholesome black beans (included in analysis). Request less cheese (½ Tbs. per taco) and tomatillo sauce on the side. (Tomatillo sauce not included in analysis; 70 calories, 8 g fat per Tbs.)
CALORIES: Moderate (805)   ✓ CHOLESTEROL: Good Choice (95 mg)
✓ FAT: Good Choice (24 g)   SODIUM: High (1960 mg)*
PROTEIN: 51 g, CARBOHYDRATE: 95 g, FIBER: 13 g

MAHI TACOS – SPECIAL REQUEST ☺

A house specialty...marinated mahi filets with cabbage and two grilled flour tortillas, tomatillo sauce and pico de gallo, served with our classic Mexican rice and wholesome black beans. Request no jack or cheddar cheese, less margarine (½ Tbs.) and tomatillo sauce on the side. (Tomatillo sauce not included in analysis; 70 cal, 8 g fat per Tbs.)
CALORIES: Moderate (820)   ✓ CHOLESTEROL: Good Choice (125 mg)
✓ FAT: Good Choice (25 g)   SODIUM: High (2045 mg)*
PROTEIN: 51 g, CARBOHYDRATE: 97 g, FIBER: 14 g

CHICKEN FAJITAS ☺

Char-broiled chicken breast with onions, tomatoes, red and green bell peppers...sautéed in garlic butter. Served with Mexican rice and fresh black beans. (Analysis does not include tortillas or sour cream.)
✓ CALORIES: Good Choice (675)   ✓ CHOLESTEROL: Good Choice (80 mg)
FAT: Moderate (26 g)   SODIUM: High (1475 mg)*
PROTEIN: 43 g, CARBOHYDRATE: 69 g, FIBER: 13 g

STEAK FAJITAS – SPECIAL REQUEST ☺

Top sirloin steak with onions, tomatoes, and red and green peppers...sautéed in garlic butter. Served with Mexican rice and fresh black beans. Request less margarine (½ Tbs).
(Analysis does not include tortillas or sour cream.)
✓ CALORIES: Good Choice (655)   ✓✓ CHOLESTEROL: Excellent Choice (55 mg)
✓ FAT: Good Choice (23 g)   SODIUM: High (1430 mg)*
PROTEIN: 44 g, CARBOHYDRATE: 69 g, FIBER: 13 g

SHRIMP FAJITAS ☺

Sautéed shrimp with onions, tomatoes, and red and green bell peppers. Served with Mexican rice and fresh black beans. (Analysis does not include tortillas or sour cream.)
✓ CALORIES: Good Choice (605)   CHOLESTEROL: Moderate (210 mg)
✓ FAT: Good Choice (21 g)   SODIUM: High (1585 mg)*
PROTEIN: 37 g, CARBOHYDRATE: 69 g, FIBER: 13 g

FRENCH GOURMET

A casual French restaurant and bakery with a "country-French" atmosphere introduces you to lighter, Mediterranean-style specialties from the south of France. For these dishes, cuts of meat are chosen for their leanness and are completely trimmed of fat. The use of olive oil, garlic and fresh herbs results in a healthy, robust style of cooking. Four dinner entrées are marked with a heart symbol indicating a dish prepared with no added saturated fats. Our passion for delicious, creative food has made our catering company a local favorite and tradition for the past 26 years. For more information about the French Gourmet and our wide range of products, please visit our catering website at www.thefrenchgourmet.com. $$

The French Gourmet
960 Turquoise Street, San Diego, CA 92109 (800) 929-1984

GRILLED SALMON
Grilled filet of fresh salmon, served with papaya salsa, steamed seasonal vegetables and herbed rice. (Rice not included in analysis.)
✓ CALORIES: Good Choice (740)   ✓ CHOLESTEROL: Good Choice (125 mg)
✓ FAT: Good Choice (23 g)♥   SODIUM: High (1420 mg)*
PROTEIN: 55 g, CARBOHYDRATE: 76 g, FIBER: 6 g

MEDITERRANEAN-STYLE CHICKEN SAUSAGE
Chicken sausage with lots of Italian flavor - sun-dried tomatoes, pine nuts, basil, parsley, bell peppers and white wine, served with rosemary potatoes and steamed seasonal vegetables.
✓ CALORIES: Good Choice (430)   CHOLESTEROL: Moderate (160 mg)
✓✓ FAT: Excellent Choice (15 g)   SODIUM: High (1310 mg)*
PROTEIN: 46 g, CARBOHYDRATE: 34 g, FIBER: 10 g

RATATOUILLE
Ratatouille served with steamed seasonal vegetables and your choice of herbed rice or couscous. (Analysis is for rice, couscous similar.)
✓ CALORIES: Good Choice (445)   ✓✓ CHOLESTEROL: Excellent Choice (0 mg)
✓✓ FAT: Excellent Choice (6 g)♥   SODIUM: High (1565 mg)*
PROTEIN: 11 g, CARBOHYDRATE: 88 g, FIBER: 9 g

PACIFIC RIM AVOCADO AND SHRIMP SALAD
✓✓ CALORIES: Excellent Choice (375)   CHOLESTEROL: Moderate (275 mg)
✓ FAT: Good Choice (19 g)♥   SODIUM: Moderate (920 mg)*
PROTEIN: 34 g, CARBOHYDRATE: 21 g, FIBER: 9 g

SALAD NICOISE
Traditional French salad - mixed greens tossed with potatoes, green beans, tuna, boiled egg and olives, topped with anchovies. (Dressing not included in analysis.)
✓ CALORIES: Good Choice (585)   CHOLESTEROL: Moderate (245 mg)
✓✓ FAT: Excellent Choice (14 g)   SODIUM: High (1250 mg)*
PROTEIN: 36 g, CARBOHYDRATE: 79 g, FIBER: 10 g

See page 43 for key to symbols: * ♥ † ☺ and $

Menus

FRESH Seafood Restaurant & Bar, located in the heart of La Jolla, offers fresh seafood from around the world and seasonal specialties prepared with an eclectic flair. A stunning covered patio for dining year-round highlights the casual, yet stylish atmosphere. Open for lunch and dinner. $$-$$$

Fresh Seafood Restaurant & Bar

1044 Wall Street, La Jolla, CA 92037
(858) 551-7575

SCALLOP CEVICHE (APPETIZER) †

with three citrus marinade. (Orange crisps not included in analysis.)

✓✓ CALORIES: Excellent Choice (130) ✓ CHOLESTEROL: Good Choice (35 mg)
✓✓ FAT: Excellent Choice (1 g)♥ SODIUM: High (450 mg)*
PROTEIN: 17 g, CARBOHYDRATE: 16 g, FIBER: 1 g

GRILLED ATLANTIC SALMON – SPECIAL REQUEST ⏾

with haricot vert, red onion salad and Dijon mustard sauce.
Request less oil (1 tsp.) and less Dijon sauce (1 Tbs).

✓✓ CALORIES: Excellent Choice (400) ✓ CHOLESTEROL: Good Choice (100 mg)
✓ FAT: Good Choice (24 g)♥ ✓✓ SODIUM: Excellent Choice (115 mg)*
PROTEIN: 37 g, CARBOHYDRATE: 11 g, FIBER: 3 g

PAN ROASTED SEA BASS – SPECIAL REQUEST

with steamed shellfish in a bouillabaisse.
Request less oil in preparation (1 Tbs.) and no oil on the fennel garnish.

✓ CALORIES: Good Choice (580) CHOLESTEROL: High (325 mg)
✓ FAT: Good Choice (25 g)♥ SODIUM: Moderate (720 mg)*
PROTEIN: 73 g, CARBOHYDRATE: 12 g, FIBER: 2 g

POACHED SEAFOOD SALAD – SPECIAL REQUEST ⏾

with shaved fennel, bell pepper, roast cipollini onions, baby greens and Meyer lemon vinaigrette.
Request less oil (¼ oz.) and less vinaigrette (1½ oz). (Fried shallots not included in analysis.)

✓✓ CALORIES: Excellent Choice (415) CHOLESTEROL: Moderate (290 mg)
✓ FAT: Good Choice (25 g)♥ ✓ SODIUM: Good Choice (495 mg)*
PROTEIN: 34 g, CARBOHYDRATE: 16 g, FIBER: 4 g

Located in the Gaslamp Quarter's most photographed building, the former home of Wyatt Earp's Gambling Hall and Saloon, G5 – Georges on Fifth also has the distinction of serving the only hand–selected, "center-cut" and aged Prime Certified Angus Beef® in San Diego. G5 has been voted "Best of the Best" Steak Houses by 600,000 San Diegans...www.BestOf.com, July 2002, and was the featured San Diego Restaurant in Wine Enthusiast Magazine, April 2002. Enjoy our Grammy-nominated pianist Tom Barabas Wednesday – Saturday. Reservations recommended. Please visit our website at www.georgesonfifth.com. $$-$$$

G5 – Georges on Fifth 835 Fifth Ave., San Diego 92101   (619) 702-0444

TOWER OF TROPICAL TUNA TARTARE (APPETIZER) † ♻
Served with a hoisin glaze, citrus ponzu broth and tropical fruit salsa.
✓ CALORIES: Good Choice (200)   ✓ CHOLESTEROL: Good Choice (40 mg)
✓✓ FAT: Excellent Choice (2 g)♥   SODIUM: High (435 mg)*
PROTEIN: 21 g, CARBOHYDRATE: 23 g, FIBER: 2 g

JUMBO SEA SCALLOPS – SPECIAL REQUEST ♻
Pan seared with wild rice dust, sun dried tomato tapenade, green goddess dressing, watercress and new potatoes. Request less dressing (1 Tbs).
✓ CALORIES: Good Choice (660)   CHOLESTEROL: Moderate (165 mg)
✓ FAT: Good Choice (20 g)♥   SODIUM: High (1300 mg)*
PROTEIN: 44 g, CARBOHYDRATE: 86 g, FIBER: 9 g

TOP SIRLOIN STEAK ♻
Sliced rum-brined USDA prime with mango salsa, grilled pineapple and plantain.
✓ CALORIES: Good Choice (520)   CHOLESTEROL: Moderate (160 mg)
✓✓ FAT: Excellent Choice (13 g)   ✓✓ SODIUM: Excellent Choice (155 mg)*
PROTEIN: 57 g, CARBOHYDRATE: 44 g, FIBER: 3 g

SUSHI-GRADE AHI
Flash-seared with hoisin glaze, fried rice, tropical fruit salsa and cilantro oil.
(Fried wontons not included in analysis.)
✓✓ CALORIES: Excellent Choice (435)   ✓ CHOLESTEROL: Good Choice (115 mg)
✓✓ FAT: Excellent Choice (12 g)♥   ✓ SODIUM: Good Choice (325 mg)*
PROTEIN: 38 g, CARBOHYDRATE: 41 g, FIBER: 3 g

SALMON – SPECIAL REQUEST
Sautéed with coriander crust, sun dried cherry fennel relish and montrachet risotto.
Request no basil oil.
✓ CALORIES: Good Choice (570)   ✓ CHOLESTEROL: Good Choice (145 mg)
✓ FAT: Good Choice (23 g)   SODIUM: Moderate (630 mg)*
PROTEIN: 52 g, CARBOHYDRATE: 35 g, FIBER: 1 g

STIR-FRY SEASONAL VEGETABLES ♻
Served with shiitake mushrooms, asparagus, baby bok choy, water chestnuts, broccoli, carrots, and snow peas in a teriyaki sauce with fried or steamed rice (analysis includes fried rice).
✓✓ CALORIES: Excellent Choice (365)   ✓✓ CHOLESTEROL: Excellent Choice (50 mg)
✓✓ FAT: Good Choice (4 g)♥   SODIUM: High (2130 mg)*
PROTEIN: 13 g, CARBOHYDRATE: 73 g, FIBER: 11 g

The Gulf Coast Grill was born out of love for good times and good food. Our menu is inspired by the flavorful and diversified cuisines of the Gulf Coast. This area, from the Gulf of Mexico to the Gulf of Campeche, offers a wide variety and style of cooking with Cajun, Creole, French, Latin American, Spanish and Caribbean influences. We blend our knowledge of these cuisines and their culinary techniques with the freshest ingredients to create what we call the "Best of Both Gulfs," a unique and exciting fusion of Latin and Southern flavors. $$

Gulf Coast Grill

4130 Park Blvd., San Diego, CA 92103
(619) 295-2244

JERK MARINATED CHICKEN SKEWERS WITH HONEY DRIZZLE (½ ORDER) †

Analysis is for ½ order, assuming it is shared between two people.
Analysis does not include jicama cole slaw.

✓ CALORIES: Good Choice (250)   CHOLESTEROL: Moderate (95 mg)
✓ FAT: Good Choice (6 g)   ✓ SODIUM: Good Choice (200 mg)*
PROTEIN: 35 g, CARBOHYDRATE: 14 g, FIBER: 0 g

GRILLED VEGETABLE QUESADILLA 🍎

with caramelized onions, spinach, tomato, corn and pepper jack cheese with salsa fresca.
(Analysis does not include cilantro lime crema and avocado salsa.)
Order as an entrée; optional chicken and shrimp (not included in analysis).

✓ CALORIES: Good Choice (560)   ✓✓ CHOLESTEROL: Excellent Choice (50 mg)
✓ FAT: Good Choice (24 g)   SODIUM: High (1285 mg)*
PROTEIN: 22 g, CARBOHYDRATE: 67 g, FIBER: 9 g

CEDAR PLANK SALMON 🍎

Lightly spice charred, served medium rare with Creole ragout.
Crispy onions and cornmeal crusted potato cake not included in analysis.

✓ CALORIES: Good Choice (480)   ✓ CHOLESTEROL: Good Choice (125 mg)
✓ FAT: Good Choice (22 g)♥   SODIUM: High (2395 mg)*
PROTEIN: 49 g, CARBOHYDRATE: 21 g, FIBER: 4 g

BLACK & WHITE SESAME CRUSTED AHI – SPECIAL REQUEST

with wasabi soy glaze and seaweed salad. *Request less oil* (½ Tbs).
(Fried rice and pickled onions not included in analysis.)

✓✓ CALORIES: Excellent Choice (415)   ✓ CHOLESTEROL: Good Choice (90 mg)
✓ FAT: Good Choice (18 g)♥   SODIUM: High (1190 mg)*
PROTEIN: 52 g, CARBOHYDRATE: 9 g, FIBER: 2 g

HARRY'S BAR
and American Grill®

Modeled after the famous bar and grill by the same name in Florence, Italy, Harry's Bar and American Grill in La Jolla is the second California location. They have earned their reputation with their Harry's Grill menu which offers superb, deliciously grilled steak, chicken, lamb and fish dishes as well as their lunch menu with homemade pasta dishes, fresh salads and more. The "Bellini," their popular specialty drink, and an extensive wine list complete the well-rounded menu in this noteworthy venue. $$-$$$

Harry's Bar and American Grill
4370 La Jolla Village Drive, San Diego, CA 92121   (858) 373-1252

SPIEDINO DI GAMBERI CON RICCIOLI
Skewer of grilled prawns, goat cheese filled zucchini, roasted peppers, olive oil and lemon.
✓✓ CALORIES: Excellent Choice (435)   CHOLESTEROL: High (375 mg)
 ✓ FAT: Good Choice (25 g)   SODIUM: Moderate (810 mg)*
            PROTEIN: 45 g, CARBOHYDRATE: 4 g, FIBER: 1 g

LINGUINE CON GAMBERI E CARCIOFI
Thin flat pasta, prawns, baby artichokes, garlic, white wine, and olive oil.
✓ CALORIES: Good Choice (565)   CHOLESTEROL: Moderate (210 mg)
✓ FAT: Good Choice (16 g)♥   ✓ SODIUM: Good Choice (580 mg)*
            PROTEIN: 35 g, CARBOHYDRATE: 67 g, FIBER: 7 g

CAPELLINI AL POMODORO E BASILICO – SPECIAL REQUEST ♻
Angel hair pasta, fresh tomatoes, basil and garlic. Request less oil (1 Tbs).
✓ CALORIES: Good Choice (485)   ✓✓ CHOLESTEROL: Excellent Choice (5 mg)
✓ FAT: Good Choice (17 g)♥   ✓✓ SODIUM: Excellent Choice (295 mg)*
            PROTEIN: 13 g, CARBOHYDRATE: 71 g, FIBER: 6 g

GRIGLIATA MISTA DI PESCE – SPECIAL REQUEST
Mixed seafood grill of freshwater prawns, calamari and fresh fish. Served with vegetable of the day. Request less lemon sauce (1 Tbs). Roasted potatoes not included in analysis.
✓ CALORIES: Good Choice (530)   CHOLESTEROL: High (480 mg)
 FAT: Moderate (27 g)♥   ✓ SODIUM: Good Choice (365 mg)*
            PROTEIN: 62 g, CARBOHYDRATE: 10 g, FIBER: 3 g

LINGUINE AI SAPORI MEDITERRANEI
Thin flat pasta, Manila clams, grilled prawns and spicy tomato sauce.
✓ CALORIES: Good Choice (720)   CHOLESTEROL: High (395 mg)
✓✓ FAT: Excellent Choice (14 g)♥   SODIUM: High (1180 mg)*
            PROTEIN: 69 g, CARBOHYDRATE: 71 g, FIBER: 5 g

Step inside Il Fornaio and take a culinary journey through Italy. Early mornings bring rustic, crisp, crusted breads hot from the oven accompanied by the scent of fresh brewed espresso. During lunch and dinner hours, pastas and flavorful sauces simmer while meats and vegetables roast over hot coals. In the tradition of Italy's thousandfold trattorias, the sights, sounds and aromas of authentic Italian cuisine are recreated fresh every day at Il Fornaio's authentic Italian restaurants and bakeries. $$

Il Fornaio

1333 First Street, Coronado, CA 92118   (619) 437-4911
1555 Camino Del Mar, #301, Del Mar, CA 92014   (858) 755-8876

PIZZA VEGETARIANA CHEESELESS ☙

Baby artichokes, button mushrooms, roasted bell peppers and tomato sauce.
- ✓ CALORIES: Good Choice (695)
- ✓ FAT: Good Choice (18 g)♥
- ✓✓ CHOLESTEROL: Excellent Choice (0 mg)
- SODIUM: High (1260 mg)

PROTEIN: 16 g, CARBOHYDRATE: 118 g, FIBER: 9 g

LINGUINE MARE CHIARO – SPECIAL REQUEST ☙

*Fresh mussels, clams, scallops and shrimp, served over pasta
with marinara sauce. Request less oil (½ Tbs).*
- ✓ CALORIES: Good Choice (730)
- ✓✓ FAT: Excellent Choice (13 g)♥
- CHOLESTEROL: Moderate (255 mg)
- SODIUM: Moderate (755 mg)*

PROTEIN: 65 g, CARBOHYDRATE: 84 g, FIBER: 6 g

CAPELLINI AL POMODORO NATURALE – SPECIAL REQUEST ☙

*Cappelini pasta topped with homemade marinara
sauce and basil. Request less oil (1 Tbs).*
- ✓ CALORIES: Good Choice (530)
- ✓ FAT: Good Choice (16 g)♥
- ✓✓ CHOLESTEROL: Excellent Choice (0 mg)
- ✓✓ SODIUM: Excellent Choice (295 mg)*

PROTEIN: 13 g, CARBOHYDRATE: 81 g, FIBER: 6 g

SALMONE – SPECIAL REQUEST ☙

*Grilled fresh salmon with lemon sauce, served with vegetables and potatoes.
Request potatoes and vegetables steamed.*
- ✓ CALORIES: Good Choice (515)
- ✓ FAT: Good Choice (18 g)♥
- ✓ CHOLESTEROL: Good Choice (120 mg)
- ✓✓ SODIUM: Excellent Choice (275 mg)*

PROTEIN: 51 g, CARBOHYDRATE: 42 g, FIBER: 8 g

Kemo Sabe, meaning "trusted friend," has become just that to the eclectic palates of San Diegans. A member of David and Lesley Cohn's Fifth Ave. favorites and the brainchild of Chef Deborah Scott, Kemo Sabe brings the Pacific Rim together with Thai, Asian, Southwest and Pacific Island influences. $$-$$$

Kemo Sabe 3958 5th Ave., San Diego, (619) 220-6802

Located in stylish Little Italy, this hot spot features San Diego's most creative cuisine that tells a story that spans the artic region to the South of Mexico. Arranged beautifully, with amazing attention to symmetry, color, contrast and form, Chef Scott's dishes are a tribute to the human spirit and its creativity. $-$$

Indigo Grill 1536 India St., San Diego (Little Italy) (619) 234-6802

Indigo Grill: MEZCAL CURED SALMON CEVICHE (½ ORDER) †🍎

Appetizer of salmon, juniper crust, cucumber and wild dill. (Analysis is for ½ order.)
✓✓ CALORIES: Excellent Choice (100) ✓✓ CHOLESTEROL: Excellent Choice (30 mg)
✓✓ FAT: Excellent Choice (4 g)♥ SODIUM: High (425 mg)*
PROTEIN: 12 g, CARBOHYDRATE: 4 g, FIBER: 1 g

Indigo Grill: STACKED BEET SALAD (½ ORDER) † – SPECIAL REQUEST 🍎

Appetizer of orange, warm beet greens, orange-caraway dressing, and beet chips.
Request less cheese (½ Tbs). (Analysis is for ½ order, assuming it is shared.)
✓ CALORIES: Good Choice (165) ✓✓ CHOLESTEROL: Excellent Choice (0 mg)
✓ FAT: Good Choice (8 g)♥ SODIUM: Moderate (305 mg)*
PROTEIN: 4 g, CARBOHYDRATE: 21 g, FIBER: 4 g

Indigo Grill: ALDERWOOD PLANK SALMON (½ PORTION) 🍎

With cucumber-dill moleto served with squid ink pasta and oaxacan cheese.
(Analysis does not include horseradish flatbread.)
✓ CALORIES: Good Choice (530) ✓ CHOLESTEROL: Good Choice (145 mg)
✓ FAT: Good Choice (23 g) SODIUM: Moderate (885 mg)*
PROTEIN: 33 g, CARBOHYDRATE: 48 g, FIBER: 3 g

KEMO SABE: SKIRTS ON FIRE – SPECIAL REQUEST 🍎

Charbroiled skirt steak, Thai chile, Mandarin-serrano relish and chile black beans.
Request less beans (½ cup). (Analysis does not include rice sticks.)
✓ CALORIES: Good Choice (660) ✓ CHOLESTEROL: Good Choice (120 mg)
✓ FAT: Good Choice (24 g) SODIUM: Moderate (685 mg)*
PROTEIN: 72 g, CARBOHYDRATE: 37 g, FIBER: 11 g

Kemo Sabe: BLACKENED SATAY CHICKEN BREAST STACK (½ ORDER) 🍎

Layered jerk chicken, chili corn cake, melon salsa, and 10 spice grilled plantain. (Analysis is for ½ order, and does not include melon buerre blanc sauce or balsamic reduction drizzled on the plate.)
✓ CALORIES: Good Choice (710) ✓✓ CHOLESTEROL: Excellent Choice (70 mg)
✓ FAT: Good Choice (22 g) SODIUM: Moderate (780 mg)*
PROTEIN: 28 g, CARBOHYDRATE: 108 g, FIBER: 6 g

Menus

J. Taylor's menu showcases contemporary American cuisine with a sophisticated flair. J. Taylor's is a casually elegant, romantic restaurant with a crackling fireplace, orchids, cathedral ceilings and French doors opening to an open courtyard and patio dining area, which features decorative waterfalls and an herb garden. J. Taylor's is open seven days per week from 6a.m. to 10p.m. and serves breakfast, lunch and dinner. Jacket and tie are not required. $$$

J. Taylor's Restaurant at L'Auberge Del Mar

1540 Camino del Mar, Del Mar, CA 92014   (858) 793-6460

(The following items appear on the "Chef's Menu," which varies daily.)
Please ask your server for the daily selection.

CHILLED CUCUMBER SOUP †

✓✓ CALORIES: Excellent Choice (110)   ✓✓ CHOLESTEROL: Excellent Choice (0 mg)
✓✓ FAT: Good Choice (8 g)♥   SODIUM: High (1590 mg)*
PROTEIN: 1 g, CARBOHYDRATE: 8 g, FIBER: 1 g

RHUBARB SOUP †

✓✓ CALORIES: Excellent Choice (145)   ✓✓ CHOLESTEROL: Excellent Choice (0 mg)
✓✓ FAT: Excellent Choice (0 g)   ✓✓ SODIUM: Excellent Choice (5 mg)*
PROTEIN: 1 g, CARBOHYDRATE: 37 g, FIBER: 2 g

CITRUS MARINATED TUNA TARTAR

with coriander, yuzu powder, smoked salt and sea urchin.
(Toasted brioche not included in analysis.)
✓✓ CALORIES: Excellent Choice (115)   ✓✓ CHOLESTEROL: Excellent Choice (60 mg)
✓✓ FAT: Excellent Choice (2 g)♥   SODIUM: Moderate (655 mg)*
PROTEIN: 22 g, CARBOHYDRATE: 2 g, FIBER: 1 g

HEIRLOOM TOMATO SALAD

with lobster, tomato water and a smoked coriander cracker.
✓✓ CALORIES: Excellent Choice (365)   ✓ CHOLESTEROL: Good Choice (95 mg)
✓✓ FAT: Excellent Choice (9 g)   SODIUM: High (1540 mg)*
PROTEIN: 31 g, CARBOHYDRATE: 39 g, FIBER: 4 g

GRILLED SEA BASS ☽

Steamed spinach, braised red lentils, clam and baby vegetable nage.
✓ CALORIES: Good Choice (725)   ✓ CHOLESTEROL: Good Choice (95 mg)
✓✓ FAT: Excellent Choice (7 g)♥   SODIUM: Moderate (920 mg)*
PROTEIN: 80 g, CARBOHYDRATE: 93 g, FIBER: 36 g

Jamba's philosophy is simple: what you put into your body feeds your spirit, gives you energy to do the things you love, and inspires a balanced life. And what better way to do that than with sun-kissed fruit-filled smoothies, energizing fresh-squeezed juices, vitamin-packed boosts, and delicious baked goods that give you the extra oomph you need to get going. All smoothies include one FREE Juice Boost & are available in a Sixteen (16 oz.), Original (24 oz.), or Power (32 oz.) size. $

Jamba Juice — with 23 San Diego County locations.
Call 1-888-JAMBA12 or visit www.jambajuice.com for your nearest location.

STRAWBERRY NIRVANA® SMOOTHIE *(16 oz.)* ♨
Enlightened base, frozen strawberries, apple strawberry juice blend, ice, and frozen bananas.
- ✓✓ CALORIES: Excellent Choice (160)
- ✓✓ CHOLESTEROL: Excellent Choice (5 mg)
- ✓✓ FAT: Excellent Choice (0 g)
- ✓✓ SODIUM: Excellent Choice (230 mg)

PROTEIN: 6 g, CARBOHYDRATE: 34 g, FIBER: 3 g

MANGO MANTRA® SMOOTHIE *(16 oz.)* ♨
Enlightened base, frozen mangos, fresh orange juice, ice, and frozen peaches.
- ✓✓ CALORIES: Excellent Choice (170)
- ✓✓ CHOLESTEROL: Excellent Choice (5 mg)
- ✓✓ FAT: Excellent Choice (½ g)
- ✓✓ SODIUM: Excellent Choice (230 mg)

PROTEIN: 7 g, CARBOHYDRATE: 36 g, FIBER: 2 g

CARIBBEAN PASSION® SMOOTHIE *(16 oz.)* ♨
Passion fruit juice blend, orange sherbet, frozen strawberries, frozen peaches and ice.
- ✓✓ CALORIES: Excellent Choice (290)
- ✓✓ CHOLESTEROL: Excellent Choice (5 mg)
- ✓✓ FAT: Excellent Choice (1½ g)
- ✓✓ SODIUM: Excellent Choice (40 mg)

PROTEIN: 2 g, CARBOHYDRATE: 67 g, FIBER: 3 g

PROTEIN BERRY PIZZAZZ™ SMOOTHIE *(16 oz.)* ♨
Soymilk, frozen strawberries, frozen bananas, ice and Protein Boost.
- ✓✓ CALORIES: Excellent Choice (280)
- ✓✓ CHOLESTEROL: Excellent Choice (0 mg)
- ✓✓ FAT: Excellent Choice (1 g)♥
- ✓✓ SODIUM: Excellent Choice (170 mg)

PROTEIN: 15 g, CARBOHYDRATE: 56 g, FIBER: 4 g

STRAWBERRIES WILD® SMOOTHIE *(16 oz.)* ♨
Apple strawberry juice blend, nonfat vanilla frozen yogurt, frozen strawberries, frozen bananas, and ice.
- ✓✓ CALORIES: Excellent Choice (290)
- ✓✓ CHOLESTEROL: Excellent Choice (0 mg)
- ✓✓ FAT: Excellent Choice (0 g)
- ✓✓ SODIUM: Excellent Choice (115 mg)

PROTEIN: 4 g, CARBOHYDRATE: 69 g, FIBER: 3 g

RAZZMATAZZ™ SMOOTHIE *(16 oz.)* ♨
Raspberry juice, strawberries, banana, orange sherbet and ice.
- ✓✓ CALORIES: Excellent Choice (310)
- ✓✓ CHOLESTEROL: Excellent Choice (5 mg)
- ✓✓ FAT: Excellent Choice (1½ g)
- ✓✓ SODIUM: Excellent Choice (45 mg)

PROTEIN: 2 g, CARBOHYDRATE: 73 g, FIBER: 3 g

HONEY BERRY BRAN BREAD: *(1 mini loaf) with raisins, blueberries and spices. Good source of protein, fiber & iron!*
CAL: 320, FAT: 12 g♥, CHOLESTEROL: 30 mg, SODIUM: 360 mg, PROTEIN: 6 g, CARBOHYDRATE: 48 g, FIBER: 6 g

Nutrition analysis supplied by Jamba Juice.

See page 43 for key to symbols ♥ * ♨ † and $

There are many reasons to eat at Jimbo's…Naturally! Drink at our Java-Juice Bar or take home our Flavours To Go. For one, we use whole foods – ingredients with all their nutrition intact. We also use as many organically grown ingredients in our deli dishes as are available. Our Java-Juice Bar offers exclusively organic coffee drinks and smoothies made from organically grown fruits and vegetables. Our meat dishes feature hormone and antibiotic-free meat and poultry. In addition, you'll find no additives, preservatives or anything artificial in any of our food.
What you will find is delicious, nutritious dishes from around the world. Come see how tasty healthy dining can be at Jimbo's…Naturally! $

Jimbo's…Naturally!

Del Mar: 12853 El Camino Real, San Diego, CA 92130   (858) 793-7755
Escondido: 1633 S. Centre City Parkway, Escondido, CA 92025   (760) 489-7755
Carlsbad: 1923 Calle Barcelona, Ste. 149, Carlsbad, CA 92009   (760) 334-7755

GARDEN NUT AU GRATIN (½ POUND) ☺

A hearty vegetable casserole layered with brown rice & nuts, seasoned with an Italian tomato sauce.
✓✓ CALORIES: Excellent Choice (290)   ✓✓ CHOLESTEROL: Excellent Choice (10 mg)
✓ FAT: Good Choice (16 g)   SODIUM: Moderate (650 mg)*
PROTEIN: 9 g, CARBOHYDRATE: 29 g, FIBER: 5 g

HEALTH SALAD (½ POUND) ☺

Medley of fresh vegetables tossed in a dill vinaigrette. A great summer salad!
✓✓ CALORIES: Excellent Choice (210)   ✓✓ CHOLESTEROL: Excellent Choice (0 mg)
✓ FAT: Good Choice (18 g)♥   ✓✓ SODIUM: Excellent Choice (135 mg)*
PROTEIN: 2 g, CARBOHYDRATE: 10 g, FIBER: 3 g

SPINACH PIE (¹⁄₆ PIE)

A whole wheat crust filled with organic spinach, eggs, spices and a blend of feta and ricotta cheese. Good any time of the day.
✓✓ CALORIES: Excellent Choice (355)   ✓ CHOLESTEROL: Good Choice (105 mg)
FAT: Moderate (26 g)   ✓ SODIUM: Good Choice (505 mg)*
PROTEIN: 13 g, CARBOHYDRATE: 17 g, FIBER: 2 g

VEGGIE BURGER ☺

Vegetarian burger made to order. In a hurry? Grab one from our Flavours To Go case.
✓✓ CALORIES: Excellent Choice (370)   ✓✓ CHOLESTEROL: Excellent Choice (20 mg)
✓✓ FAT: Excellent Choice (13 g)♥   SODIUM: High (1355 mg)*
PROTEIN: 15 g, CARBOHYDRATE: 50 g, FIBER: 8 g

TABOULI SALAD (¼ POUND) †

A Mediterranean wheat salad made with fresh parsley, tomato and mint, tossed with a lemony olive oil dressing.
✓✓ CALORIES: Excellent Choice (100)   ✓✓ CHOLESTEROL: Excellent Choice (0 mg)
✓✓ FAT: Excellent Choice (5 g)♥   ✓ SODIUM: Good Choice (135 mg)*
PROTEIN: 2 g, CARBOHYDRATE: 14 g, FIBER: 4 g

HARVEST BERRY MUFFIN † ☺

A wheat-free whole grain fruited muffin.
CALORIES: Moderate (320)   ✓✓ CHOLESTEROL: Excellent Choice (0 mg)
✓✓ FAT: Excellent Choice (5 g)♥   ✓ SODIUM: Good Choice (105 mg)*
PROTEIN: 9 g, CARBOHYDRATE: 75 g, FIBER: 9 g

At Ki's, we serve an array of food and drinks made from high-quality fruits, vegetables, grains, eggs, dairy, and poultry products. Our goal is to serve low-fat, great-tasting, healthy food and drinks at an affordable price. Along with this, we strive to have an atmosphere of friendliness while providing service in a quick and efficient manner. Every customer is special at Ki's. $

Ki's Restaurant & Juice Bar

2591 S. Coast Hwy. 101, Cardiff by the Sea, CA 92007   (760) 436-5236

GRILLED SALMON SALAD (DINNER MENU) – SPECIAL REQUEST ♨

with baby greens, roasted peppers and orange basil vinaigrette.
<u>*Request dressing on the side*</u> *(not included in analysis).*

✓✓ CALORIES: Excellent Choice (225)   ✓✓ CHOLESTEROL: Excellent Choice (70 mg)
✓✓ FAT: Excellent Choice (10 g)♥   ✓✓ SODIUM: Excellent Choice (285 mg)*
PROTEIN: 27 g, CARBOHYDRATE: 7 g, FIBER: 3 g

TOFU BURRITO – SPECIAL REQUEST ♨

Tofu, green peppers, tomatoes, and onions sautéed in soy,
olive oil and spices. <u>*Request less oil*</u> *(½ Tbs).*

✓ CALORIES: Good Choice (615)   ✓✓ CHOLESTEROL: Excellent Choice (0 mg)
✓ FAT: Good Choice (21 g)♥   SODIUM: High (1445 mg)*
PROTEIN: 29 g, CARBOHYDRATE: 84 g, FIBER: 14 g

GRILLED TEMPEH SANTA FE ♨

with avocado salsa, grilled veggies and roasted potatoes.

✓✓ CALORIES: Excellent Choice (650)   ✓✓ CHOLESTEROL: Excellent Choice (0 mg)
FAT: Moderate (37 g)♥   ✓ SODIUM: Good Choice (425 mg)*
PROTEIN: 34 g, CARBOHYDRATE: 56 g, FIBER: 13 g

PAN SEARED HERBED CHICKEN BREAST

with creamy asiago cheese polenta and sautéed vegetables.

✓✓ CALORIES: Excellent Choice (440)   ✓ CHOLESTEROL: Good Choice (130 mg)
✓ FAT: Good Choice (16 g)   ✓ SODIUM: Good Choice (425 mg)*
PROTEIN: 52 g, CARBOHYDRATE: 21 g, FIBER: 4 g

The Original Made-to-Order Fresh Mexican Restaurant! At La Salsa you'll find a variety of delicious Mexican recipes and tastes all prepared individually to your order and liking. A fresh salsa bar also allows you to garnish with a wide variety of salsas and trimmings. No prepackaged burritos, no MSG, no microwaves. Tell us what you want...we'll make it fresh! For more info & locations, visit www.lasalsa.com. $

La Salsa's San Diego area locations: Airport, Carmel Country Plaza, Clairemont Mesa, Coronado, Costa Verde, Downtown, Encinitas, Escondido, Hillcrest, La Mesa, Oceanside, Pacific Beach and Santee.

Chips not included in analyses below.

TWO SOFT TACOS PLATTER WITH CHICKEN

Two soft corn tortilla tacos filled with charbroiled chicken, Jack and cheddar cheeses, lettuce and tomatoes. Served with black beans, rice, and salsa.

✓ CALORIES: Good Choice (735)   ✓ CHOLESTEROL: Good Choice (90 mg)
✓ FAT: Good Choice (23 g)   SODIUM: High (1350 mg)
PROTEIN: 47 g, CARBOHYDRATE: 103 g, FIBER: 12 g

CHICKEN CHILE-LIME SALAD – SPECIAL REQUEST

Chicken, Romaine, Cotija cheese, tomatoes & avocado, with our own Chile–Lime dressing. <u>Request no tortilla strips & dressing on the side</u> (neither incl. in analysis). Mango Salsa is an excellent dressing alternative.

✓✓ CALORIES: Excellent Choice (290)   ✓✓ CHOLESTEROL: Excellent Choice (65 mg)
✓ FAT: Good Choice (16 g)   SODIUM: Moderate (805 mg)
PROTEIN: 31 g, CARBOHYDRATE: 15 g, FIBER: 6 g

CALIFORNIA VEGGIE BURRITO – SPECIAL REQUEST

Black beans, avocado, rice, lettuce and fresh salsa wrapped in a flour tortilla. <u>Request no cheese</u>.

✓ CALORIES: Good Choice (545)   ✓✓ CHOLESTEROL: Excellent Choice (0 mg)
✓ FAT: Good Choice (19 g)   SODIUM: High (1280 mg)
PROTEIN: 19 g, CARBOHYDRATE: 89 g, FIBER: 9 g

THREE PEPPER FAJITA BURRITO WITH STEAK – SPECIAL REQUEST

Sirloin steak, fresh fire-roasted red and green bell peppers, poblano peppers, onions and garlic, with rice, avocado and salsa. <u>Request no cheese</u>.

✓ CALORIES: Good Choice (570)   ✓✓ CHOLESTEROL: Excellent Choice (40 mg)
✓ FAT: Good Choice (20 g)   SODIUM: High (1890 mg)
PROTEIN: 27 g, CARBOHYDRATE: 79 g, FIBER: 6 g

BLACK BEAN & CHEESE BURRITO WITH CHICKEN

With freshly made beans and Jack and Cheddar cheese in a flour tortilla. Pinto beans also available, making the dish slightly lower in carbs & calories, higher in fiber.

✓ CALORIES: Good Choice (695)   CHOLESTEROL: Moderate (200 mg)
✓ FAT: Good Choice (22 g)   SODIUM: High (1420 mg)
PROTEIN: 43 g, CARBOHYDRATE: 85 g, FIBER: 9 g

SIDE OF PINTO BEANS (with cheese)

CAL: 230, FAT: 4 g♥, CHOLESTEROL: 5 mg, SODIUM: 605 mg, PROTEIN: 33 g, CARBOHYDRATE: 59 g, FIBER: 14 g

SIDE OF RICE

CAL: 155, FAT: 5 g♥, CHOLESTEROL: 5 mg, SODIUM: 560 mg; PROTEIN: 4 g, CARBOHYDRATE: 29 g, FIBER: 1 g

Nutrition information supplied by La Salsa.

Leucadia
Pizzeria & Italian Restaurant

Leucadia Pizzeria is a full-service Italian restaurant and is known for its specialty gourmet pizzas and pastas. We have a large selection of salads and low-fat salad dressing for you to enjoy. Any pizza or calzone can be made with non-fat mozzarella cheese! The ambiance is upscale casual, appropriate for either a quick lunch or friendly dinner. Both indoor and patio dining are available. The full menu is available for delivery to most of Coastal North County. Reservations are not required but are accepted for large parties. $

Leucadia Pizzeria

Encinitas: 315 S. Coast Hwy. 101	(760) 942-2222
La Jolla/UTC: 7748 Regents Rd.	(858) 597-2222
Rancho Santa Fe: 16085 San Dieguito Rd.	(858) 759-2222
Carmel Mt. Ranch: 12075 Carmel Mtn. Rd.	(858) 675-2222

Pizzas can be ordered with veggie cheese if desired.

BROCCOLI–EGGPLANT–MUSHROOM PIZZA – 9-INCH (½ PIZZA) ☺

Grilled eggplant, red onions, broccoli, mushrooms, sun-dried tomatoes, fresh basil, mozzarella cheese, and tomato sauce. (Analysis is for ½ of a 9-inch pizza.)

✓ CALORIES: Good Choice (580)   ✓✓ CHOLESTEROL: Excellent Choice (20 mg)
✓✓ FAT: Excellent Choice (15 g)   ✓ SODIUM: Good Choice (360 mg)*
PROTEIN: 18 g, CARBOHYDRATE: 95 g, FIBER: 11 g

LITE PIZZA – 9-INCH (½ PIZZA) – SPECIAL REQUEST

Delicious and nutritious pizza with feta cheese, fresh broccoli, spinach and red onions (no sauce). Request non-fat mozzarella. (Analysis is for ½ of a 9-inch pizza.)

✓ CALORIES: Good Choice (510)   ✓✓ CHOLESTEROL: Excellent Choice (15 mg)
✓✓ FAT: Excellent Choice (4 g)   ✓ SODIUM: Good Choice (565 mg)*
PROTEIN: 24 g, CARBOHYDRATE: 93 g, FIBER: 4 g

TOMATO–BASIL ANGEL HAIR PASTA – SPECIAL REQUEST

Angel hair pasta mixed with a light tomato basil sauce and a touch of garlic. Request no butter.

✓✓ CALORIES: Excellent Choice (435)   ✓✓ CHOLESTEROL: Excellent Choice (0 mg)
✓✓ FAT: Excellent Choice (14 g)♥   ✓ SODIUM: Good Choice (565 mg)*
PROTEIN: 12 g, CARBOHYDRATE: 65 g, FIBER: 5 g

PASTA WITH MARINARA SAUCE

Homemade marinara sauce served over your choice of hot pasta.

✓✓ CALORIES: Excellent Choice (310)   ✓✓ CHOLESTEROL: Excellent Choice (0 mg)
✓✓ FAT: Excellent Choice (4 g)♥   ✓✓ SODIUM: Excellent Choice (220 mg)*
PROTEIN: 10 g, CARBOHYDRATE: 58 g, FIBER: 4 g

GRILLED CHICKEN SALAD (ENTRÉE SIZE) – SPECIAL REQUEST ☺

Charbroiled breast of chicken on a bed of mixed greens topped with feta cheese, tomatoes, olives and red onions. Request dressing on the side (not included in analysis).

✓✓ CALORIES: Excellent Choice (390)   ✓ CHOLESTEROL: Good Choice (125 mg)
✓ FAT: Good Choice (18 g)   SODIUM: Moderate (840 mg)*
PROTEIN: 41 g, CARBOHYDRATE: 16 g, FIBER: 5 g

LOEWS
CORONADO BAY RESORT
SAN DIEGO

In between sunrise over the bay and sunset beyond the Pacific, you have plenty of time to savor the best San Diego restaurants. More than a mere restaurant, Azzura Point combines innovative California cuisine with sweeping views in a relaxed classic California ambiance to critical acclaim. Sample the seasonal menus or take in the spectacular San Diego sunsets in the adjacent lounge. Open Tuesday through Sunday, 6 p.m. to 10 p.m. Reservations recommended. $$$

Enjoy the Market Café with casual all-day dockside dining as you overlook the resort's bustling marina. Savor fare such as seasonal salads, sandwiches and pizzas that showcase local flavors and regional ingredients. Open daily 6 a.m. to 10 p.m. $-$$

Azzura Point & Market Café
at Loews Coronado Bay Resort & Spa
4000 Coronado Bay Rd., Coronado, CA 92118   (619) 424-4000

AZZURA POINT: POACHED AHI TUNA – SPECIAL REQUEST †
with infused achiote-ginger oil, oro blanco grapefruit, ocean aioli, friseé and crispy capers. Request ocean aioli on the side (not included in analysis; 1 Tbs. = 75 cal, 8 g fat). Analysis does not include crispy capers.
✓✓ CALORIES: Excellent Choice (130)   ✓✓ CHOLESTEROL: Excellent Choice (40 mg)
✓✓ FAT: Excellent Choice (3 g)♥   ✓✓ SODIUM: Excellent Choice (30 mg)
PROTEIN: 20 g, CARBOHYDRATE: 3 g, FIBER: 1 g

MARKET CAFÉ: GRILLED FISH TACOS – SPECIAL REQUEST ☺
Served with black beans, guacamole & pico de gallo. Request less oil (½ Tbs.) & less cheese (1 Tbs).
✓ CALORIES: Good Choice (725)   ✓ CHOLESTEROL: Good Choice (90 mg)
✓ FAT: Good Choice (23 g)   SODIUM: High (1375 mg)*
PROTEIN: 53 g, CARBOHYDRATE: 79 g, FIBER: 21 g

MARKET CAFÉ: ANGEL HAIR PASTA – SPECIAL REQUEST ☺
with fresh and sun dried tomatoes, baby spinach, roasted garlic and fresh basil. Request less oil (1 Tbs.) and less parmesan cheese (1 Tbs).
✓ CALORIES: Good Choice (555)   ✓✓ CHOLESTEROL: Excellent Choice (5 mg)
✓ FAT: Good Choice (19 g)   SODIUM: High (1415 mg)*
PROTEIN: 19 g, CARBOHYDRATE: 86 g, FIBER: 11 g

MARKET CAFÉ: MARKET CHICKEN CAESAR WRAP – SPECIAL REQUEST ☺
with grilled chicken, sun dried tomatoes and parmesan cheese wrapped in a spinach tortilla. Request dressing on the side (not included in analysis; 1 Tbs. = 90 cal, 9 g fat). Analysis does not include salt used to season chicken or side dishes.
✓ CALORIES: Good Choice (715)   ✓ CHOLESTEROL: Good Choice (95 mg)
✓ FAT: Good Choice (25 g)   SODIUM: High (1910 mg)*
PROTEIN: 50 g, CARBOHYDRATE: 71 g, FIBER: 7 g

MARKET CAFÉ: MANGO AND PAPAYA CHICKEN SALAD – SPECIAL REQUEST ☺
Grilled chicken breast with papaya, mango, kiwi and dates atop a bed of mesclun greens. Request dressing on the side (not included in analysis). Analysis does not include salt used to season chicken.
✓ CALORIES: Good Choice (700)   CHOLESTEROL: Moderate (170 mg)
✓ FAT: Good Choice (19 g)   ✓✓ SODIUM: Excellent Choice (190 mg)*
PROTEIN: 70 g, CARBOHYDRATE: 66 g, FIBER: 12 g

MARKET CAFÉ: BERRY BERRY GOOD HEALTHY KIDS SMOOTHIE:
CAL: 205, FAT: 3g♥, CHOLESTEROL: 0, SODIUM: 120 mg, PROTEIN: 10 g, CARBOHYDRATE: 37 g, FIBER: 9 g

Los Cabos, located on the tip of the Baja California peninsula, is famous for its world class fishing and seafood. We combine the flavors and casual dining traditions of Baja with mainland Mexico's mesquite grilled cooking. We use only olive and canola oils, lean beef, and skinless boneless chicken breast. Unlike traditional Mexican fare, we have taken the influences of Mexico and combined them with the freshness and flair of San Diego, to make a menu, which is not only unique but delicious as well. $

Los Cabos 12955 El Camino Real, Ste. G-7, San Diego, CA 92130   (858) 792-2226
(in the Del Mar Highlands Town Center across from the Edwards Cinema)

SEAFOOD ENCHILADAS 🍎

Lobster, shrimp, scallops with leeks, roasted bell peppers and tomatoes, topped with traditional salsa. Served with choice of accompaniments (see below).
- ✓✓ CALORIES: Excellent Choice (315)
- ✓✓ FAT: Excellent Choice (3 g)♥
- ✓ CHOLESTEROL: Good Choice (115 mg)
- ✓ SODIUM: Good Choice (480 mg)*
- PROTEIN: 26 g, CARBOHYDRATE: 39 g, FIBER: 5 g

CABOS CATCH

Yellowfin grilled over mesquite, with choice of salsa of the day and tortillas (2 corn tortillas included in analysis). Served with choice of accompaniments (see below).
- ✓✓ CALORIES: Excellent Choice (450)
- ✓✓ FAT: Excellent Choice (10 g)♥
- ✓ CHOLESTEROL: Good Choice (100 mg)
- ✓✓ SODIUM: Excellent Choice (95 mg)*
- PROTEIN: 55 g, CARBOHYDRATE: 28 g, FIBER: 3 g

CHICKEN PALMILLA

A marinated skinless chicken breast charbroiled, sliced and served with corn salsa and tortillas (2 corn tortillas included in analysis). Served with choice of accompaniments (see below).
- ✓ CALORIES: Good Choice (545)
- ✓ FAT: Good Choice (17 g)♥
- ✓ CHOLESTEROL: Good Choice (150 mg)
- ✓ SODIUM: Good Choice (305 mg)*
- PROTEIN: 58 g, CARBOHYDRATE: 35 g, FIBER: 4 g

CABOS FISH TACO PLATE

Two wahoo fish tacos mesquite grilled and topped with Mexican cole slaw and salsa fresca. Served with choice of accompaniments (see below).
- ✓✓ CALORIES: Excellent Choice (285)
- ✓✓ FAT: Excellent Choice (8 g)♥
- ✓✓ CHOLESTEROL: Excellent Choice (60 mg)
- ✓✓ SODIUM: Excellent Choice (295 mg)*
- PROTEIN: 19 g, CARBOHYDRATE: 29 g, FIBER: 4 g

RICE (6 oz.)
CALORIES: 180, FAT: 3 g♥, CHOLESTEROL: 0, SODIUM: 250 mg, PROTEIN: 4 g, CARBOHYDRATE: 34 g, FIBER: 2 g

WHITE BEANS (4 oz.)
CALORIES: 160, FAT: 0, CHOLESTEROL: 0, SODIUM: 505 mg, PROTEIN: 11 g, CARBOHYDRATE: 29 g, FIBER: 7 g

BLACK BEANS (4 oz.)
CALORIES: 145, FAT: 1 g♥, CHOLESTEROL: 0, SODIUM: 500 mg, PROTEIN: 10 g, CARBOHYDRATE: 26 g, FIBER: 10 g

MEXICAN COLE SLAW (6 oz.) 🍎
CALORIES: 95, FAT: 7 g♥, CHOLESTEROL: 0, SODIUM: 295 mg, PROTEIN: 2 g, CARBOHYDRATE: 8 g, FIBER: 3 g

See page 43 for key to symbols: * ♥ † 🍎 and $

Lotsa Pasta
Fresh Pasta • Restaurant • Market

With the finest fresh homemade pastas and sauces made every day, Lotsa Pasta is located in the heart of Pacific Beach, and has been consistently voted as one of San Diego's most popular restaurants. Lotsa Pasta uses only the finest ingredients to give its pasta and sauces the best taste and texture you'll find anywhere. Please visit us at www.yumm.com or just come in person and enjoy our specialties for yourself! $-$$

Lotsa Pasta 1762 Garnet Ave., Pacific Beach, CA 92109   (858) 581-6777

ROASTED GARLIC SOUP (8 oz.) †
✓✓ CALORIES: Excellent Choice (110)   ✓✓ CHOLESTEROL: Excellent Choice (0)
✓✓ FAT: Excellent Choice (0)   ✓ SODIUM: Good Choice (165 mg)*
PROTEIN: 3 g, CARBOHYDRATE: 24 g, FIBER: 1 g

TUSCANO SALAD ♻
Crisp romaine, tomatoes, cucumbers, red onions and feta cheese with a light vinaigrette dressing.
✓✓ CALORIES: Excellent Choice (305)   ✓✓ CHOLESTEROL: Excellent Choice (60 mg)
✓ FAT: Good Choice (22 g)   SODIUM: Moderate (895 mg)*
PROTEIN: 12 g, CARBOHYDRATE: 16 g, FIBER: 4 g

SALMON CAESAR SALAD – SPECIAL REQUEST ♻
Our large Caesar salad topped with pieces of fresh grilled salmon.
Request dressing on the side, (not included in analysis: 85 calories, 9 g fat per Tbs).
✓✓ CALORIES: Excellent Choice (440)   CHOLESTEROL: Moderate (160 mg)
✓ FAT: Good Choice (20 g)♥   ✓ SODIUM: Good Choice (425 mg)*
PROTEIN: 59 g, CARBOHYDRATE: 4 g, FIBER: 2 g

PUTTANESCA SAUCE WITH SPINACH FETTUCCINE (DINNER PORTION) ♻
(Poot-an-ness-kuh) A classic Italian favorite of roma tomatoes, anchovies, garlic, chili peppers, capers and olives. Served with our spinach fettuccine.
✓ CALORIES: Good Choice (585)   ✓ CHOLESTEROL: Good Choice (110 mg)
✓✓ FAT: Excellent Choice (15 g)♥   SODIUM: High (1230 mg)*
PROTEIN: 21 g, CARBOHYDRATE: 89 g, FIBER: 8 g

TOMATO BASIL MARINARA WITH SPINACH LINGUINI (DINNER PORTION) ♻
A favorite choice for kids, this sauce has no garlic and the slightly sweet flavor of carrots. Served with our spinach linguini.
✓ CALORIES: Good Choice (510)   ✓ CHOLESTEROL: Good Choice (110 mg)
✓✓ FAT: Excellent Choice (5 g)♥   SODIUM: Moderate (755 mg)*
PROTEIN: 21 g, CARBOHYDRATE: 93 g, FIBER: 8 g

RED CLAM SAUCE WITH GARLIC SCALLION PASTA (DINNER PORTION)
Tender sea clams simmered in white wine, tomatoes, garlic, fresh herbs and a touch of red chili pepper with our garlic, scallion and parsley fettucine.
✓ CALORIES: Good Choice (540)   ✓ CHOLESTEROL: Good Choice (140 mg)
✓✓ FAT: Excellent Choice (6 g)♥   SODIUM: Moderate (635 mg)*
PROTEIN: 29 g, CARBOHYDRATE: 87 g, FIBER: 6 g

McCORMICK & SCHMICK'S
SEAFOOD RESTAURANTS

McCormick & Schmick's Fresh Seafood Restaurant is committed to delivering excellence in service, traditionalism, quality and value. We have versatile dining areas; located next to PETCO Park and the San Diego Convention Center, our fantastic semi-private dining area accommodates parties of up to 200 people. Please note our Fresh List changes daily to ensure the highest quality of seafood, meat and poultry dishes are available to our guests. We also offer specially priced appetizers in a Happy Hour setting, everyday from 3 p.m. – 7 p.m. Plan your next special event now; for reservations or inquiries please call (619) 645-6545 or email sandiegobanquets@msmg.com. $$

McCormick & Schmick's Seafood Restaurant
675 L Street, San Diego, CA 92101   (619) 645-6545

MAHI MAHI WITH TERIYAKI JASMINE RICE ♨
Request mahi mahi grilled with oil (1 tsp.) and veggies cooked with less oil (½ Tbs.)
- ✓ CALORIES: Good Choice (740)
- ✓✓ FAT: Excellent Choice (15 g)♥
- CHOLESTEROL: Moderate (190 mg)
- SODIUM: High (1610 mg)*
- PROTEIN: 58 g, CARBOHYDRATE: 89 g, FIBER: 4 g

CAJUN SEARED RARE AHI
(Analysis does not include wonton cup or soy sauce.)
- ✓ CALORIES: Good Choice (555)
- ✓✓ FAT: Excellent Choice (8 g)♥
- ✓✓ CHOLESTEROL: Excellent Choice (75 mg)
- SODIUM: High (4710 mg)*
- PROTEIN: 45 g, CARBOHYDRATE: 74 g, FIBER: 4 g

SEARED AHI NICOISE SALAD – SPECIAL REQUEST ♨
Request no basil oil (not included in analysis).
- ✓ CALORIES: Good Choice (660)
- ✓ FAT: Good Choice (22 g)
- CHOLESTEROL: Moderate (245 mg)
- SODIUM: High (2590 mg)*
- PROTEIN: 33 g, CARBOHYDRATE: 83 g, FIBER: 11 g

SEAFOOD STIR-FRY – SPECIAL REQUEST ♨
Request less oil (1 Tbs). (Analysis does not include fried rice noodles.)
- ✓ CALORIES: Good Choice (635)
- ✓ FAT: Good Choice (17 g)♥
- ✓ CHOLESTEROL: Good Choice (110 mg)
- SODIUM: High (1935 mg)*
- PROTEIN: 41 g, CARBOHYDRATE: 77 g, FIBER: 3 g

ROASTED BEETS AND HERB CHEVRE CHEESE SALAD ♨
- ✓✓ CALORIES: Excellent Choice (345)
- ✓✓ FAT: Excellent Choice (11 g)
- ✓✓ CHOLESTEROL: Excellent Choice (20 mg)
- ✓ SODIUM: Good Choice (350 mg)*
- PROTEIN: 12 g, CARBOHYDRATE: 48 g, FIBER: 14 g

Delicious, Fresh and Authentic. This is not your ordinary quick-service restaurant. We never start your meal until you place your order. All of our food is prepared fresh. We use only the best quality ingredients including quality meats and seafood, fresh vegetables, real sour cream, real guacamole, cheese, and fresh tortillas. All of our salsas and guacamole are handcrafted fresh daily. And remember, *WE DON'T NEED TO ADD LARD or MSG TO TASTE THIS GOOD!!!* Fresh, well-prepared food doesn't need it. $

Mi Ranchito

12812 Rancho Penasquitos Blvd., San Diego, CA 92129   (858) 484-4548

"LIGHT" VEGGIE BURRITO
A whole wheat tortilla with black beans, rice, lettuce and salsa fresca.
- ✓ CALORIES: Good Choice (660)
- ✓✓ CHOLESTEROL: Excellent Choice (0 mg)
- ✓ FAT: Good Choice (19 g)♥
- SODIUM: High (2715 mg)*

PROTEIN: 23 g, CARBOHYDRATE: 105 g, FIBER: 20 g

GRILLED CHICKEN BURRITO
Grilled chicken with salsa fresca and cheese.
- ✓ CALORIES: Good Choice (615)
- ✓ CHOLESTEROL: Good Choice (115 mg)
- ✓ FAT: Good Choice (18 g)
- SODIUM: High (1190 mg)*

PROTEIN: 48 g, CARBOHYDRATE: 67 g, FIBER: 3 g

MAHI MAHI TACO
Grilled mahi mahi with salsa fresca and white sauce.
- ✓✓ CALORIES: Excellent Choice (200)
- ✓✓ CHOLESTEROL: Excellent Choice (50 mg)
- ✓✓ FAT: Excellent Choice (8 g)
- ✓✓ SODIUM: Excellent Choice (180 mg)*

PROTEIN: 13 g, CARBOHYDRATE: 19 g, FIBER: 3 g

GRILLED CHICKEN TACO
Grilled chicken served with lettuce, salsa fresca and cheese.
- ✓✓ CALORIES: Excellent Choice (265)
- ✓✓ CHOLESTEROL: Excellent Choice (60 mg)
- ✓✓ FAT: Excellent Choice (9 g)
- ✓ SODIUM: Good Choice (545 mg)*

PROTEIN: 27 g, CARBOHYDRATE: 20 g, FIBER: 3 g

SALMON TACO
Grilled salmon with salsa fresca, white sauce and cheese.
- ✓✓ CALORIES: Excellent Choice (285)
- ✓✓ CHOLESTEROL: Excellent Choice (55 mg)
- ✓✓ FAT: Excellent Choice (15 g)
- ✓ SODIUM: Good Choice (545 mg)*

PROTEIN: 19 g, CARBOHYDRATE: 19 g, FIBER: 3 g

SHRIMP TACO
Sautéed shrimp, salsa fresca, cheese and white sauce.
- ✓✓ CALORIES: Excellent Choice (270)
- ✓ CHOLESTEROL: Good Choice (115 mg)
- ✓✓ FAT: Excellent Choice (15 g)
- ✓ SODIUM: Good Choice (540 mg)*

PROTEIN: 16 g, CARBOHYDRATE: 20 g, FIBER: 3 g

NINE-TEN

We are dedicated to the pursuit of culinary excellence, shopping daily to obtain the freshest local ingredients from local farms. Nine-Ten's unique fish selection is flown in daily from the North Atlantic and Pacific regions. We pay attention to the details that set Nine-Ten apart, from smoking our own salmon to turning out fresh, house-made desserts each day. As we change our menu daily, the following dishes are typical of the items we feature in our "Evolving California Cuisine." Located in the European-style Grande Colonial Hotel, which overlooks the shores of La Jolla's beautiful coves and beaches, Nine-Ten has received numerous awards, including "Best New Restaurant" from both The Reader and The La Jolla Light. $$-$$$

Nine-Ten Restaurant

910 Prospect Street, La Jolla, CA 92037   (858) 964-5400

LOBSTER AND PEA TENDRILS SALAD – SPECIAL REQUEST ♂
Request less avocado (¼ of avocado).
✓ CALORIES: Good Choice (620)   CHOLESTEROL: Moderate (275 mg)
✓ FAT: Good Choice (25 g)♥   SODIUM: High (1045 mg)*
        PROTEIN: 64 g, CARBOHYDRATE: 41 g, FIBER: 15 g

SEARED SEA SCALLOPS AND SPRING VEGETABLE SALAD WITH
BLACK TRUFFLE VINAIGRETTE – SPECIAL REQUEST ♂
Request less dressing (1 oz).
✓ CALORIES: Good Choice (470)   ✓✓ CHOLESTEROL: Excellent Choice (35 mg)
✓ FAT: Good Choice (23 g)♥   ✓✓ SODIUM: Excellent Choice (260 mg)*
        PROTEIN: 31 g, CARBOHYDRATE: 34 g, FIBER: 12 g

BLACK BASS WITH BROCCOLINI, ARTICHOKES, PEARL ONIONS
AND TANGERINE VINAIGRETTE ♂
✓ CALORIES: Good Choice (530)   ✓✓ CHOLESTEROL: Excellent Choice (50 mg)
✓ FAT: Good Choice (23 g)♥   ✓✓ SODIUM: Excellent Choice (220 mg)*
        PROTEIN: 32 g, CARBOHYDRATE: 54 g, FIBER: 7 g

STRAWBERRY SORBET †
(Analysis for ½ cup)
✓✓ CALORIES: Excellent Choice (125)   ✓✓ CHOLESTEROL: Excellent Choice (0)
✓✓ FAT: Excellent Choice (0)   ✓✓ SODIUM: Excellent Choice (0)
        PROTEIN: 0, CARBOHYDRATE: 32 g, FIBER: 2 g

Menus

At 150 Grand Cafe, we offer a light and airy atmosphere in our Library Dining Room, with a central skylight and windows, where you are invited to browse through a large collection of cookbooks. Our Garden Room showcases many plants and a fountain. The cuisine includes a wide variety of intriguing choices, based on the seasons and availability of specific items, drawing upon classical French, California, Latino and some Asian influences. Come join us for a special meal in our unique and inviting atmosphere. Lunch served Monday – Saturday, 11:30 a.m. – 2:30 p.m. Dinner served Monday – Saturday, 5 p.m. – 9 p.m. Visit us online to see a virtual tour of our dining room at www.150grand.com. $$-$$$

150 Grand Cafe

150 West Grand Ave., Escondido, CA 92025 (760) 738-6868

CALAMARI MARTINI (APPETIZER) – HEALTHY DINING PREPARATION† ✿

Avocado, cucumber, onion, cilantro, and tomato with citrus dressing.

✓ CALORIES: Good Choice (160)   CHOLESTEROL: High (240 mg)
✓ FAT: Good Choice (7 g)♥   SODIUM: Moderate (230 mg)*
PROTEIN: 16 g, CARBOHYDRATE: 8 g, FIBER: 1 g

GRILLED CHICKEN SALAD – HEALTHY DINING PREPARATION ✿

with avocado, red peppers, roasted corn and citrus vinaigrette.
(Dressing not included in analysis; 80 cals, 9 g fat per Tbs).

✓✓ CALORIES: Excellent Choice (435)   ✓ CHOLESTEROL: Good Choice (95 mg)
✓ FAT: Good Choice (21 g)   ✓✓ SODIUM: Excellent Choice (115 mg)*
PROTEIN: 41 g, CARBOHYDRATE: 25 g, FIBER: 10 g

GRILLED CHICKEN BREAST – HEALTHY DINING PREPARATION ✿

Served with wild rice, pine nuts, balsamic reduction and green beans.

✓ CALORIES: Good Choice (555)   CHOLESTEROL: Good Choice (95 mg)
✓✓ FAT: Excellent Choice (9 g)   SODIUM: Moderate (685 mg)*
PROTEIN: 49 g, CARBOHYDRATE: 71 g, FIBER: 9 g

GRILLED ATLANTIC SALMON – HEALTHY DINING PREPARATION ✿

with mixed berry coulis, berries, roasted fingerling potatoes, and watercress.

✓✓ CALORIES: Excellent Choice (390)   ✓ CHOLESTEROL: Good Choice (80 mg)
✓ FAT: Good Choice (18 g)♥   SODIUM: High (1030 mg)*
PROTEIN: 31 g, CARBOHYDRATE: 26 g, FIBER: 4 g

The whimsical dining room of the Pacific Coast Grill, with its
industrial feel and artistic decor, sets the stage for beyond-the-
ordinary cuisine. The culinary staff draws its inspiration from
diverse elements of Pacific Coast cuisine, which can be tasted in
house specialties such as lobster tacos and tequila glazed
seafood. Open for lunch & dinner daily & Sunday brunch. $$-$$$

Pacific Coast Grill 437 S. Highway 101, Solana Beach 92075 (858) 794-4632

Adjoining the legendary Belly Up, one of the finest music venues in the world, the Wild
Note Café stands on its own for haute food and cool atmosphere and is as unique as
the Cedros Design District surrounding it. Chef Izzy Balderas has created an eclectic
menu that is as diverse as the music next door. From his Mexican roots to his Thai-
inspired dishes, the no-holds-barred approach produces anything but boring food.
Come in and hang…it's about the music man, and the food. $-$$

Wild Note Cafe 141 S. Cedros Ave., Solana Beach 92075 (858) 720-9000

PACIFIC COAST GRILL: TEQUILA GLAZED PRAWNS AND SCALLOPS – SPECIAL REQUEST ♻

with sticky rice, steamed broccoli and cilantro chile sauce. _Request less oil (½ Tbs)._
✓ CALORIES: Good Choice (715) CHOLESTEROL: Moderate (250 mg)
✓ FAT: Good Choice (25 g)♥ SODIUM: Moderate (755 mg)*
PROTEIN: 57 g, CARBOHYDRATE: 61 g, FIBER: 5 g

PACIFIC COAST GRILL: LOBSTER TACOS ♻

with roasted corn salsa, black beans and tortillas. (Analysis includes 4 corn tortillas.)
✓ CALORIES: Good Choice (500) ✓ CHOLESTEROL: Good Choice (80 mg)
✓✓ FAT: Excellent Choice (5 g)♥ SODIUM: High (1235 mg)
PROTEIN: 38 g, CARBOHYDRATE: 80 g, FIBER: 14 g

WILD NOTE CAFE: DIJON HERB CRUSTED SALMON – SPECIAL REQUEST ♻

with Israeli couscous, vegetables, and lemon-tarragon buerre blanc. _Request vegetables steamed
and buerre blanc sauce on the side_ (sauce not included in analysis).
✓ CALORIES: Good Choice (590) ✓ CHOLESTEROL: Good Choice (95 mg)
FAT: Moderate (26 g)♥ ✓ SODIUM: Good Choice (505 mg)*
PROTEIN: 46 g, CARBOHYDRATE: 46 g, FIBER: 6 g

WILD NOTE CAFE: THAI TOFU STIR FRY (LUNCH PORTION) ♻

with fresh spinach, sticky rice, spicy peanut sauce and stir fry vegetables.
(Analysis for lunch portion.)
✓ CALORIES: Good Choice (500) ✓✓ CHOLESTEROL: Excellent Choice (0 mg)
FAT: Moderate (26 g) SODIUM: Moderate (625 mg)*
PROTEIN: 20 g, CARBOHYDRATE: 54 g, FIBER: 7 g

WILD NOTE CAFE: VEGGIE BURGER – SPECIAL REQUEST ♻

with house made hummus, lettuce and tomato. _Request side salad
with dressing on the side instead of fries_ (dressing not included in analysis).
✓✓ CALORIES: Excellent Choice (450) ✓✓ CHOLESTEROL: Excellent Choice (10 mg)
✓✓ FAT: Excellent Choice (14 g) ✓ SODIUM: Good Choice (550 mg)*
PROTEIN: 13 g, CARBOHYDRATE: 69 g, FIBER: 8 g

Menus

Pat & Oscar's started out in San Diego over 10 years ago as a single take-out restaurant. Today our restaurants total 21, stretching throughout Southern California. And to think, we built it all on breadsticks! But we're also committed to serving other great foods like the ones listed below – in a clean, relaxed and friendly atmosphere. Please come by soon and see for yourself! $

PAT & OSCAR'S

Carmel Mtn. Ranch: 12045 Carmel Mtn. Road	(858) 592-0222
Carlsbad: 2525 El Camino Real #105	(760) 730-2921
Carlsbad: 965 Palomar Airport Road	(760) 929-7040
Del Mar/Carmel Valley: 3881 Valley Centre Drive	(858) 720-3525
Down Town: 501 1st Avenue	(619) 515-0877
El Cajon: 375 Pkwy. Plaza	(619) 440-1400
Mira Mesa: 10673 Westview Parkway	(858) 621-6100
Mission Valley: 8590 Rio San Diego Drive	(619) 295-6200
National City: 3030 Plaza Bonita Road #106	(619) 472-2701

BARBEQUE CHICKEN PIZZA – 10-INCH (2 SLICES)
BBQ chicken, red onions, cilantro & BBQ sauce. (Analysis is for 2 slices, ⅓ of a small pizza.)
✓✓ CALORIES: Excellent Choice (440) ✓✓ CHOLESTEROL: Excellent Choice (50 mg)
✓✓ FAT: Excellent Choice (14 g) SODIUM: Moderate (765 mg)*
PROTEIN: 21 g, CARBOHYDRATE: 56 g, FIBER: 2 g

GOURMET VEGETARIAN PIZZA – 10-INCH (2 SLICES)
Feta, broccoli, tomatoes, carrots, spinach and pesto. (Analysis is for 2 slices, ⅓ of a small pizza.)
✓ CALORIES: Good Choice (475) ✓✓ CHOLESTEROL: Excellent Choice (45 mg)
✓ FAT: Good Choice (20 g) SODIUM: Moderate (800 mg)*
PROTEIN: 18 g, CARBOHYDRATE: 55 g, FIBER: 3 g

TURKEY POCKET SANDWICH
Roasted turkey breast with Roma tomatoes and shredded lettuce on fresh homemade bread.
✓ CALORIES: Good Choice (645) ✓ CHOLESTEROL: Good Choice (130 mg)
✓✓ FAT: Excellent Choice (7 g) SODIUM: High (2530 mg)*
PROTEIN: 49 g, CARBOHYDRATE: 95 g, FIBER: 5 g

VEGGIE POCKET SANDWICH – SPECIAL REQUEST ✂
Provolone cheese, mushrooms, red onions, green peppers, olives, Roma tomatoes and shredded lettuce on fresh homemade bread. Request less cheese (1 oz. included in analysis) and fat-free dressing (not included in analysis).
✓ CALORIES: Good Choice (680) ✓✓ CHOLESTEROL: Excellent Choice (20 mg)
✓ FAT: Good Choice (23 g) SODIUM: High (1175 mg)*
PROTEIN: 23 g, CARBOHYDRATE: 101 g, FIBER: 9 g

GREEK SALAD – SPECIAL REQUEST ✂
Tomatoes, olives, cucumbers, beets, red onions, feta cheese and peppers. Request fat-free dressing (not included in analysis).
✓✓ CALORIES: Excellent Choice (265) ✓✓ CHOLESTEROL: Excellent Choice (55 mg)
✓✓ FAT: Excellent Choice (15 g) SODIUM: Moderate (820 mg)*
PROTEIN: 13 g, CARBOHYDRATE: 21 g, FIBER: 6 g

LEMON CHICKEN SANDWICH ✂
Lemon marinated chicken with lemon seasoning, Roma tomatoes and shredded lettuce on fresh homemade bread.
CALORIES: Moderate (820) ✓ CHOLESTEROL: Good Choice (145 mg)
✓ FAT: Good Choice (19 g) SODIUM: High (1455 mg)*
PROTEIN: 66 g, CARBOHYDRATE: 92 g, FIBER: 6 g

Pick Up Stix Fresh Asian Kitchen prepares traditional Asian food adapted to American tastes by reducing the oil and adding wine, vinegar and soy sauce to create our flavorful entrees. Our food is prepared in an open-style kitchen, treating guests to a show of the art of Asian cooking as each meal is cooked-to-order with only the finest ingredients. $

Pick Up Stix

San Diego area locations: Carlsbad, Carmel Mountain Ranch, Chula Vista, Clairemont Mesa, Del Mar, El Cajon, Encinitas, Escondido, Hillcrest, La Jolla, La Mesa, Mira Mesa, Mission Valley, Murphy Canyon, Pacific Beach, Point Loma, Scripps Ranch, Torrey Highlands, and Vista. Please visit www.pickupstix.com for details.

CALIFORNIA ROLL (2 PIECES) †

Made fresh throughout the day! With shaved ginger and Japanese wasabi mustard.
(Analysis is for 2 pieces.)
✓✓ CALORIES: Excellent Choice (145)   ✓✓ CHOLESTEROL: Excellent Choice (10 mg)
✓ FAT: Good Choice (8 g)   SODIUM: Moderate (325 mg)
PROTEIN: 4 g, CARBOHYDRATE: 15 g, FIBER: <1 g

CHICKEN WITH VEGETABLES ᗏ

Steamed white meat chicken with broccoli, carrots, zucchini, mushrooms and water chestnuts in a sauce of white wine, garlic and soy. (Analysis does not include rice; see separate analysis below.)
✓ CALORIES: Good Choice (650)   CHOLESTEROL: Moderate (165 mg)
✓✓ FAT: Excellent Choice (10 g)   SODIUM: High (2170 mg)*
PROTEIN: 68 g, CARBOHYDRATE: 69 g, FIBER: 7 g

GARLIC SHRIMP ᗏ

Plump shrimp stir-fried with zucchini, broccoli, onions, mushrooms, and water chestnuts in our special garlic sauce. (Analysis does not include rice; see separate analysis below.)
✓ CALORIES: Good Choice (690)   CHOLESTEROL: High (340 mg)
✓ FAT: Good Choice (24 g)♥   SODIUM: High (2470 mg)*
PROTEIN: 45 g, CARBOHYDRATE: 72 g, FIBER: 6 g

CHINESE CHICKEN SALAD WITH FAT-FREE SPICY LIME CILANTRO DRESSING ᗏ

Oven roasted chicken breast over fresh greens & Mandarin oranges, sprinkled with sunflower seeds & topped with Chinese croutons. Analysis includes 4 oz. fat-free Spicy Lime Cilantro dressing served on the side.
✓ CALORIES: Good Choice (590)   ✓ CHOLESTEROL: Good Choice (90 mg)
✓✓ FAT: Excellent Choice (15 g)   SODIUM: High (1140 mg)*
PROTEIN: 42 g, CARBOHYDRATE: 74 g, FIBER: 9 g

BUDDHA'S FEAST ᗏ

An array of fresh vegetables in white wine sauce.
(Analysis does not include rice; see analysis below.)
✓✓ CALORIES: Excellent Choice (370)   ✓✓ CHOLESTEROL: Excellent Choice (5 mg)
✓✓ FAT: Excellent Choice (1 g)♥   SODIUM: High (1645 mg)*
PROTEIN: 11 g, CARBOHYDRATE: 80 g, FIBER: 10 g

Rice *(6 oz):* CAL: 220, FAT: ½ g♥, CHOL: 0, SOD: <5 mg; PROTEIN: 5 g, CARB: 48 g, FIBER: 1 g

See page 43 for key to symbols: * ♥ † ᗏ and $ *Healthy Dining in San Diego* **91**

PIZZA NOVA

Pizza Nova is the gourmet pizza restaurant that has everybody talking. When people taste our incredibly delicious wood-fired California pizzas, scrumptious salads, rotisserie, and pastas, they can't wait to tell their friends how wonderfully delicious they are. Pizza Nova uses only the finest ingredients and creates each menu selection with dedicated attention to detail. The results keep Pizza Nova customers coming back for more. Try us for lunch or dinner. We're sure you'll agree. $

Pizza Nova

Hillcrest: 3955 Fifth Avenue (Village Hillcrest)	(619) 296-6682
Point Loma: 5120 North Harbor Drive (On the Bay)	(619) 226-0268
Solana Beach: 945 Lomas Santa Fe Drive	(858) 259-0666

WHITE BEAN AND VEGETABLE SOUP *(10 oz.)* – SPECIAL REQUEST †
Fresh vegetable soup with white beans and pesto. <u>Request no parmesan cheese</u>.
✓✓ CALORIES: Excellent Choice (105)   ✓✓ CHOLESTEROL: Excellent Choice (10 mg)
✓✓ FAT: Excellent Choice (4 g)♥   SODIUM: Moderate (215 mg)*
PROTEIN: 6 g, CARBOHYDRATE: 16 g, FIBER: 3 g

SUNDRIED TOMATO LINGUINE *(½ ORDER)* – SPECIAL REQUEST
Linguine topped with pesto, sundried tomatoes and pine nuts. <u>Request no butter</u>.
✓✓ CALORIES: Excellent Choice (450)   ✓✓ CHOLESTEROL: Excellent Choice (5 mg)
✓✓ FAT: Excellent Choice (11 g)   ✓✓ SODIUM: Excellent Choice (190 mg)*
PROTEIN: 16 g, CARBOHYDRATE: 73 g, FIBER: 5 g

10-INCH MARGHERITA PIZZA *(½ PIZZA)*
Sliced roma tomatoes, fresh basil, garlic, mozzarella and fontina cheese.
Can be prepared without cheese, upon request. (Analysis for ½ of a 10" pizza.)
✓ CALORIES: Good Choice (530)   ✓✓ CHOLESTEROL: Excellent Choice (25 mg)
✓ FAT: Good Choice (19 g)   SODIUM: Moderate (820 mg)*
PROTEIN: 14 g, CARBOHYDRATE: 71 g, FIBER: 3 g

10-INCH MEDITERRANEAN PIZZA *(½ PIZZA)* ☺
Fire-roasted Portobello mushrooms, onions, zucchini, kalamata olives and tomatoes with mozzarella and feta cheese. <u>Request less mozzarella cheese</u> (1½ oz). (Analysis for ½ of a 10" pizza.)
✓ CALORIES: Good Choice (610)   ✓✓ CHOLESTEROL: Excellent Choice (35 mg)
✓ FAT: Good Choice (25 g)   SODIUM: High (1425 mg)*
PROTEIN: 17 g, CARBOHYDRATE: 79 g, FIBER: 3 g

BROCCOLI WITH PENNE ☺
Broccoli, fresh herbs, garlic, sundried tomatoes, extra virgin olive oil and parmesan cheese.
✓ CALORIES: Good Choice (485)   ✓✓ CHOLESTEROL: Excellent Choice (10 mg)
✓ FAT: Good Choice (19 g)   ✓ SODIUM: Good Choice (330 mg)*
PROTEIN: 18 g, CARBOHYDRATE: 62 g, FIBER: 6 g

Just minutes from downtown San Diego, The Prado adds a new dimension to David and Lesley Cohn's successful culinary portfolio of award-winning restaurants. Set in the rich landscape of landmark buildings and finely manicured gardens, The Prado restaurant is located at the historic House of Hospitality in the center of San Diego's famous Balboa Park. The Prado has an eye-catching décor that blends with the natural beauty of the environment. Specializing in Latin and Italian fusion, The Prado features a menu (that will delight all palates) created with the freshest ingredients of the Southern California region. A full bar with an extensive wine list featuring The Prado's signature drinks to complement the distinctive dining experience. Reservations are recommended. $$-$$$

The Prado at Balboa Park

1549 El Prado, San Diego, CA 92101   (619) 557-9441

CILANTRO GRILLED MAHI MAHI ☼

with sweet potato mash and chipotle shrimp salsa.

✓ CALORIES: Good Choice (515)   CHOLESTEROL: Moderate (165 mg)
✓ FAT: Good Choice (22 g)   ✓ SODIUM: Good Choice (530 mg)*
PROTEIN: 33 g, CARBOHYDRATE: 49 g, FIBER: 10 g

STEAMED RED BEET STACK

Tossed in a black-truffle champagne vinaigrette, whipped goat cheese and micro intensity greens.

✓✓ CALORIES: Excellent Choice (160)   ✓✓ CHOLESTEROL: Excellent Choice (5 mg)
✓✓ FAT: Excellent Choice (14 g)   ✓✓ SODIUM: Excellent Choice (195 mg)*
PROTEIN: 3 g, CARBOHYDRATE: 6 g, FIBER: 1 g

PRESSED SALAD – SPECIAL REQUEST ☼

with organic baby arugula, shaved asiago cheese, strawberries, candied walnuts and figs dressed in sherry shallot vinaigrette. <u>Request less dressing</u> (½ oz).

✓✓ CALORIES: Excellent Choice (345)   ✓✓ CHOLESTEROL: Excellent Choice (15 mg)
✓ FAT: Good Choice (22 g)   ✓ SODIUM: Good Choice (310 mg)*
PROTEIN: 10 g, CARBOHYDRATE: 33 g, FIBER: 6 g

Located in Mission Valley's Hazard Center, Prego offers a modern interpretation of a Tuscan villa, modeled after a small countryside Italian village, with a large walled piazza, olive trees, and sparkling fountains. Regional Italian cuisine features such specialties as homemade pasta, grilled fresh fish, spit-roasted meats and fowl, and pizza baked in an oak-fired oven. Fresh breadsticks and pastries are baked on the premises daily. Lunch is served on weekdays, dinner every day. $$

Prego Ristorante 1370 Frazee Road, San Diego, CA 92108 (619) 294-4700

LINGUINE ALLE VONGOLE – SPECIAL REQUEST

Flat pasta ribbons, Manila clams, fresh-water prawns, white wine, garlic, and extra virgin olive oil. Request less oil (1 Tbs).

✓ CALORIES: Good Choice (705)   CHOLESTEROL: Moderate (200 mg)
✓ FAT: Good Choice (17 g)♥   ✓ SODIUM: Good Choice (510 mg)*
PROTEIN: 46 g, CARBOHYDRATE: 87 g, FIBER: 5 g

PENNE AI VEGETALI 🍎

Pasta tubes, grilled zucchini, eggplant, broccoli, basil, diced tomatoes, garlic, and extra virgin olive oil.

✓ CALORIES: Good Choice (565)   ✓✓ CHOLESTEROL: Excellent Choice (0 mg)
✓ FAT: Good Choice (16 g)♥   ✓✓ SODIUM: Excellent Choice (20 mg)*
PROTEIN: 16 g, CARBOHYDRATE: 91 g, FIBER: 7 g

SPAGHETTI DI MARE – SPECIAL REQUEST

Spaghetti, shrimp, scallops, Manila clams, black mussels, and tomato sauce. Request less oil (½ Tbs).

✓ CALORIES: Good Choice (725)   CHOLESTEROL: High (305 mg)
✓✓ FAT: Excellent Choice (15 g)♥   SODIUM: Moderate (865 mg)*
PROTEIN: 72 g, CARBOHYDRATE: 71 g, FIBER: 4 g

RISOTTO PREGO – SPECIAL REQUEST

Arborio rice, grilled chicken, asparagus, and saffron. (Parmigiano not included in analysis.) Request no butter and less oil (½ Tbs).

✓ CALORIES: Good Choice (555)   ✓ CHOLESTEROL: Good Choice (85 mg)
✓ FAT: Good Choice (20 g)   SODIUM: High (1090 mg)*
PROTEIN: 31 g, CARBOHYDRATE: 60 g, FIBER: 2 g

POLLO ALA DIAVOLA 🍎

Mesquite grilled chicken breast marinated in spicy mustard greens and served with fresh steamed vegetables and roasted potatoes.

CALORIES: Moderate (780)   CHOLESTEROL: High (305 mg)
✓ FAT: Good Choice (20 g)   ✓ SODIUM: Good Choice (515 mg)*
PROTEIN: 117 g, CARBOHYDRATE: 30 g, FIBER: 5 g

Mexican & Vegetarian Cuisine

Ranchos' food is made fresh daily with the finest ingredients. When oil is required, we use only a little. Our rice and beans are 100% vegetarian and vegan. Our mole and sauces are made from scratch. We try to get as much organic fruits and vegetables as possible, fresh fish, with lots of vegan and vegetarian options. Check out our all-organic raw food selections. For our non-dairy smoothies, we use organic apple juice, fresh squeezed orange juice, or organic soy milk. $

Ranchos Cocina

1830 Sunset Cliffs Blvd. #H, Ocean Beach   (619) 226-7619
3910 30th Street, San Diego   (619) 574-1288

Fresh Salmon

Served with brown rice & steamed veggies. (Guacamole & tortillas not included in analysis.)
✓✓ CALORIES: Excellent Choice (405)   ✓ CHOLESTEROL: Good Choice (125 mg)
✓✓ FAT: Excellent Choice (14 g)♥   ✓✓ SODIUM: Excellent Choice (125 mg)*
PROTEIN: 48 g, CARBOHYDRATE: 18 g, FIBER: 3 g

Eggplant Enchiladas – Special Request 🍎

with pico de gallo and ranchero sauce. Request brown rice and black beans.
✓✓ CALORIES: Excellent Choice (305)   ✓✓ CHOLESTEROL: Excellent Choice (0 mg)
✓✓ FAT: Excellent Choice (2 g)♥   ✓✓ SODIUM: Excellent Choice (275 mg)*
PROTEIN: 12 g, CARBOHYDRATE: 62 g, FIBER: 12 g

Veggie Fajitas with Tofu – Special Request 🍎

Lots of veggies and 2 corn tortillas. (Guacamole not included in analysis.)
Request brown rice and black beans.
✓✓ CALORIES: Excellent Choice (335)   ✓✓ CHOLESTEROL: Excellent Choice (0 mg)
✓✓ FAT: Excellent Choice (4 g)♥   ✓✓ SODIUM: Excellent Choice (130 mg)*
PROTEIN: 17 g, CARBOHYDRATE: 62 g, FIBER: 12 g

Mushroom Ranchero – Special Request 🍎

Fresh mushrooms, corn tortillas, pico de gallo, and ranchero sauce. Request brown rice and black beans.
✓✓ CALORIES: Excellent Choice (305)   ✓✓ CHOLESTEROL: Excellent Choice (0 mg)
✓✓ FAT: Excellent Choice (3 g)♥   ✓ SODIUM: Good Choice (305 mg)*
PROTEIN: 14 g, CARBOHYDRATE: 61 g, FIBER: 12 g

Steamed Veggie Plate – Special Request 🍎

Served on a bed of black beans, with 2 corn tortillas.
Request brown rice. (Guacamole not included in analysis.)
✓✓ CALORIES: Excellent Choice (335)   ✓✓ CHOLESTEROL: Excellent Choice (0 mg)
✓✓ FAT: Excellent Choice (3 g)♥   ✓✓ SODIUM: Excellent Choice (210 mg)*
PROTEIN: 15 g, CARBOHYDRATE: 68 g, FIBER: 15 g

See page 43 for key to symbols: * ♥ † 🍎 and $

rice|Jones®

Why riceJones? "As a little girl growing up in Vietnam, I was used to having the freshest ingredients that came to my mother's kitchen from the villages nearby. Shrimp that still jumped in the baskets, fish that swam until paid for, and vegetables that were freshly pulled in the morning. At riceJones, Vietnamese and California cuisines are separate but 'together,' with the name 'rice' representing East Asia, and 'Jones' representing America," explains Anh Long, creator of the restaurant in Hillcrest. Menu items are reasonably priced with generous portions, and the cooking is light and healthy (no MSG is used). Full bar and tapas menu daily. $-$$

rice Jones
3687 Fifth Avenue, San Diego, CA 92103 (619) 291-1887

TOFU SPRING ROLL (½ ORDER) † ♨
*Salad rolls filled with rice noodles, lettuce, cucumber and fresh herbs
in rice paper with tofu, served with peanut sauce.*
- ✓ CALORIES: Good Choice (205)
- ✓ FAT: Good Choice (6 g)♥
- ✓✓ CHOLESTEROL: Excellent Choice (0 mg)
- SODIUM: High (705 mg)*

PROTEIN: 7 g, CARBOHYDRATE: 30 g, FIBER: 2 g

CHICKEN NOODLE SOUP
*Slices of chicken over rice noodles in a flavorful broth, topped with green onion, cilantro,
and a twist of lime – a Vietnamese all-time favorite. (Analysis for soup only.)*
- ✓ CALORIES: Good Choice (520)
- ✓✓ FAT: Excellent Choice (5 g)
- ✓ CHOLESTEROL: Good Choice (95 mg)
- SODIUM: High (1560 mg)*

PROTEIN: 39 g, CARBOHYDRATE: 77 g, FIBER: 4 g

BUN, SHRIMP – SPECIAL REQUEST ♨
*Rice noodles, shredded lettuce, cucumber, fresh herbs, bean sprouts, and grilled shrimp.
Request dressing on the side (not included in analysis; 5 cal, 0 fat, 125 mg sodium per Tbs).*
- ✓✓ CALORIES: Excellent Choice (380)
- ✓✓ FAT: Excellent Choice (7 g)♥
- CHOLESTEROL: Moderate (220 mg)
- SODIUM: Moderate (650 mg)*

PROTEIN: 28 g, CARBOHYDRATE: 50 g, FIBER: 5 g

GRILLED EGGPLANT ♨
with zucchini, red pepper, green onion, garlic, served with Jones rice.
- ✓ CALORIES: Good Choice (490)
- ✓✓ FAT: Excellent Choice (15 g)♥
- ✓✓ CHOLESTEROL: Excellent Choice (0 mg)
- SODIUM: High (1530 mg)*

PROTEIN: 13g, CARBOHYDRATE: 81 g, FIBER: 16 g

LEMONGRASS CHICKEN – SPECIAL REQUEST
Lemongrass marinated chicken with steamed rice and veggies. Request less oil (1 Tbs).
- ✓ CALORIES: Good Choice (685)
- ✓ FAT: Good Choice (22 g)
- ✓ CHOLESTEROL: Good Choice (125 mg)
- SODIUM: High (1250 mg)*

PROTEIN: 52 g, CARBOHYDRATE: 65 g, FIBER: 2 g

CHICKEN NOODLE TOSS – SPECIAL REQUEST ♨
Angel hair pasta tossed with shiitake mushrooms, mixed veggies and chicken. Request less oil (½ Tbs).
- ✓ CALORIES: Good Choice (730)
- ✓ FAT: Good Choice (17 g)
- ✓ CHOLESTEROL: Good Choice (125 mg)
- SODIUM: High (2655 mg)*

PROTEIN: 66 g, CARBOHYDRATE: 80 g, FIBER: 12 g

Roppongi Restaurant & Sushi Bar, located in the Village of La Jolla, is Zagat rated "One of the Top 5 Most Popular San Diego Restaurants." Serves a lunch and dinner menu of New Asian cuisine – blending Japanese, Chinese, Vietnamese, Thai, and Indian flavors using European cooking techniques. $$-$$$

Roppongi Restaurant & Sushi Bar
875 Prospect Street, La Jolla, CA 92037   (858) 551-5252

SASHIMI SALAD †☺
- ✓✓ CALORIES: Excellent Choice (175)
- ✓✓ FAT: Excellent Choice (3 g)♥
- ✓✓ CHOLESTEROL: Excellent Choice (30 mg)
- SODIUM: High (1775 mg)*
- PROTEIN: 17 g, CARBOHYDRATE: 20 g, FIBER: 3 g

ALASKAN HALIBUT WITH URCHIN – SPECIAL REQUEST ☺
Pan seared Alaskan halibut with urchin sauce served with edamame and pea tendrils. Request no butter.
- ✓ CALORIES: Good Choice (640)
- ✓ FAT: Good Choice (24 g)♥
- CHOLESTEROL: Moderate (205 mg)
- ✓ SODIUM: Good Choice (475 mg)*
- PROTEIN: 71 g, CARBOHYDRATE: 31 g, FIBER: 9 g

POLYNESIAN DUNGENESS CRAB STACK
Mango, pea shoots, cucumber, tomato, avocado and peanuts served with spicy ginger lime dressing. (Analysis does not include brioche.)
- ✓✓ CALORIES: Excellent Choice (350)
- ✓✓ FAT: Excellent Choice (15 g)♥
- ✓✓ CHOLESTEROL: Excellent Choice (45 mg)
- SODIUM: Moderate (855 mg)*
- PROTEIN: 20 g, CARBOHYDRATE: 37 g, FIBER: 6 g

MISO MARINATED BLACK COD – SPECIAL REQUEST ☺
with Chinese broccoli, wilted arugula and balsamic reduction. Request butter sauce on the side (not included in analysis).
- ✓ CALORIES: Good Choice (495)
- ✓ FAT: Good Choice (25 g)
- ✓ CHOLESTEROL: Good Choice (145 mg)
- SODIUM: Moderate (705 mg)*
- PROTEIN: 40 g, CARBOHYDRATE: 21 g, FIBER: 3 g

INDONESIAN TIGER SHRIMP SKEWER
Skewered tiger prawns served with tomato horseradish sauce and mango salsa.
- ✓✓ CALORIES: Excellent Choice (335)
- ✓✓ FAT: Excellent Choice (10 g)♥
- CHOLESTEROL: Moderate (190 mg)
- SODIUM: High (1160 mg)*
- PROTEIN: 22 g, CARBOHYDRATE: 44 g, FIBER: 2 g

HIBACHI GRILLED SEABASS – SPECIAL REQUEST ☺
with roasted vegetables, mashed potatoes and papaya ponzu. Request less oil (1 tsp).
- ✓ CALORIES: Good Choice (670)
- ✓ FAT: Good Choice (25 g)
- ✓ CHOLESTEROL: Good Choice (110 mg)
- SODIUM: High (5245 mg)*
- PROTEIN: 58 g, CARBOHYDRATE: 57 g, FIBER: 11 g

We offer pizzas with a variety of sauces, a blend of three real cheeses, superior meats, fresh vegetables, and dough made fresh in our restaurants. Round Table Pizza offers many locations in San Diego County for your convenience. Please visit our website: www.roundtablepizza.com. $

Round Table Pizza San Diego area locations: Encinitas, Escondido, La Mesa, Oceanside, Pacific Beach, Perris, Poway, Rancho Bernardo, Rancho Penasquitos, Rancho San Diego, Santee, Solana Beach, Spring Valley, Temecula, Tierrasanta, UCSD, University City, Vista.

Analyses below are for original (thin crust) pizza; pan crust adds approx. 2 g fat & 80 cal per slice.

GUINEVERE'S GARDEN DELIGHT® PIZZA (2 SLICES)

Our zesty red sauce, three cheeses, mushrooms, black olives, Roma tomatoes,
yellow onions, and green peppers. (Analysis for 2 slices of a large pizza.)
✓✓ CALORIES: Excellent Choice (420)   ✓✓ CHOLESTEROL: Excellent Choice (40 mg)
✓✓ FAT: Excellent Choice (14 g)   SODIUM: High (1100 mg)
PROTEIN: 18 g, CARBOHYDRATE: 50 g, FIBER: 4 g

GOURMET VEGGIE™ PIZZA (2 SLICES)

Our creamy garlic sauce, three cheeses, artichoke hearts, zucchini, spinach,
Portabella mushrooms, Roma tomatoes, red & green onions, Italian herb seasoning
and lots of chopped garlic. (Analysis for 2 slices of a large pizza.)
✓✓ CALORIES: Excellent Choice (440)   ✓✓ CHOLESTEROL: Excellent Choice (40 mg)
✓ FAT: Good Choice (18 g)   SODIUM: Moderate (960 mg)
PROTEIN: 20 g, CARBOHYDRATE: 52 g, FIBER: 4 g

CHICKEN & GARLIC GOURMET™ PIZZA (2 SLICES)

Our creamy garlic sauce, three cheeses, grilled white-meat chicken, Portobello mushrooms, Roma
tomatoes, red & green onions, Italian herb seasoning and lots of chopped garlic.
(Analysis for 2 slices of a large pizza.)
✓ CALORIES: Good Choice (460)   ✓✓ CHOLESTEROL: Excellent Choice (50 mg)
✓ FAT: Good Choice (18 g)   SODIUM: High (1140 mg)
PROTEIN: 26 g, CARBOHYDRATE: 50 g, FIBER: 2 g

HAWAIIAN PIZZA (2 SLICES)

Tender slices of ham and juicy pineapple tidbits. Baked with a blend of 3 cheeses
on our zesty red sauce. (Analysis for 2 slices of a large pizza.)
✓✓ CALORIES: Excellent Choice (420)   ✓✓ CHOLESTEROL: Excellent Choice (50 mg)
✓✓ FAT: Excellent Choice (14 g)   SODIUM: High (1240 mg)
PROTEIN: 20 g, CARBOHYDRATE: 50 g, FIBER: 2 g

MAUI ZAUI™ PIZZA (2 SLICES)

Tender ham, crisp bacon, juicy pineapple, Roma tomatoes, red and green onions.
Baked with a blend of 3 cheeses on our zesty red sauce (or Polynesian sauce).
(Analysis for 2 slices of a large pizza with zesty red sauce).
✓ CALORIES: Good Choice (480)   ✓✓ CHOLESTEROL: Excellent Choice (50 mg)
✓ FAT: Good Choice (18 g)   SODIUM: High (1380 mg)
PROTEIN: 22 g, CARBOHYDRATE: 50 g, FIBER: 2 g

GARDEN SALAD (SMALL): CAL: 100, FAT: 3½ g, CHOL: 0, SODIUM: 220 mg, PROT: 2 g, CARB: 14 g, FIBER: 2 g

Nutrition information supplied by Round Table Pizza.

Royal India and Royal India Express offer a large selection of vegetarian meals, as well as chicken, lamb and seafood, and fresh homemade breads, desserts and yogurt. Meals are cooked to order and can be requested mild, medium, or hot. Many of our most popular dishes are prepared using the tandoor, a tall cylindrical clay oven that allows the fat to drip away while retaining the flavor. Please visit us at the new fine dining Royal India in the Gaslamp district ($$), or our Royal India Express locations. $

Royal India Exquisite Restaurant, Bar & Lounge

Gaslamp/Downtown: 329 Market Street, San Diego 92101   (619) 269-9999

or (888) MY CURRY

Royal India Express

UTC: 4545 La Jolla Village Dr.; #E22, San Diego 92122   (858) 453-5300

Mission Valley: 1640 Cam. del Rio N., #FC7, San Diego 92108   (619) 501-9999

Downtown: 423 Horton Plaza, #379, San Diego 92101   (619) 795-4444

CHICKEN TIKKA KABAB

Tandoori-prepared boneless chicken marinated with fresh herbs and spices.

✓✓ CALORIES: Excellent Choice (380)   CHOLESTEROL: Moderate (195 mg)

✓✓ FAT: Excellent Choice (8 g)   ✓ SODIUM: Good Choice (305 mg)*

PROTEIN: 71 g, CARBOHYDRATE: 1 g, FIBER: 0 g

CHICKEN CURRY WITH VEGETABLES

✓✓ CALORIES: Excellent Choice (390)   ✓ CHOLESTEROL: Good Choice (115 mg)

✓ FAT: Good Choice (20 g)   ✓ SODIUM: Good Choice (510 mg)*

PROTEIN: 44 g, CARBOHYDRATE: 9 g, FIBER: 3 g

KARAHI CHICKEN – SPECIAL REQUEST ☺

Boneless chicken sautéed with bell peppers, onion and tomatoes in a delicately spiced curry. Request less oil (½ Tbs).

✓✓ CALORIES: Excellent Choice (410)   ✓ CHOLESTEROL: Good Choice (105 mg)

✓✓ FAT: Excellent Choice (14 g)   SODIUM: Moderate (660 mg)*

PROTEIN: 37 g, CARBOHYDRATE: 33 g, FIBER: 7 g

PRAWN PEPPER MASALA – SPECIAL REQUEST ☺

Prawns cooked with fresh green peppers, onions and spices. Request less oil (½ Tbs).

✓✓ CALORIES: Excellent Choice (340)   CHOLESTEROL: Moderate (250 mg)

✓✓ FAT: Excellent Choice (10 g)♥   SODIUM: Moderate (865 mg)*

PROTEIN: 33 g, CARBOHYDRATE: 32 g, FIBER: 7 g

ALOO GOBI – SPECIAL REQUEST ☺

Cauliflower and potatoes cooked with herbs and spices. Request less oil (½ Tbs).

✓✓ CALORIES: Excellent Choice (240)   ✓✓ CHOLESTEROL: Excellent Choice (0 mg)

✓✓ FAT: Excellent Choice (8 g)♥   ✓✓ SODIUM: Excellent Choice (90 mg)*

PROTEIN: 8 g, CARBOHYDRATE: 38 g, FIBER: 10 g

BENGAN BHARTHA – SPECIAL REQUEST ☺

Eggplant baked in clay oven with onions, peas and tomatoes. Request less oil (½ Tbs).

✓✓ CALORIES: Excellent Choice (300)   ✓✓ CHOLESTEROL: Excellent Choice (0 mg)

✓✓ FAT: Excellent Choice (9 g)♥   SODIUM: Moderate (740 mg)*

PROTEIN: 12 g, CARBOHYDRATE: 49 g, FIBER: 15 g

See page 43 for key to symbols: * ♥ † ☺ and $ *Healthy Dining in San Diego*   **99**

Fresh, flavorful, bold, distinctive Baja-inspired food is the hallmark of Rubio's Fresh Mexican Grill.® Rubio's was founded on fresh authentic food, and we continue our commitment to freshness and to accommodating our guests on any kind of diet—with the ability to customize orders and a whole line of HealthMex® products, each with less than 20% of calories from fat. Complete nutritional information is available at rubios.com. $

Rubio's® San Diego area locations: Carlsbad, Carmel Mountain Ranch, Chula Vista, College Grove, Coronado, Del Mar, Eastlake, El Cajon, Encinitas, Escondido, Fashion Valley, Grossmont Center, Kearny Mesa, La Jolla, Mira Mesa, Mission Bay, Mission Gorge, Mission Valley, Oceanside, Pacific Beach, Parkway Plaza, Point Loma, Poway, Ramona, Rancho Bernardo, Rancho Del Rey, Rancho San Diego, San Marcos, Scripps Ranch, SDSU, Solana Beach, Torrey Highlands, UCSD, UTC, Viejas, & Vista. Visit rubios.com for a map of your local Rubio's & other Orange County/Inland Empire locations.

HEALTHMEX CHICKEN TACO
Grilled all-white meat chicken, crisp lettuce or shredded cabbage, roasted chipotle salsa and salsa fresca in a soft, stone-ground corn tortilla.
✓✓ CALORIES: Excellent Choice (170)   ✓✓ CHOLESTEROL: Excellent Choice (30 mg)
✓✓ FAT: Excellent Choice (3 g)   ✓ SODIUM: Good Choice (390 mg)
PROTEIN: 13 g, CARBOHYDRATE: 23 g, FIBER: 2 g

HEALTHMEX MAHI MAHI TACO
Grilled Mahi Mahi, crisp lettuce or shredded cabbage, roasted chipotle salsa and salsa fresca in a soft, stone-ground corn tortilla.
✓✓ CALORIES: Excellent Choice (180)   ✓✓ CHOLESTEROL: Excellent Choice (15 mg)
✓✓ FAT: Excellent Choice (3 g)   ✓✓ SODIUM: Excellent Choice (190 mg)
PROTEIN: 14 g, CARBOHYDRATE: 22 g, FIBER: 2 g

HEALTHMEX CHICKEN BURRITO
Grilled all-white meat chicken with rice, black beans, roasted chipotle salsa and salsa fresca in a warm whole wheat tortilla. Served with rice (see separate analysis below) instead of chips.
✓ CALORIES: Good Choice (530)   ✓✓ CHOLESTEROL: Excellent Choice (70 mg)
✓✓ FAT: Excellent Choice (10 g)   SODIUM: High (1670 mg)
PROTEIN: 35 g, CARBOHYDRATE: 77 g, FIBER: 7 g

HEALTHMEX MAHI MAHI BURRITO
Grilled Mahi Mahi with rice, black beans, roasted chipotle salsa and salsa fresca in a warm whole wheat tortilla. Served with rice (see separate analysis below) instead of chips.
✓ CALORIES: Good Choice (540)   ✓✓ CHOLESTEROL: Excellent Choice (35 mg)
✓✓ FAT: Excellent Choice (11 g)   SODIUM: High (1170 mg)
PROTEIN: 37 g, CARBOHYDRATE: 75 g, FIBER: 7 g

HEALTHMEX CHICKEN SALAD ☺
Grilled all white meat chicken and salsa fresca atop crisp lettuce, shredded cabbage and Rubio's fat-free Serrano-grape dressing (dressing included in this analysis and also listed below).
✓✓ CALORIES: Excellent Choice (260)   ✓✓ CHOLESTEROL: Excellent Choice (70 mg)
✓✓ FAT: Excellent Choice (2 g)   SODIUM: High (1050 mg)
PROTEIN: 27 g, CARBOHYDRATE: 34 g, FIBER: 6 g

INDIVIDUAL SIDES: RICE SERVED WITH HEALTHMEX BURRITOS
CALORIES: 80, FAT: 1 g, CHOLESTEROL: 0, SODIUM: 210 mg, PROTEIN: 3 g, CARBOHYDRATE: 14 g, FIBER: 1 g

FAT-FREE SERRANO GRAPE DRESSING *(per 38 gram, or approx. 2½ Tbs.)*
CALORIES: 40, FAT: 0, CHOLESTEROL: 0, SODIUM: 135 mg, PROTEIN: 0, CARBOHYDRATE: 9 g, FIBER: 0

Nutrition analysis supplied by Rubio's. Please check rubios.com for updates on product & nutrition information.

Ruby's Diner is the authentic 1940s diner! Step back in time to 40s memorabilia, gleaming red and white interiors and friendly, courteous service. Ruby's offers items to please every palate, including a variety of salads, sandwiches, and home style breakfasts. Swing into Ruby's today and experience great food and great service with a 40s flair. $

Ruby's Diner

with 3 San Diego County locations to serve you!

5630 Paseo del Norte, Ste. 130, Carlsbad 92008   (760) 931-RUBY
640 Camino del Rio N., #360P, San Diego 92108   (619) 294-RUBY
1 Pierview Way, Oceanside 92054   (760) 433-RUBY

For locations outside San Diego County, call 1-800 HEY RUBY or visit our website at www.rubys.com.

EGG WHITE OMELETTE

Egg whites with low-fat American cheese, mushrooms, tomato & spinach, served with fresh fruit.

✓✓ CALORIES: Excellent Choice (340)   ✓✓ CHOLESTEROL: Excellent Choice (35 mg)
✓ FAT: Good Choice (20 g)   SODIUM: High (1105 mg)
PROTEIN: 31 g, CARBOHYDRATE: 11 g, FIBER: 2 g

SKINNY LUNCH (GRILLED CHICKEN BREAST)

with salsa, fresh fruit and low-fat cottage cheese.

✓✓ CALORIES: Excellent Choice (350)   ✓ CHOLESTEROL: Good Choice (105 mg)
✓✓ FAT: Excellent Choice (6 g)   SODIUM: High (1045 mg)
PROTEIN: 48 g, CARBOHYDRATE: 24 g, FIBER: 2 g

VEGWICH

Avocado, low-fat American cheese, tomato, not-fat mayo, lettuce & spinach on toasted wheat bread.

✓ CALORIES: Good Choice (455)   ✓✓ CHOLESTEROL: Excellent Choice (40 mg)
✓ FAT: Good Choice (22 g)   SODIUM: High (1505 mg)
PROTEIN: 21 g, CARBOHYDRATE: 51 g, FIBER: 7 g

DE "LITE" FUL CHICKEN BURGER

*A tender grilled chicken breast with tomato, red onion,
low-fat American cheese, and non-fat mayo on a whole wheat bun.*

✓ CALORIES: Good Choice (685)   ✓ CHOLESTEROL: Good Choice (130 mg)
FAT: Moderate (30 g)   SODIUM: High (1675 mg)
PROTEIN: 52 g, CARBOHYDRATE: 55 g, FIBER: 6 g

TURKEY RUBYBURGER – SPECIAL REQUEST

with a full ⅓ lb. of lean ground turkey. Request no margarine or Ruby sauce.

✓ CALORIES: Good Choice (490)   ✓ CHOLESTEROL: Good Choice (145 mg)
✓ FAT: Good Choice (19 g)   ✓ SODIUM: Good Choice (485 mg)
PROTEIN: 35 g, CARBOHYDRATE: 43 g, FIBER: 1 g

VEGGIE RUBYBURGER – SPECIAL REQUEST

with a tasty vegetable, rice, oats & wheat Garden Burger patty. Request no margarine or mayonnaise.

✓ CALORIES: Good Choice (500)   ✓✓ CHOLESTEROL: Excellent Choice (5 mg)
✓✓ FAT: Excellent Choice (9 g)♥   SODIUM: High (1085 mg)
PROTEIN: 19 g, CARBOHYDRATE: 85 g, FIBER: 8 g

Nutrition analysis supplied by Ruby's.

Fresh...Simple...Homemade. That's been our philosophy since the early 1970s when we first opened our doors to this community. It is this commitment to freshness, quality, and even a surprise or two that has kept St. Germain's Cafe on the forefront of the California dining experience. Open 7 a.m. - 4 p.m. daily. Dinner Fridays and Saturdays until 10 p.m. $

St. Germain's Cafe 1010 S. Hwy. 101, Encinitas, CA 92024 (760) 753-5411

EGG BEATERS BIG SCRAMBLE – SPECIAL REQUEST ♨

with mushrooms, onion, tomato and bell pepper. Served with two slices of toast and fresh fruit. <u>Request Egg Beaters</u>. (Analysis does not include butter on toast.)
- ✓✓ CALORIES: Excellent Choice (375)
- ✓✓ FAT: Excellent Choice (5 g)♥
- ✓✓ CHOLESTEROL: Excellent Choice (0 mg)
- SODIUM: Moderate (695 mg)*

PROTEIN: 27 g, CARBOHYDRATE: 59 g, FIBER: 4 g

EGG BEATERS SPANISH OMELETTE – SPECIAL REQUEST ♨

Topped with mild Spanish sauce and served with two slices of toast and fresh fruit. <u>Request Egg Beaters and no cheese</u>. (Analysis does not include butter on toast.)
- ✓✓ CALORIES: Excellent Choice (370)
- ✓✓ FAT: Excellent Choice (5 g)♥
- ✓✓ CHOLESTEROL: Excellent Choice (0 mg)
- SODIUM: Moderate (815 mg)*

PROTEIN: 27 g, CARBOHYDRATE: 59 g, FIBER: 4 g

EGG BEATERS SPINACH & MUSHROOM OMELETTE – SPECIAL REQUEST ♨

Fresh spinach and mushrooms sautéed. Includes two slices of toast and fresh fruit. <u>Request Egg Beaters with no cheese</u> (cheese adds 110 calories and 9 g fat). (Analysis does not include butter on toast.)
- ✓✓ CALORIES: Excellent Choice (385)
- ✓✓ FAT: Excellent Choice (5 g)♥
- ✓✓ CHOLESTEROL: Excellent Choice (0 mg)
- SODIUM: Moderate (740 mg)*

PROTEIN: 29 g, CARBOHYDRATE: 61 g, FIBER: 5 g

FAMOUS VEGETARIAN BURGER ♨

Made from lentils, walnuts, onions and delicious spices, and topped with lettuce, tomato and onion. Served with fresh fruit and cafe potatoes. (Analysis does not include potatoes or cheese.)
- ✓ CALORIES: Good Choice (580)
- ✓✓ FAT: Excellent Choice (14 g)♥
- ✓✓ CHOLESTEROL: Excellent Choice (45 mg)
- SODIUM: Moderate (995 mg)*

PROTEIN: 26 g, CARBOHYDRATE: 94 g, FIBER: Not available

TERIYAKI CHICKEN SANDWICH

Marinated in our own teriyaki sauce, crowned with pineapple, and topped with lettuce and tomato. (Analysis includes fresh fruit.)
- ✓ CALORIES: Good Choice (600)
- ✓✓ FAT: Excellent Choice (9 g)
- ✓ CHOLESTEROL: Good Choice (130 mg)
- SODIUM: High (1190 mg)

PROTEIN: 60 g, CARBOHYDRATE: 72 g, FIBER: 8 g

WEST INDIES CHICKEN SANDWICH

Spiced with our unique Cajun spices and charbroiled. (Analysis includes fresh fruit.)
- ✓ CALORIES: Good Choice (595)
- ✓✓ FAT: Excellent Choice (9 g)
- ✓ CHOLESTEROL: Good Choice (130 mg)
- SODIUM: High (1260 mg)

PROTEIN: 61 g, CARBOHYDRATE: 71 g, FIBER: 8 g

Zagat-rated among the 5 most popular San Diego restaurants. Serving gourmet pizza, refreshing salads, fresh pastas and specialty entrées at reasonable prices. Please visit www.sammyspizza.com $

Sammy's Woodfired Pizza

Carlsbad:	(760) 438-1212	Costa Verde:	(858) 404-9898
Del Mar:	(858) 259-6600	Downtown:	(619) 230-8888
La Jolla:	(858) 456-5222	Mission Valley:	(619) 298-8222
	Scripps Ranch:	(858) 695-0900	

OAK ROASTED SALMON ON PONZU SALAD ☼

Shredded cabbage, cucumber, edamame and ponzu sauce.

✓ CALORIES: Good Choice (470)
✓ FAT: Good Choice (19 g)♥
   CHOLESTEROL: Good Choice (110 mg)
   SODIUM: High (2200 mg)
Protein: 50 g, Carbohydrate: 21 g, Fiber: 5 g

ROAST CHICKEN PESTO WRAP – SPECIAL REQUEST ☼

Onions, feta cheese, bell peppers, romaine lettuce, and kalamata olives. <u>Request non-fat honey mustard dressing and lettuce wraps in place of tortilla.</u>
(Analysis for wrap only, does not include cole slaw or French fries.)

✓ CALORIES: Good Choice (480)
✓ FAT: Good Choice (20 g)
   CHOLESTEROL: Moderate (155 mg)
   SODIUM: High (1485 mg)
PROTEIN: 52 g, CARBOHYDRATE: 22 g, FIBER: 5 g

TOMATO ANGEL HAIR PASTA – SPECIAL REQUEST ☼

Roma tomatoes, fresh basil and garlic. <u>Request less oil</u> *(1 Tbs).*

✓ CALORIES: Good Choice (700)
✓ FAT: Good Choice (18 g)♥
   ✓✓ CHOLESTEROL: Excellent Choice (15 mg)
   ✓✓ SODIUM: Excellent Choice (65 mg)*
PROTEIN: 24 g, CARBOHYDRATE: 115 g, FIBER: 9 g

CHINESE CHICKEN SALAD (INDIVIDUAL SIZE) – SPECIAL REQUEST ☼

Chinese greens, bell peppers, sesame seeds, cilantro, scallions and Mandarin oranges. <u>Request non-fat honey mustard dressing</u> *(included in analysis).*

✓✓ CALORIES: Excellent Choice (450)
✓✓ FAT: Excellent Choice (12 g)
   ✓ CHOLESTEROL: Good Choice (85 mg)
   SODIUM: High (1010 mg)
PROTEIN: 40 g, CARBOHYDRATE: 47 g, FIBER: 8 g

CHOPPED CHICKEN SALAD (INDIVIDUAL SIZE) – SPECIAL REQUEST ☼

Chicken breast, lettuce, tomatoes, olives, fat-free mozzarella, and basil. <u>Request non-fat honey mustard dressing</u> *(included in analysis),* <u>fat-free cheese and less olives</u> *(2 Tbs).*

✓✓ CALORIES: Excellent Choice (425)
✓✓ FAT: Excellent Choice (11 g)
   ✓ CHOLESTEROL: Good Choice (90 mg)
   SODIUM: High (3690 mg)
PROTEIN: 52 g, CARBOHYDRATE: 30 g, FIBER: 6

VEGETARIAN PIZZA (½ PIZZA) – SPECIAL REQUEST

Grilled eggplant, onions, bell peppers, fontina, garlic, zucchini and Roma tomatoes with mozzarella. <u>Request fat-free mozzarella</u> *(1 cup). (Analysis is for ½ of a pizza.)*

   CALORIES: Moderate (845)
✓ FAT: Good Choice (19 g)
   ✓✓ CHOLESTEROL: Excellent Choice (20 mg)
   SODIUM: High (1940 mg)
PROTEIN: 37 g, CARBOHYDRATE: 127 g, FIBER: 6 g

FRESH TOMATO BASIL SOUP – SPECIAL REQUEST † ☼

With shaved Romano cheese. <u>Request no herb oil.</u>
CAL: 110, FAT: 5 g, CHOLESTEROL: 5 g, SOD: 900 mg, PROTEIN: 7 g, CARB: 10 g, FIBER: 3 g

See page 43 for key to symbols ♥ ✳ ☼ † and $

Healthy Dining in San Diego **103**

Sandy Crabbe, owner of The SandCrab Cafe, offers seafood with a difference. A California version of an East Coast Crab House, various seafood combinations are offered, as well as a la carte, including stone crab claws, mussels, and seafood gumbo. Open for lunch and dinner 7 days: Monday through Thursday 11 a.m. to 9 p.m., Friday 11 a.m. to 10 p.m., Saturday noon to 10 p.m., Sunday noon to 9 p.m. A different way to dine; fun for the whole family. $$

SandCrab Cafe

2229 Micro Place, Escondido, CA 92029   (760) 480-CRAB (2722)

Directions: From Hwy 78 exit Nordahl south to Mission, turn right onto Mission, then first left onto Barham, left on Opper, then another left onto Micro Place.

SEAFOOD GUMBO
Spicy!

✓✓ CALORIES: Excellent Choice (255)   ✓✓ CHOLESTEROL: Excellent Choice (70 mg)
✓✓ FAT: Excellent Choice (6 g)♥   ✓✓ SODIUM: Excellent Choice (255 mg)*
PROTEIN: 21 g, CARBOHYDRATE: 30 g, FIBER: 2 g

SNOW CRAB CLUSTERS
One pound. Cooked in our own special broth of savory spices.
(Analysis does not include butter served on the side.)

✓✓ CALORIES: Excellent Choice (145)   ✓✓ CHOLESTEROL: Excellent Choice (70 mg)
✓✓ FAT: Excellent Choice (1 g)♥   SODIUM: High (1970 mg)*
PROTEIN: 31 g, CARBOHYDRATE: 1 g, FIBER: 0

STONE CRAB CLAWS
Cooked in our own special broth of savory spices.
(Analysis does not include butter served on the side.)

✓✓ CALORIES: Excellent Choice (195)   ✓ CHOLESTEROL: Good Choice (95 mg)
✓✓ FAT: Excellent Choice (1 g)♥   SODIUM: High (2625 mg)*
PROTEIN: 42 g, CARBOHYDRATE: 1 g, FIBER: 0

ALL CRAB COMBO ♨
Snow crab, blue crab, stone crab claws, king crab leg, new potatoes and corn on the cob. (Sausage and bread not included in analysis.)

✓✓ CALORIES: Excellent Choice (360)   ✓✓ CHOLESTEROL: Excellent Choice (65 mg)
✓✓ FAT: Excellent Choice (3 g)♥   SODIUM: High (3615 mg)*
PROTEIN: 28 g, CARBOHYDRATE: 58 g, FIBER: 3 g

FISHERMAN'S SAMPLER (½ SERVING)
Shrimp, clams, snow crab clusters, crawfish, New Zealand mussels, stone crab claws, lobster tail, new potatoes and corn on the cob all cooked in our own special broth of savory spices.
(Analysis for ½ of a one large serving. Sausage and bread not included in analysis.)

✓✓ CALORIES: Excellent Choice (395)   CHOLESTEROL: High (300 mg)
✓✓ FAT: Excellent Choice (4 g)♥   SODIUM: High (2965 mg)*
PROTEIN: 58 g, CARBOHYDRATE: 31 g, FIBER: 3 g

Home of the famous California Burrito. Thanks to you, we have been serving you in San Diego since 1987. We believe that fresher is better. That is why our food is prepared every day on our premises, and our tortillas, meat, poultry and produce are delivered daily. We use 100% corn oil and no preservatives. We thank you again for the opportunity of letting us serve you. And to you who haven't tried our food, we dare you to do so!!! We also offer frequent eater cards, an ATM machine and a fresh salsa bar when you dine-in at all our locations. For your convenience, we are open 24/7. $

Santana's Mexican Grill

San Marcos: 580 S. Pacific St. (760)736-4648
Pt. Loma: 1480 Rosecrans St. (619)226-2033
Bay Park: 1525 Morena Blvd. (619)276-6010

Mission Hills: 719 W. Washington St. (619)574-8710
Pacific Beach: 2303 Garnet Ave. (858)483-1227
Sports Arena: 3742 Midway Dr. (619)523-9517

GRILLED CHICKEN TACO
Wrapped in 2 corn tortillas with guacamole and Mexican salsa.
✓✓ CALORIES: Excellent Choice (410)   ✓✓ CHOLESTEROL: Excellent Choice (55 mg)
✓✓ FAT: Excellent Choice (13 g)   ✓ SODIUM: Good Choice (350 mg)*
PROTEIN: 22g, CARBOHYDRATE: 55 g, FIBER: 9 g

GRILLED ACHIOTE CHICKEN TACO
Wrapped in 2 corn tortillas with lettuce, cheddar and enchilado cheeses.
✓ CALORIES: Good Choice (485)   ✓ CHOLESTEROL: Good Choice (85 mg)
✓ FAT: Good Choice (19 g)   ✓ SODIUM: Good Choice (345 mg)*
PROTEIN: 29 g, CARBOHYDRATE: 54 g, FIBER: 8 g

CARNE ASADA TACO
Wrapped in 2 corn tortillas with guacamole and Mexican salsa.
✓ CALORIES: Good Choice (490)   ✓✓ CHOLESTEROL: Excellent Choice (60 mg)
✓ FAT: Good Choice (21 g)   ✓ SODIUM: Good Choice (335 mg)*
PROTEIN: 22 g, CARBOHYDRATE: 54 g, FIBER: 9 g

SHRIMP BOWL
Grilled shrimp, Mexican salsa and achiote sauce with rice and a zest of lemon.
✓✓ CALORIES: Excellent Choice (235)   CHOLESTEROL: Moderate (250 mg)
✓✓ FAT: Excellent Choice (4 g)♥   SODIUM: High (1120 mg)*
PROTEIN: 29 g, CARBOHYDRATE: 19 g, FIBER: 2 g

VEGGIE BOWL 🍎
with beans, rice, lettuce, Mexican salsa and guacamole (nominal extra charge for fifth item).
✓✓ CALORIES: Excellent Choice (430)   ✓✓ CHOLESTEROL: Excellent Choice (5 mg)
✓ FAT: Good Choice (19 g)♥   SODIUM: High (1475 mg)*
PROTEIN: 13 g, CARBOHYDRATE: 54 g, FIBER: 14 g

Beans: CALORIES: 205, FAT: 7 g, CHOLESTEROL: 5 mg, SODIUM: 285 mg; PROTEIN: 10 g, CARB: 27 g, FIBER: 9 g
Rice: CALORIES: 170, FAT: 5 g♥, CHOLESTEROL: 0, SODIUM: 670 mg; PROTEIN: 3 g, CARB: 27 g, FIBER: 1 g

See page 43 for key to symbols: * ♥ † 🍎 and $ *Healthy Dining in San Diego* **105**

Sizzler invites you to treat yourself to the famous Sizzlin' menu, including the seafood and chicken items shown below, or their All-you-care-to-eat Salad, Soup, Appetizer & Dessert Bars featuring over 80 items to choose from, including 22 salad toppings. $-$$

Sizzler San Diego locations:

El Cajon: 1030 Fletcher Pkwy.   (619) 596-1695   Oceanside: 3805 Plaza Dr.   (760) 630-1551
Escondido: 355 N. Escondido Bl. (760) 741-2568   Point Loma: 2855 Midway Dr. (619) 224-3347
National City: 1325 Plaza Bl.   (619) 477-2590   San Diego: 4445 Imperial Ave. (619) 263-5731
San Diego: 3755 Murphy Canyon Road, Ste. S   (858) 278-6988

GRILLED SALMON ⏃

Eight fire-grilled ounces of herb-seasoned salmon, served with sizzling veggies and your choice of sides (steamed broccoli & baked potato recommended, see analysis for potato below, broccoli included in analysis). Tartar sauce not included in analysis.
✓✓ CALORIES: Excellent Choice (425)   ✓ CHOLESTEROL: Good Choice (130 mg)
   ✓ FAT: Good Choice (20 g)   ✓ SODIUM: Good Choice (525 mg)*
          PROTEIN: 49 g, CARBOHYDRATE: 13 g, FIBER: 6 g

GRILLED SHRIMP SKEWERS – SPECIAL REQUEST (2 SKEWERS)

Two sizzling skewers of fire-grilled succulent shrimp, brushed with garlic and sitting on a bed of sizzlin' onions and peppers. Served with rice pilaf.
<u>Request less garlic margarine</u> (½ oz). Cheese toast not included in analysis.
✓ CALORIES: Good Choice (520)   CHOLESTEROL: Moderate (275 mg)
✓ FAT: Good Choice (24 g)   SODIUM: High (1450 mg)
          PROTEIN: 35 g, CARBOHYDRATE: 42 g, FIBER: 2 g

PETITE LUNCH SIZZLER STEAK ⏃

Served with your choice of sides (steamed broccoli and baked potato recommended, see analysis for potato below, broccoli included in analysis). Also found on Senior Menu.
✓✓ CALORIES: Excellent Choice (320)   ✓ CHOLESTEROL: Good Choice (110 mg)
✓✓ FAT: Excellent Choice (13 g)   SODIUM: High (2195 mg)
          PROTEIN: 40 g, CARBOHYDRATE: 10 g, FIBER: 5 g

DOUBLE LEMON HERB CHICKEN

Ten generous ounces of Sizzler's boneless, skinless chicken breasts covered with lemon herb sauce and sprinkled with parsley. Served with rice pilaf (included in analysis) and cheese toast (not included in analysis).
✓ CALORIES: Good Choice (670)   CHOLESTEROL: Moderate (215 mg)
✓ FAT: Good Choice (18 g)   SODIUM: High (1045 mg)
          PROTEIN: 83 g, CARBOHYDRATE: 39 g, FIBER: 1 g

DOUBLE HIBACHI CHICKEN ⏃

Two boneless, skinless chicken breasts seasoned with tangy hibachi sauce, fire-grilled to perfection. Served with your choice of sides (steamed broccoli and baked potato recommended, see analysis for potato below, broccoli included in analysis). Hibachi sauce served on the side is not included in analysis.
✓✓ CALORIES: Excellent Choice (430)   CHOLESTEROL: Moderate (195 mg)
✓✓ FAT: Excellent Choice (8 g)   ✓ SODIUM: Good Choice (535 mg)
          PROTEIN: 75 g, CARBOHYDRATE: 11 g, FIBER: 5 g

⏃SIZZLIN' VEGGIES *(4 oz.)*: CAL.: 65, FAT: 3 g♥, CHOL.: 0, SOD.: 5 mg, PRO.: 1 g, CARB.: 8 g, FIBER: 2 g
⏃BAKED POTATO, PLAIN *(12 oz.)*: CAL.: 375, FAT: 1 g♥, CHOL.: 0, SOD.: 155 mg, PRO: 8 g, CARB.: 86 g, FIB: 9 g
RICE PILAF *(5 oz.)*: CAL.: 195, FAT: 4 g, CHOL.: 0, SOD.: 685 mg, PRO: 4 g, CARB.: 37 g, FIBER: 1 g
⏃STEAMED BROCCOLI, PLAIN *(5 oz.)*: CAL.: 40, FAT: 0, CHOL.: 0, SOD.: 40 mg, PRO: 4 g, CARB.: 7 g, FIBER: 4 g

Souplantation®
salads · soups · bakery

Souplantation is the biggest, the best, the PREMIER, salad experience restaurant. All of our soups, chilis, muffins, and prepared salads are made from scratch. We serve fresh, healthful and wholesome food, which is perfect for everyday family dining. At Souplantation, there's LOTS TO FEEL GOOD ABOUT! Complete nutrition information available at www.souplantation.com. $

Souplantation Locations:

Carlsbad: 1860 Marron Rd.   (760) 434-9100   Mission Gorge: 6171 Msn. Gorge Rd.   (619) 280-7087
Del Mar: 3804 Valley Centre Dr.   (858) 481-3225   Point Loma: 3960 W. Pt. Loma Blvd.   (619) 222-7404
Kearny Mesa: 7095 Clairemont Mesa Blvd.   (858) 715-6824   R. Bernardo: 17210 Bernardo Ctr. Dr.   (858) 675-3353
La Mesa: 9158 Fletcher Pkwy.   (619) 462-4232   Temecula: 26420 Ynez Rd.   (909) 296-3922
Mira Mesa: 8105 Mira Mesa Blvd.   (858) 566-1172   Vista: 1860 University Dr.   (760) 630-9217

FRESH TOSSED SALADS (1 CUP) †

Classic Greek, Ensalada Azteca with Turkey, Roma Tomato with Mozzarella and Basil, Won Ton Chicken Happiness, Strawberry Fields with Caramelized Walnuts, Watercress and Orange.

✓ CALORIES: Good Choice (90 – 180)   ✓✓ CHOLESTEROL: Excellent Choice (0 – 25 mg)
✓ FAT: Good Choice (4 – 9 g), some♥   SODIUM: Excellent to Moderate (75 – 320 mg)
PROTEIN: 1 – 6 g, CARBOHYDRATE: 4 – 15 g, FIBER: 1 – 4 g

SIGNATURE PREPARED SALADS (½ CUP) †

Baja Bean & Cilantro, Carrot Raisin, German Potato, Mandarin Noodle w/Broccoli, Mandarin Shells w/Almonds, Marinated Summer Vegetables, Moroccan Marinated Vegetable, Oriental Ginger Slaw w/Krab, Penne Pasta w/Chicken, Southern Dill Potato, Spicy Southwestern Rice & Beans, Spicy Southwestern Pasta, Summer Barley w/Black Beans.

✓✓ CALORIES: Excellent Choice (70 – 180)   ✓✓ CHOLESTEROL: Excellent Choice (0 – 5 mg)
✓✓ FAT: Excellent Choice (0 – 3 g)♥   SODIUM: Excellent to High (80 – 480 mg)
PROTEIN: 1 – 9 g, CARBOHYDRATE: 8 – 29 g, FIBER: 2 – 5 g

SOUPS & CHILIS (1 CUP) †

Soups: Autumn Root Veg. with Wild Rice, Big Chunk Chicken Noodle, Bombay Lentil, Chicken Tortilla, Garden Fresh Veg., Hungarian Veg., Old Fashioned Veg., Classic or Spicy 4 Bean Minestrone, Ratatouille Provencale, Sweet Tomato Onion, Tomato Parmesan & Vegetable, Vegetable Medley; Chilis: 3 Bean Turkey, Deep Kettle House, Santa Fe Black Bean, Vegetarian, White Bean & Chicken.

✓ CAL: Good (Soups 80 – 160, Chilis 150 – 230)   ✓✓ CHOLESTEROL: Excellent Choice (0 – 30 mg)
✓✓ FAT: Excellent Choice (1 – 3½ g), some♥   SODIUM: High (480 – 990 mg)
PROTEIN: 1 – 17 g, CARBOHYDRATE: 5 – 28 g, FIBER: 1 – 9 g

FRESH BAKED MUFFINS & BREADS †

Muffins: Apple Cinnamon Bran, Cranberry Orange Bran, Fruit Medley Bran, Buttermilk Corn Bread, Chili Corn, Tangy Lemon, Cappuccino Chip; Breads (1 piece): Quattro Formaggio, Garlic Asiago Focaccia.

✓✓ CALORIES: Excellent Choice (80 – 160)   ✓✓ CHOLESTEROL: Excellent Choice (0 – 25 mg)
✓✓ FAT: Excellent Choice (½– 4 g, Breads 5 g)♥   SODIUM: Good to Moderate (110 – 320 mg)
PROTEIN: 2 – 4 g, CARBOHYDRATE: 17 – 28 g, FIBER: 1 – 2 g

DESSERTS & YOGURT BAR (½ CUP) †

Fat-free: Apple Medley, Banana Royale, Jello, Chocolate Frozen Yogurt; Low-fat: Chocolate, Butterscotch, Tapioca, and Rice Puddings; Nutty Waldorf Salad; or one small Chocolate Chip Cookie.

✓✓ CALORIES: Excellent Choice (10 – 140)   ✓✓ CHOLESTEROL: Excellent Choice (0 – 10 mg)
✓✓ FAT: Excellent Choice (0 – 3 g)   SODIUM: (most 5 – 80 mg; puddings 50 – 430 mg)
PROTEIN: 1 – 4 g, CARBOHYDRATE: 10 – 26 g, FIBER: 0 – 3 g

Nutrition analysis supplied by Souplantation.

Spoons restaurants offer full service with a menu featuring ribs, hamburgers, French fries, fajitas (steak and chicken), tacos, pasta platters, salads and Tex-Mex appetizers such as nachos, "buffalo" wings and mozzarella sticks. Spoons offers booth and table seating in a casual, highly energetic atmosphere. In addition, each restaurant has a lounge, which also serves food. Spoons provides the customer with a fresh, value-oriented alternative to traditional quick-service restaurants. Spoons is open for lunch and dinner from 11a.m. to 11p.m. and feature the same menu all day. $-$$

Spoons Grill & Bar   2725 Vista Way, Oceanside, CA 92054 (760) 757-7070

CHOPPED CHINESE CHICKEN SALAD – REGULAR ☺

with almonds, celery, pickled ginger, cilantro, wonton strips and scallions tossed with sesame and Chinese dressing.
✓✓ CALORIES: Excellent Choice (430)   ✓✓ CHOLESTEROL: Excellent Choice (55 mg)
✓ FAT: Good Choice (20 g)   SODIUM: High (1125 mg)*
PROTEIN: 25 g, CARBOHYDRATE: 38 g, FIBER: 5 g

SOUTHWEST BBQ CHICKEN SALAD – REGULAR – SPECIAL REQUEST ☺

with fire-roasted corn, tomatoes, olives, avocado, jicama, tortilla strips and jack and cheddar cheese tossed in honey vinaigrette dressing. <u>Request dressing on the side</u> (1 Tbs. = 60 cals., 6 g fat). (Analysis does not include red corn tortilla strips or dressing.)
✓ CALORIES: Good Choice (485)   ✓ CHOLESTEROL: Good Choice (95 mg)
✓ FAT: Good Choice (25 g)   SODIUM: Moderate (970 mg)*
PROTEIN: 34 g, CARBOHYDRATE: 34 g, FIBER: 8 g

TURKEY BURGER – SPECIAL REQUEST ☺

99% fat-free all white meat turkey breast topped with lettuce, tomatoes and Grey Poupon mustard on a wheat bun. <u>Request side salad with dressing on the side, instead of French fries</u>. (Analysis for turkey burger and side salad without dressing.)
✓ CALORIES: Good Choice (690)   ✓ CHOLESTEROL: Good Choice (115 mg)
✓ FAT: Good Choice (25 g)   SODIUM: High (2235 mg)*
PROTEIN: 55 g, CARBOHYDRATE: 64 g, FIBER: 7 g

SPICY CHICKEN TACOS

Two soft flour tortillas stuffed with spicy chicken and all the fixings, pico de gallo and salsa. Served with rice and beans (not included in analysis, see analysis below).
✓ CALORIES: Good Choice (500)   ✓ CHOLESTEROL: Good Choice (110 mg)
✓ FAT: Good Choice (21 g)   SODIUM: Moderate (945 mg)*
PROTEIN: 42 g, CARBOHYDRATE: 35 g, FIBER: 3 g

VEGGIE FAJITA PLATTER ☺

Vegetable fajitas with sautéed onions and peppers served with Mexican rice, refried beans, 3 tortillas and all the fixings. (Rice, beans and tortillas not included in analysis, see analysis below.)
✓✓ CALORIES: Excellent Choice (365)   ✓✓ CHOLESTEROL: Excellent Choice (45 mg)
✓ FAT: Good Choice (25 g)   SODIUM: High (1470 mg)*
PROTEIN: 12 g, CARBOHYDRATE: 27 g, FIBER: 6 g

CHICKEN FAJITA PLATTER ☺

Fajita chicken served atop sautéed onions and peppers served with Mexican rice, refried beans, 3 tortillas and all the fixings. (Rice, beans and tortillas not included in analysis, see analysis below.)
✓ CALORIES: Good Choice (490)   ✓ CHOLESTEROL: Good Choice (145 mg)
✓ FAT: Good Choice (23 g)   SODIUM: Moderate (855 mg)*
PROTEIN: 49 g, CARBOHYDRATE: 20 g, FIBER: 4 g

REFRIED BEANS: CALORIES: 180, FAT: 10 g♥, CHOL: 0, SOD: 800 mg*; PROT: 6 g, CARB: 18 g, FIBER: 6 g
MEXICAN RICE: CALORIES: 105, FAT: 2 g♥, CHOL: 0, SOD: 815 mg*; PROT: 2 g, CARB: 19 g, FIBER: 0
FLOUR TORTILLA: *(Each 6" tortilla)* CAL: 175, FAT: 4 g, CHOL: 0, SOD: 360 mg; PROT: 5 g, CARB: 29 g, FIB: 2 g

SUBWAY® restaurants are committed to serving fresh, high quality, nutritious foods. We bake Italian breads fresh throughout each day and use fresh veggies. Each sandwich and salad is made to your exact specifications, right before your eyes. We offer a variety of fat-free condiments and dressings. To further reduce fat and calorie intake, try mustard, vinegar, or our fat-free dressings. Baked Lay's Low-Fat Potato Crisps and Fat-Free Rold Gold Pretzels are also offered. Party Platters and Giant 6' Party Subs are available for your healthy entertaining! $

Over 150 San Diego County **SUBWAY**® locations. For the one nearest you, call (619) 688-9255.

All regular Subway Sandwiches include: *Onions, Lettuce, Tomatoes, Pickles, Green Peppers and Olives.* **Available upon request:** *Cheese, Olive Oil Blend, Mayonnaise, Bacon, Light Mayonnaise, Mustard, Vinegar, Salt, Pepper and Hot Peppers.* **Nutritional Information stated below is for 6" regular (not double meat) wheat or Italian Subs** and includes bread, meat/poultry, and all veggies. No cheese or condiments are included in values stated below. Addition of ingredients from standard sandwich formula may alter nutrition content. Check www.subway.com for future updates to nutrition information.

SWEET ONION CHICKEN TERIYAKI

✓✓ CALORIES: Excellent Choice (380)
✓✓ FAT: Excellent Choice (5 g)
✓✓ CHOLESTEROL: Excellent Choice (50 mg)
SODIUM: High (1230 mg)
PROTEIN: 26 g, CARBOHYDRATE: 59 g, FIBER: 4 g

SUBWAY CLUB®

✓✓ CALORIES: Excellent Choice (320)
✓✓ FAT: Excellent Choice (6 g)
✓✓ CHOLESTEROL: Excellent Choice (35 mg)
SODIUM: High (1310 mg)
PROTEIN: 24 g, CARBOHYDRATE: 47 g, FIBER: 4 g

HAM

✓✓ CALORIES: Excellent Choice (290)
✓✓ FAT: Excellent Choice (5 g)
✓✓ CHOLESTEROL: Excellent Choice (20 mg)
SODIUM: High (1280 mg)
PROTEIN: 18 g, CARBOHYDRATE: 47 g, FIBER: 4 g

OVEN ROASTED CHICKEN BREAST

✓✓ CALORIES: Excellent Choice (330)
✓✓ FAT: Excellent Choice (5 g)
✓✓ CHOLESTEROL: Excellent Choice (45 mg)
SODIUM: High (1020 mg)
PROTEIN: 24 g, CARBOHYDRATE: 47 g, FIBER: 4 g

ROAST BEEF

✓✓ CALORIES: Excellent Choice (290)
✓✓ FAT: Excellent Choice (5 g)
✓✓ CHOLESTEROL: Excellent Choice (15 mg)
SODIUM: Moderate (920 mg)
PROTEIN: 19 g, CARBOHYDRATE: 45 g, FIBER: 4 g

TURKEY BREAST

✓✓ CALORIES: Excellent Choice (280)
✓✓ FAT: Excellent Choice (4½ g)
✓✓ CHOLESTEROL: Excellent Choice (20 mg)
SODIUM: High (1020 mg)
PROTEIN: 18 g, CARBOHYDRATE: 46 g, FIBER: 4 g

VEGGIE DELITE®

✓✓ CALORIES: Excellent Choice (230)
✓✓ FAT: Excellent Choice (3 g)♥
✓✓ CHOLESTEROL: Excellent Choice (0 mg)
✓ SODIUM: Good Choice (520 mg)
PROTEIN: 9 g, CARBOHYDRATE: 44 g, FIBER: 4 g

Nutrition analysis supplied by Subway®

See page 43 for key to symbols: * ♥ † ☺ and $

Healthy Dining in San Diego 109

Susan's Healthy Gourmet is a one-of-a-kind service that provides delicious, fresh meals for the home that free you of shopping, cooking and clean up. Award winning bakery goods made from scratch and extensive a la carte selections supplement a complete weekly menu of low-fat, low-sodium, and low-cholesterol items offered in three daily calorie levels. All meals are prepared for pick-up or delivery every Monday and Friday. $

Susan's Healthy Gourmet - Meals for the Home and Office

For information & to order call: (858) 456-1366, 1-888-EZ-MEALS (396-3257)
17851 Sky Park Circle, Suite G, Irvine, CA 92614   www.susanshealthygourmet.com

RUTH'S POT ROAST ☺

A family recipe served with garlic mashed potatoes, gravy, green beans and squash.

✓✓ CALORIES: Excellent Choice (380)   ✓✓ CHOLESTEROL: Excellent Choice (70 mg)
✓✓ FAT: Excellent Choice (7 g)   ✓ SODIUM: Good Choice (440 mg)
PROTEIN: 36 g, CARBOHYDRATE: 42 g, FIBER: 8 g

OLD-FASHIONED TURKEY DINNER ☺

A holiday meal made healthy! Roasted turkey with a turkey gravy,
herb stuffing, sweet potatoes, cabbage, broccoli and cranberry sauce.

✓✓ CALORIES: Excellent Choice (430)   ✓✓ CHOLESTEROL: Excellent Choice (70 mg)
✓✓ FAT: Excellent Choice (8 g)   ✓ SODIUM: Good Choice (420 mg)
PROTEIN: 35 g, CARBOHYDRATE: 57 g, FIBER: 5 g

SALMON WITH TARRAGON CHEESE SAUCE ☺

A salmon fillet topped with a tantalizing herb cheddar sauce,
served over wild rice with cauliflower and vegetable ratatouille.

✓✓ CALORIES: Excellent Choice (380)   ✓✓ CHOLESTEROL: Excellent Choice (70 mg)
✓ FAT: Good Choice (19 g)   ✓✓ SODIUM: Excellent Choice (265 mg)
PROTEIN: 29 g, CARBOHYDRATE: 23 g, FIBER: 4 g

SALMON WRAP (½ WRAP) ☺

Poached salmon, combined with cucumbers, fresh
dill and capers in a green onion wrap and served with an apple.

✓✓ CALORIES: Excellent Choice (330)   ✓✓ CHOLESTEROL: Excellent Choice (45 mg)
✓✓ FAT: Excellent Choice (10 g)♥   ✓ SODIUM: Good Choice (590 mg)
PROTEIN: 21 g, CARBOHYDRATE: 42 g, FIBER: 12 g

HONEY MUSTARD CHICKEN ☺

Tender grilled chicken breast served over brown rice and topped with a citrus
honey mustard glaze, served with butternut squash and sugar snap peas.

✓✓ CALORIES: Excellent Choice (415)   ✓ CHOLESTEROL: Good Choice (100 mg)
✓✓ FAT: Excellent Choice (4 g)   ✓✓ SODIUM: Excellent Choice (295 mg)
PROTEIN: 46 g, CARBOHYDRATE: 50 g, FIBER: 7 g

SPINACH CREPES ☺

A savory spinach, mushroom, sherry, garlic and feta cheese filling,
delicately folded into a crepe, served with broccoli and savory green beans.

✓✓ CALORIES: Excellent Choice (395)   ✓✓ CHOLESTEROL: Excellent Choice (55 mg)
✓✓ FAT: Excellent Choice (12 g)   SODIUM: Moderate (805 mg)
PROTEIN: 23 g, CARBOHYDRATE: 50 g, FIBER: 6 g

Nutrition analysis provided by Susan's Healthy Gourmet.

Since 1979, Leo Sciuto and his sons have been serving San Diegans a tasty mix of Mexican food & spirits at their 4 popular Tio Leo's locations. Leo's main objective was to serve not only great food, but also generous portions with reasonable prices. Come and taste for yourself! www.tioleos.com $

Tio Leo's

Del Mar: 3510 Valley Centre Drive   (858) 350-1468
Mission Gorge: 6333 Mission Gorge Rd.   (619) 280-9940
Mira Mesa: 10787 Camino Ruiz   (858) 695-1461
Morena/Napa: 5302 Napa Street   (619) 542-1462

LETTUCE WRAP TACOS ♂

Spicy chopped chicken, peanuts, chopped eggplant, pico de gallo and avocado.
✓ CALORIES: Good Choice (590)   ✓ CHOLESTEROL: Good Choice (95 mg)
FAT: Moderate (40 g)   ✓✓ SODIUM: Excellent Choice (215 mg)*
PROTEIN: 42 g, CARBOHYDRATE: 21 g, FIBER: 11 g

POLLO ASADA TACOS ♂

Two grilled chicken tacos with Tio Leo's special seasoning.
Includes two whole wheat tortillas. Served with black beans and Mexican coleslaw.
✓ CALORIES: Good Choice (735)   ✓ CHOLESTEROL: Good Choice (120 mg)
✓ FAT: Good Choice (24 g)   SODIUM: High (1470 mg)*
PROTEIN: 61 g, CARBOHYDRATE: 81 g, FIBER: 20 g

GRILLED EGGPLANT TACOS ♂

Two delicious marinated eggplant tacos grilled to perfection and served with cabbage, pico de gallo and feta cheese in a corn tortilla. Served with black beans and Mexican coleslaw.
✓ CALORIES: Good Choice (700)   ✓✓ CHOLESTEROL: Excellent Choice (25 mg)
✓ FAT: Good Choice (24 g)   SODIUM: Moderate (810 mg)*
PROTEIN: 26 g, CARBOHYDRATE: 105 g, FIBER: 29 g

VEGETARIAN BURRITO ♂

Black beans, pinto beans, rice and cheese rolled in a flour tortilla with pico de gallo. Served with Mexican coleslaw.
✓ CALORIES: Good Choice (740)   ✓✓ CHOLESTEROL: Excellent Choice (15 mg)
✓ FAT: Good Choice (22 g)   SODIUM: High (1320 mg)*
PROTEIN: 27 g, CARBOHYDRATE: 112 g, FIBER: 19 g

POLLO ASADA RICE BOWL ♂

Chicken breast with Spanish rice, black beans, pico de gallo & avocado. Served with tortillas (not included in analysis).
✓ CALORIES: Good Choice (585)   ✓ CHOLESTEROL: Good Choice (95 mg)
✓✓ FAT: Excellent Choice (12 g)   SODIUM: High (1200 mg)
PROTEIN: 50 g, CARBOHYDRATE: 70 g, FIBER: 14 g

BLACK BEAN TOSTADA ♂

Black beans with feta cheese, avocado, lettuce and pico de gallo. (Analysis does not include shell.)
✓✓ CALORIES: Excellent Choice (410)   ✓✓ CHOLESTEROL: Excellent Choice (20 mg)
✓✓ FAT: Excellent Choice (12 g)   SODIUM: Moderate (865 mg)*
PROTEIN: 22 g, CARBOHYDRATE: 57 g, FIBER: 21 g

One of Southern California's most prestigious restaurants, Top of The Cove offers a unique and memorable atmosphere for your business and social affairs. The 100-year-old bungalow is perched high on a bluff in the heart of La Jolla and presents spectacular views of La Jolla Cove. You and your guests dine in timeless elegance at beautifully appointed tables overlooking the Pacific. Top of the Cove has developed an award-winning eclectic menu that combines culinary influences from around the globe. Guests will enjoy the timeless elegance of the atmosphere and professional and personal attention of a staff that wants to ensure a memorable occasion. $$$

Top of the Cove
1216 Prospect Street, La Jolla, CA 92037   (858) 454-7779

EDAMAME SALAD

✓✓ CALORIES: Excellent Choice (410)
✓ FAT: Good Choice (22 g)
✓✓ CHOLESTEROL: Excellent Choice (15 mg)
SODIUM: High (1960 mg)*
PROTEIN: 19 g, CARBOHYDRATE: 36 g, FIBER: 12 g

HALIBUT WITH CHINESE BLACK BEAN SAUCE – SPECIAL REQUEST
Request less oil (1 Tbs).
✓ CALORIES: Good Choice (595)
✓ FAT: Good Choice (24 g)♥
✓ CHOLESTEROL: Good Choice (130 mg)
SODIUM: High (2355 mg)*
PROTEIN: 73 g, CARBOHYDRATE: 16 g, FIBER: 2 g

NICOISE SALAD STACK – SPECIAL REQUEST
Fingerling potatoes, green beans, baby greens, tomatoes, and olive tapenade.
Request no dressing on the greens.
✓✓ CALORIES: Excellent Choice (330)
✓✓ FAT: Excellent Choice (12 g)♥
✓✓ CHOLESTEROL: Excellent Choice (50 mg)
SODIUM: High (1125 mg)*
PROTEIN: 34 g, CARBOHYDRATE: 21 g, FIBER: 5 g

SPICY TUNA/RADISH CAKE (½ ORDER)
(Analysis for half order; does not include soy sauce.)
✓ CALORIES: Good Choice (495)
✓ FAT: Good Choice (21 g)♥
✓✓ CHOLESTEROL: Excellent Choice (50 mg)
SODIUM: High (1385 mg)*
PROTEIN: 33 g, CARBOHYDRATE: 44 g, FIBER: 5 g

TRATTORIA
LA STRADA
CUCINA TOSCANA

Trattoria La Strada has flourished for over 14 years in the Gaslamp District on the corner of Fifth Avenue and G Street. Chef and co-owner Roberto Bernardoni comes from an Italian family that has operated restaurants in Florence for three generations. The large windows of the spacious dining room overlook the busy street, while the open kitchen allows guests to watch authentic Tuscan specialties being prepared. Large party facilities and patio dining are available, as well as a full bar with live music on weekend evenings. La Strada has won the "Best of the Best Five Star Diamond Award," was twice voted "Best Italian Dinner" in Metropolitan Magazine, won the 1998 through 2002 "Insegna del Ristorante Italiano" awards, and has been named one of the top ten Italian restaurants in the United States. $$

Trattoria La Strada 702 Fifth Avenue, San Diego, CA 92101 (619) 239-3400

SALMONE AL ROSMARINO ♨
Salmon fillet with fresh spinach, shallots and white wine.
- ✓ CALORIES: Good Choice (465)
- ✓ FAT: Good Choice (23 g)
- ✓ CHOLESTEROL: Good Choice (145 mg)
- ✓ SODIUM: Good Choice (385 mg)*

PROTEIN: 51 g, CARBOHYDRATE: 11 g, FIBER: 7 g

CAPELLINI IN BARCA
Angel hair pasta tossed with clams, mussels, shrimp and scallops in a white wine and tomato sauce.
- ✓ CALORIES: Good Choice (605)
- ✓✓ FAT: Excellent Choice (15 g)♥
- ✓ CHOLESTEROL: Good Choice (150 mg)
- ✓ SODIUM: Good Choice (305 mg)*

PROTEIN: 46 g, CARBOHYDRATE: 59 g, FIBER: 4 g

LINGUINE ALLE VONGOLE
Linguine pasta with manila clams, extra virgin olive oil, fresh garlic and white wine.
- ✓ CALORIES: Good Choice (600)
- ✓✓ FAT: Excellent Choice (14 g)♥
- ✓ CHOLESTEROL: Good Choice (85 mg)
- ✓✓ SODIUM: Excellent Choice (240 mg)*

PROTEIN: 43 g, CARBOHYDRATE: 70 g, FIBER: 3 g

FETTUCCINE AI FUNGHI ♨
Homemade fettuccine with porcini mushrooms, garlic, parsley and extra virgin olive oil.
- ✓✓ CALORIES: Excellent Choice (430)
- ✓✓ FAT: Excellent Choice (12 g)♥
- ✓✓ CHOLESTEROL: Excellent Choice (0 mg)
- ✓✓ SODIUM: Excellent Choice (15 mg)*

PROTEIN: 13 g, CARBOHYDRATE: 68 g, FIBER: 5 g

FETTUCCINE POMODORO E BASILICO
Fettuccine pasta tossed with tomato sauce, light garlic and extra virgin olive oil.
- ✓✓ CALORIES: Excellent Choice (415)
- ✓✓ FAT: Excellent Choice (12 g)♥
- ✓✓ CHOLESTEROL: Excellent Choice (0 mg)
- ✓✓ SODIUM: Excellent Choice (10 mg)*

PROTEIN: 11 g, CARBOHYDRATE: 66 g, FIBER: 5 g

GRILLED CHICKEN ♨
served with an assortment of grilled vegetables.
- ✓ CALORIES: Good Choice (490)
- ✓ FAT: Good Choice (18 g)
- CHOLESTEROL: Moderate (175 mg)
- ✓✓ SODIUM: Excellent Choice (160 mg)*

PROTEIN: 67 g, CARBOHYDRATE: 14 g, FIBER: 2 g

Trellises Garden Grille at the Town and Country Resort Hotel has been recognized for its impeccable service and delicious cuisine for over 45 years. Trellises' menu features creative appetizers, healthy light entrees, a variety of pastas and pizzas, fresh fish, shellfish, vegetable entrees and lavish desserts. We invite you to join us at Trellises, where celebrations and special events are our specialty. $$

Trellises Garden Grille

Town & Country Hotel 500 Hotel Circle North, San Diego, CA 92108   (619) 291-7131

TOMATO BRUSCHETTA (½ ORDER) † ♻

Tomato, garlic and fresh basil tossed in extra virgin olive oil, topped with parmesan cheese and toasted on a crisp crouton. (Analysis is for ½ of an order.)

✓ CALORIES: Good Choice (240)   ✓✓ CHOLESTEROL: Excellent Choice (5 mg)
✓ FAT: Good Choice (6 g)   SODIUM: Good Choice (490 mg)*
PROTEIN: 9 g, CARBOHYDRATE: 38 g, FIBER: 2 g

FRUIT GRANITAS † ♻

Fresh seasonal fruit ices.

✓ CALORIES: Good Choice (165)   ✓✓ CHOLESTEROL: Excellent Choice (0 mg)
✓✓ FAT: Excellent Choice (0 g)   ✓✓ SODIUM: Excellent Choice (5 mg)*
PROTEIN: 1 g, CARBOHYDRATE: 41 g, FIBER: 4 g

FRESH PACIFIC HALIBUT ♻

Steamed and served over a bed of spinach and baby carrots.

✓✓ CALORIES: Excellent Choice (365).   ✓✓ CHOLESTEROL: Excellent Choice (70 mg)
✓ FAT: Good Choice (17 g)   ✓✓ SODIUM: Excellent Choice (265 mg)*
PROTEIN: 40 g, CARBOHYDRATE: 13 g, FIBER: 5 g

FRESH ATLANTIC SALMON ♻

Poached and served on top of a bed of bok choy and grilled asparagus.

✓✓ CALORIES: Excellent Choice (400)   ✓ CHOLESTEROL: Good Choice (110 mg)
✓ FAT: Good Choice (24 g)   ✓✓ SODIUM: Excellent Choice (220 mg)*
PROTEIN: 38 g, CARBOHYDRATE: 8 g, FIBER: 4 g

ATHENIAN GREENS ♻

Fresh spinach, tomatoes, bell peppers, cucumbers and feta cheese.

✓✓ CALORIES: Excellent Choice (255)   ✓✓ CHOLESTEROL: Excellent Choice (25 mg)
✓ FAT: Good Choice (17 g)   SODIUM: Moderate (670 mg)*
PROTEIN: 11 g, CARBOHYDRATE: 21 g, FIBER: 8 g

GULF SHRIMP AND PASTA – SPECIAL REQUEST ♻

Gulf shrimp sautéed in garlic, shallots and mushrooms, served over pasta. Request less oil (1 Tbs).

✓ CALORIES: Good Choice (600)   CHOLESTEROL: Moderate (170 mg)
✓ FAT: Good Choice (19 g)   ✓ SODIUM: Good Choice (445 mg)*
PROTEIN: 34 g, CARBOHYDRATE: 73 g, FIBER: 6 g

tutto · mare

Located in The Plaza at La Jolla Village, Tutto Mare offers a variety of specialties representing the coastal regions of Italy — whole fish baked in an oak-fire oven, housemade pastas, charcoal-grilled meats, fowl and fresh fish. Hours: Monday 11:30 a.m. to 10:30 p.m., Tuesday to Thursday 11:30 a.m. to 11 p.m., Friday 11:30 a.m. to 11 p.m., Saturday 5 p.m. to 11 p.m., Sunday 5 p.m. to 10 p.m. $$

Tutto Mare

4365 Executive Drive, San Diego, CA 92121   (858) 597-1188

GRIGLIATA MISTA

Mixed grill of fresh fish, fresh water prawns and calamari. Served with roasted potatoes and steamed mixed vegetables. (Roasted potatoes not included in analysis.)
- ✓ CALORIES: Good Choice (700)
- ✓ FAT: Good Choice (18 g)♥

CHOLESTEROL: High (955 mg)
SODIUM: Moderate (665 mg)*

PROTEIN: 116 g, CARBOHYDRATE: 15 g, FIBER: 3 g

INSALATA DI ARAGOSTA ⏱

Diced lobster, mache, hearts of palm, radicchio and cannelloni beans in a lemon dressing.
- ✓✓ CALORIES: Excellent Choice (430)
- ✓✓ FAT: Excellent Choice (12 g)♥

CHOLESTEROL: Moderate (270 mg)
SODIUM: High (1055 mg)*

PROTEIN: 61 g, CARBOHYDRATE: 18 g, FIBER: 6 g

SPAGHETTINI TUTTO MARE

Thin spaghetti, black mussels, clams, fresh fish, shrimp, and garlic, in a spicy tomato sauce.
- ✓ CALORIES: Good Choice (695)
- ✓ FAT: Good Choice (21 g)♥

CHOLESTEROL: Moderate (180 mg)
- ✓ SODIUM: Good Choice (545 mg)*

PROTEIN: 50 g, CARBOHYDRATE: 72 g, FIBER: 5 g

RICCIOLI D'ORO AL TRE CROSTACEI ⏱

Angel hair pasta, shrimp, crab, and lobster, in a spicy tomato sauce.
- ✓ CALORIES: Good Choice (630)
- ✓ FAT: Good Choice (16 g)♥

CHOLESTEROL: Moderate (175 mg)
SODIUM: Moderate (615 mg)*

PROTEIN: 44g, CARBOHYDRATE: 72 g, FIBER: 6 g

LIGUINE ALLE VONGOLE

Flat pasta, manila clams, garlic, and basil in a white wine sauce.
- ✓ CALORIES: Good Choice (560)
- ✓ FAT: Good Choice (16 g)

- ✓✓ CHOLESTEROL: Excellent Choice (75 mg)
- ✓✓ SODIUM: Excellent Choice (105 mg)*

PROTEIN: 33 g, CARBOHYDRATE: 65 g, FIBER: 4 g

GRAN MISTO MARE – SPECIAL REQUEST

Italian style bouillabaisse with fresh fish, shrimp, scallops, clams, and mussels, in a tomato-lobster broth. _Request less garlic oil_ (½ Tbs).
- ✓ CALORIES: Good Choice (555)
- ✓ FAT: Good Choice (19 g)♥

CHOLESTEROL: High (350 mg)
SODIUM: High (1035 mg)*

PROTEIN: 79 g, CARBOHYDRATE: 13 g, FIBER: 2 g

See page 43 for key to symbols: * ♥ † ⏱ and $ *Healthy Dining in San Diego*

Wahoo's Fish Taco serves a unique menu featuring Mexican dishes with a Brazilian twist in a beach-casual atmosphere. Known for our charbroiled fish tacos and Banzai burritos, we also serve chicken, steak, pork, shrimp and veggie dishes. All ingredients are prepared fresh daily. $

Wahoo's Fish Taco San Diego area locations:
La Jolla: 639 Pearl Street   (858) 459-0027
Encinitas: 1006 N. El Camino Real #C   (760) 753-5060
Point Loma: 3944 W. Pt. Loma Blvd. #A   (619) 222-0020
Mission Valley: 2195 Station Village Way #A   (619) 299-4550
Visit www.wahoos.com for other locations.

CHARBROILED FISH TACO
✓✓ CALORIES: Excellent Choice (235)   ✓✓ CHOLESTEROL: Excellent Choice (55 mg)
✓✓ FAT: Excellent Choice (4 g)   ✓ SODIUM: Good Choice (325 mg)*
PROTEIN: 16 g, CARBOHYDRATE: 28 g, FIBER: 3 g

CHARBROILED CHICKEN TACO
✓✓ CALORIES: Excellent Choice (260)   ✓✓ CHOLESTEROL: Excellent Choice (50 mg)
✓✓ FAT: Excellent Choice (6 g)   ✓ SODIUM: Good Choice (305 mg)*
PROTEIN: 20 g, CARBOHYDRATE: 28 g, FIBER: 3 g

½ RICE & ½ BEAN COMBO BOWL
✓✓ CALORIES: Excellent Choice (390)   ✓✓ CHOLESTEROL: Excellent Choice (0 mg)
✓✓ FAT: Excellent Choice (3 g)   SODIUM: High (1005 mg)*
PROTEIN: 16 g, CARBOHYDRATE: 74 g, FIBER: 13 g

CHARBROILED CHICKEN BURRITO
✓ CALORIES: Good Choice (540)   ✓ CHOLESTEROL: Good Choice (110 mg)
✓ FAT: Good Choice (17 g)   SODIUM: High (1080 mg)*
PROTEIN: 46 g, CARBOHYDRATE: 49 g, FIBER: 3 g

VEGETARIAN BURRITO
✓ CALORIES: Good Choice (600)   ✓✓ CHOLESTEROL: Excellent Choice (15 mg)
✓✓ FAT: Excellent Choice (14 g)   SODIUM: High (1460 mg)*
PROTEIN: 21 g, CARBOHYDRATE: 98 g, FIBER: 12 g

CHARBROILED FISH BURRITO
✓ CALORIES: Good Choice (480)   ✓ CHOLESTEROL: Good Choice (120 mg)
✓✓ FAT: Excellent Choice (14 g)   SODIUM: High (1125 mg)*
PROTEIN: 38 g, CARBOHYDRATE: 50 g, FIBER: 4 g

Whole Foods Market is dedicated to supplying the finest, most natural, wholesome foods available, including an ever-increasing selection of organically grown ingredients. Our savory salads, delectable dressings, steamy soups, enticing entrees and many of our delicious baked goods are prepared in our own kitchen, using time honored recipes with no artificial flavors, artificial colors, artificial sweeteners or preservatives. $

Whole Foods Market

8825 Villa La Jolla Drive, La Jolla, CA 92037   (858) 642-6700
711 University Avenue (Hillcrest), San Diego, CA 92103   (619) 294-2800

EMERALD MUSHROOMS (4 oz.) † ♉

Tossed with asparagus and marinated with Asian flavors.

✓✓ CALORIES: Excellent Choice (115)   ✓✓ CHOLESTEROL: Excellent Choice (0 mg)
✓ FAT: Good Choice (7 g)   SODIUM: High (425 mg)
PROTEIN: 4 g, CARBOHYDRATE: 12 g, FIBER: 1 g

KUNG PAO TOFU (8 oz. serving)

This interpretation of Chinese "pow" is one of our most popular deli selections.

✓✓ CALORIES: Excellent Choice (200)   ✓✓ CHOLESTEROL: Excellent Choice (0 mg)
✓✓ FAT: Excellent Choice (11 g)   SODIUM: Moderate (820 mg)
PROTEIN: 13 g, CARBOHYDRATE: 15 g, FIBER: 2 g

PORTOBELLO PASTA WITH CHICKEN (8 oz.)

A touch of Italy perfect for an alfresco lunch or buffet entrée for your next gathering.

✓ CALORIES: Good Choice (455)   ✓✓ CHOLESTEROL: Excellent Choice (40 mg)
✓ FAT: Good Choice (16 g)   ✓✓ SODIUM: Excellent Choice (205 mg)
PROTEIN: 22 g, CARBOHYDRATE: 51 g, FIBER: 3 g

ASIAN GINGER SALMON (6 oz. filet)

The intense, Asian inspired sauce makes this dish a consistent favorite.

✓✓ CALORIES: Excellent Choice (250)   ✓ CHOLESTEROL: Good Choice (90 mg)
✓✓ FAT: Excellent Choice (12 g)   ✓✓ SODIUM: Excellent Choice (235 mg)
PROTEIN: 33 g, CARBOHYDRATE: 0 g, FIBER: 0 g

WARM QUINOA SALAD WITH SHRIMP AND ASPARAGUS (8 oz.)

High-protein, nutty quinoa combines well with lively flavors for this elegant dish.

✓✓ CALORIES: Excellent Choice (330)   ✓ CHOLESTEROL: Good Choice (110 mg)
✓✓ FAT: Excellent Choice (14 g)♥   ✓✓ SODIUM: Excellent Choice (270 mg)
PROTEIN: 20 g, CARBOHYDRATE: 30 g

Nutrition information for last item supplied by Whole Foods Market.

Owner and San Diego native Bruce Jackson is a graduate of Torrey Pines High School and San Diego State University. He and his wife, Momoko, opened World Curry nine years ago in Pacific Beach. World Curry offers a unique mix of curries from around the world in a casual dining setting. We make all of our dishes from scratch using the finest available ingredients. For more information about World Curry, menus, and food photos, please visit our website at www.worldcurry.com. $

World Curry

1433 Garnet Avenue, San Diego, CA 92109   (858) 270-9238

BANANA LEAF VEGETABLE CURRY – REGULAR SIZE ☙

Fantastic Singapore style vegetable curry with cauliflower, carrots, potatoes and chick peas garnished with tomatoes and cilantro. Served with Thai jasmine rice and side salad (dressing not included in analysis).

✓ CALORIES: Good Choice (550)   ✓✓ CHOLESTEROL: Excellent Choice (0 mg)
✓✓ FAT: Excellent Choice (4 g)♥   ✓✓ SODIUM: Excellent Choice (245 mg)*
PROTEIN: 12 g, CARBOHYDRATE: 114 g, FIBER: 5 g

SPINACH CURRY WITH CHICKEN – REGULAR SIZE – SPECIAL REQUEST

*A mild and smooth classic type of curry with a creamed spinach base.
<u>Request white meat chicken</u>. Served with Thai jasmine rice and side salad (dressing not included in analysis).*

CALORIES: Moderate (760)   ✓ CHOLESTEROL: Good Choice (95 mg)
✓✓ FAT: Excellent Choice (15 g)   ✓ SODIUM: Good Choice (580 mg)*
PROTEIN: 46 g, CARBOHYDRATE: 107 g, FIBER: 4 g

CARIBBEAN VEGAN CURRY – REGULAR SIZE ☙

Delicious and super healthy black beans, tomatoes, corn and pineapple slow cooked in our own columbo curry mix. Served with Thai jasmine rice and side salad (dressing not included in analysis).

✓ CALORIES: Good Choice (590)   ✓✓ CHOLESTEROL: Excellent Choice (0 mg)
✓✓ FAT: Excellent Choice (5 g)♥   ✓ SODIUM: Good Choice (310 mg)*
PROTEIN: 14 g, CARBOHYDRATE: 118 g, FIBER: 9 g

KEEMA CURRY – REGULAR SIZE ☙

A delicious minced chicken curry. Slow cooked with tomatoes, cilantro and peas. Served with Thai jasmine rice and side salad (dressing not included in analysis).

CALORIES: Moderate (775)   ✓✓ CHOLESTEROL: Excellent Choice (55 mg)
✓ FAT: Good Choice (21 g)   ✓✓ SODIUM: Excellent Choice (235 mg)*
PROTEIN: 29 g, CARBOHYDRATE: 115 g, FIBER: 9 g

In Greek and Italian cooking, only fresh and natural ingredients are used in preparing the most delicious foods. In keeping with this tradition, we created Yanni's Bistro. Yanni's Bistro is your neighborhood restaurant, where you can enjoy a delicious lunch and dinner or simply stop by for a cappuccino. It is our goal to provide you with only the best quality food and wine with the best possible service. $-$$

Yanni's Bistro

12205 Scripps Poway Parkway, Suite 101, Poway, CA 92064   (858) 527-0011

CHICKEN VESUVIO – SPECIAL REQUEST ☝

Sautéed with garlic and topped with roasted vegetables, marinara and mozzarella. <u>Request less mozzarella (1 oz.) and plain steamed vegetables</u>. (Analysis does not include rice.)
- ✓ CALORIES: Good Choice (580)   CHOLESTEROL: Moderate (190 mg)
- ✓ FAT: Good Choice (22 g)   SODIUM: Moderate (710 mg)*
  PROTEIN: 71 g, CARBOHYDRATE: 26 g, FIBER: 7 g

GOURMET SALAD – SMALL – SPECIAL REQUEST ☝

Romaine and green leaf lettuce, vine ripe tomatoes, red peppers and artichoke hearts, avocado, red onions, olives, feta & kasseri cheese and balsamic vinaigrette. <u>Request less cheese (½ oz. kasseri, 1 oz. feta) and dressing on the side</u> (not included in analysis).
- ✓✓ CALORIES: Excellent Choice (325)   ✓✓ CHOLESTEROL: Excellent Choice (25 mg)
- ✓ FAT: Good Choice (24 g)   SODIUM: Moderate (945 mg)*
  PROTEIN: 13 g, CARBOHYDRATE: 20 g, FIBER: 7 g

CHICKEN SKEWERS – SPECIAL REQUEST

Marinated in lemon, garlic, virgin olive oil, saffron, onion and peppers topped with crumbled feta and served with pita and tzatziki. <u>Request less cheese (1 oz.) and tzatziki sauce on the side</u> (not included in analysis).
- ✓ CALORIES: Good Choice (610)   CHOLESTEROL: Moderate (150 mg)
- ✓ FAT: Good Choice (25 g)   SODIUM: Moderate (730 mg)*
  PROTEIN: 61 g, CARBOHYDRATE: 32 g, FIBER: 2 g

SAN REMO SALAD – SMALL – SPECIAL REQUEST ☝

Baby field greens, goat cheese, beets, carrots, sundried tomatoes, avocado, tomatoes, red onion and house dressing. <u>Request less cheese (1 oz.) and dressing on the side</u> (not included in analysis).
- ✓✓ CALORIES: Excellent Choice (370)   ✓✓ CHOLESTEROL: Excellent Choice (30 mg)
- ✓ FAT: Good Choice (19 g)   SODIUM: Moderate (930 mg)*
  PROTEIN: 17 g, CARBOHYDRATE: 41 g, FIBER: 13 g

SALMON BRODETTO – SPECIAL REQUEST

Mussels, lobster broth, virgin olive oil, sweet onion, fresh tomatoes and garlic. <u>Request less oil (1 tsp)</u>. (Analysis does not include rice.)
- ✓ CALORIES: Good Choice (540)   ✓ CHOLESTEROL: Good Choice (145 mg)
- ✓ FAT: Good Choice (24 g)♥   SODIUM: Moderate (645 mg)*
  PROTEIN: 56 g, CARBOHYDRATE: 21 g, FIBER: 5 g

SALMON LIVORNESE – SPECIAL REQUEST ☝

Sautéed in virgin olive oil, tomato, capers, basil, garlic and olives. <u>Request plain steamed vegetables, less olive oil (½ Tbs.) and less olives (½ Tbs)</u>. (Analysis does not include rice.)
- ✓ CALORIES: Good Choice (500)   ✓ CHOLESTEROL: Good Choice (130 mg)
- ✓ FAT: Good Choice (25 g)♥   SODIUM: High (1180 mg)*
  PROTEIN: 49 g, CARBOHYDRATE: 17 g, FIBER: 5 g

See page 43 for key to symbols: * ♥ † ☝ and $ *Healthy Dining in San Diego* **119**

At Zanzibar Cafe, we pride ourselves on serving only the highest quality food & beverages available from sandwiches, salads and pizzas to eggs, baked omelettes, desserts and pastries. Our goal is to satisfy our customers by providing mouth watering cuisine and superior customer service in a comfortable environment. The cafe is open Monday through Thursday from 6:30 a.m. until 10:30 p.m. and Friday through Sunday from 6:30 a.m. until 11:30 p.m. We are open 365 days a year. Please feel free to visit our retail section while you are in our cafe. We sell all the items you need to serve wonderful coffee and tea in the comfort of your own home. Thank you for dining with us! We accept all major credit cards. $

Zanzibar Cafe

976 Garnet Avenue, San Diego, CA 92109   (858) 272-4762
711 G Street, San Diego, CA 92101   COMING Fall 2006!

ARTICHOKE HEART AND SPINACH PIZZA (2 SLICES)

Fresh spinach, feta, artichoke hearts, garlic and kalamata olives.

✓✓ CALORIES: Excellent Choice (330)   ✓✓ CHOLESTEROL: Excellent Choice (25 mg)
✓ FAT: Good Choice (17 g)   SODIUM: Moderate (755 mg)*
PROTEIN: 13 g, CARBOHYDRATE: 34 g, FIBER: 3 g

HEALTHNUT SPECIAL 🍎

*Egg white omelet with spinach, broccoli, mushroom, tomato, onion,
feta and mozzarella cheeses. Served with avocado, salsa and a bowl of fresh fruit.*

✓✓ CALORIES: Excellent Choice (445)   ✓✓ CHOLESTEROL: Excellent Choice (45 mg)
✓ FAT: Good Choice (22 g)   SODIUM: Moderate (955 mg)*
PROTEIN: 34 g, CARBOHYDRATE: 35 g, FIBER: 10 g

TRADITIONAL TURKEY SANDWICH 🍎

*Mustard, mayo, with organic greens and sliced roma tomatoes
on sourdough. Served with a red cabbage salad.*

✓ CALORIES: Good Choice (485)   ✓✓ CHOLESTEROL: Excellent Choice (50 mg)
✓ FAT: Good Choice (18 g)   SODIUM: High (1635 mg)*
PROTEIN: 32 g, CARBOHYDRATE: 48 g, FIBER: 4 g

GRILLED PORTOBELLO MUSHROOM SALAD – SPECIAL REQUEST 🍎

Exquisite sliced portobello mushrooms on mixed greens, topped with chopped walnuts, golden raisins and crumbled goat cheese. Served with foccacia bread and raspberry vinaigrette dressing on the side (dressing not included in analysis). <u>Request fewer walnuts</u> (1 Tbs).

✓ CALORIES: Good Choice (500)   ✓✓ CHOLESTEROL: Excellent Choice (30 mg)
✓ FAT: Good Choice (22 g)   ✓✓ SODIUM: Excellent Choice (250 mg)*
PROTEIN: 16 g, CARBOHYDRATE: 61 g, FIBER: 7 g

MANGO CHICKEN SALAD 🍎

with roasted almonds, jicama, goat cheese and organic greens. Served with foccacia bread and sun-dried cherry vinaigrette on the side (dressing not included in analysis).

✓ CALORIES: Good Choice (710)   ✓ CHOLESTEROL: Good Choice (105 mg)
✓ FAT: Good Choice (25 g)   ✓ SODIUM: Good Choice (495 mg)*
PROTEIN: 48 g, CARBOHYDRATE: 72 g, FIBER: 13 g

CHOPPED SUMMER SALAD WITH CHICKEN – SPECIAL REQUEST 🍎

Organic greens chopped with Greek olives, diced tomatoes, avocado, cucumbers, hearts of palm and feta cheese. Foccacia bread and citrus vinaigrette dressing served on the side. <u>Request less black olives</u> (1 oz). (Dressing not included in analysis.)

✓ CALORIES: Good Choice (475)   ✓ CHOLESTEROL: Good Choice (105 mg)
✓ FAT: Good Choice (24 g)   SODIUM: High (1030 mg)*
PROTEIN: 39 g, CARBOHYDRATE: 28 g, FIBER: 11 g

A zocalo (pronounced SO-cah-low) is a large square or plaza in the center of many towns that serves as the central meeting place where residents and out-of-town visitors gather to socialize, celebrate the local culture and enjoy a terrific meal. Until recently, San Diego had no zocalo of its own. Like the traditional zocalos, Zocalo Grill has quickly become a popular place to meet friends, enjoy an excellent meal and relish the local flavor of San Diego in historic Old Town. $$-$$$

Zocalo Grill

2444 San Diego Avenue, San Diego, CA 92110   (619) 298-9840

Spicy Seared Ahi †

with avocado relish and heirloom tomato salad. Analysis for half portion.
- ✓ CALORIES: Good Choice (175)
- ✓ FAT: Good Choice (7 g)♥
- ✓✓ CHOLESTEROL: Excellent Choice (20 mg)
- SODIUM: High (1075 mg)*

PROTEIN: 12 g, CARBOHYDRATE: 17 g, FIBER: 3 g

Steamed Mussels & Clams with Mojo Verde – Special Request †

Mojos are dipping sauces; ours is made from fresh herbs, dried chiles and meyer lemon. <u>Request less butter</u> (1 Tbs). Analysis for half portion. Sauces served on the side, (not included in analysis: 1 Tbs. mojo verde = 45 cals, 4 g fat; 1 Tbs. cilantro aioli = 75 cals, 8 g fat).
- ✓ CALORIES: Good Choice (155)
- ✓ FAT: Good Choice (7 g)
- ✓ CHOLESTEROL: Good Choice (35 mg)
- SODIUM: High (970 mg)*

PROTEIN: 12 g, CARBOHYDRATE: 9 g, FIBER: 0 g

Gazpacho Salad ☺

Baby spinach, arugula, red onion, heirloom tomatoes, sweet peppers and cilantro. Grilled focaccia croutons not included in analysis.
- ✓✓ CALORIES: Excellent Choice (285)
- FAT: Moderate (27 g)♥
- ✓✓ CHOLESTEROL: Excellent Choice (0 mg)
- ✓✓ SODIUM: Excellent Choice (255 mg)*

PROTEIN: 2 g, CARBOHYDRATE: 11 g, FIBER: 3 g

Pepita Crusted Mahi Mahi – Special Request

with avocado salsa, Mayan rice and fresh vegetables. <u>Request plain, steamed vegetables</u>.
- ✓ CALORIES: Good Choice (485)
- ✓✓ FAT: Excellent Choice (15 g)
- ✓ CHOLESTEROL: Good Choice (150 mg)
- SODIUM: Moderate (675 mg)*

PROTEIN: 48 g, CARBOHYDRATE: 40 g, FIBER: 6 g

Old Town Seafood Paella – Special Request

<u>Request less oil</u> (½ Tbs). Analysis does not include ciabatta bread.
- ✓ CALORIES: Good Choice (615)
- ✓ FAT: Good Choice (21 g)
- CHOLESTEROL: Moderate (270 mg)
- SODIUM: High (2895 mg)*

PROTEIN: 56 g, CARBOHYDRATE: 48 g, FIBER: 5 g

Part III

Chefs' Recipes

Recipes

Measure Equivalents:

3 teaspoons (tsp.) = 1 Tablespoon (Tbs.)
16 Tablespoons (Tbs.) = 1 cup
2 Tablespoons (Tbs.) = 1 ounce (oz.) for liquids
1 Tablespoon = ½ ounce

Healthy Dining is pleased to present a diverse selection of recipes created by chefs of restaurants participating in this book and other Healthy Dining books from Southern California. We are delighted that so many restaurants have elected to participate in this section, sharing some of their culinary "trade secrets."

For several years, KFMB-TV (San Diego's Channel 8) aired segments with chefs demonstrating recipes from Healthy Dining restaurants during the Thursday noon news. Many of these recipes are featured in this section of the book.

Types of Recipes

The recipes include a wide range of selections – varying ethnic and regional origins, combinations of flavors, preparation times required, preparation difficulty, and types of dishes (soups, entrees, salads, desserts, etc.)

The Recipe Index

On pages 126 to 129, you'll find the Recipe Index, first arranged by type of dish, then by the name of the restaurant that submitted the recipe. Some recipes fit into more than one category within the Recipe Index. For example, a seafood salad may be listed in both the salads and seafood categories.

Nutrition analysis and modification of the recipes

Most recipes represent dishes that appear on the restaurant's menu page in Healthy Dining. We've stated on each recipe page that "This nutrition analysis corresponds to the recipe below. The restaurant version may differ." This notice indicates: (1) The recipe originally submitted to us for nutrition analysis was in bulk quantity and was adjusted to make 2 to 6 servings. In the process, we may have reformulated the recipe slightly so that amounts are expressed in convenient units – for example, ½ cup and not $7/12$ of a cup, or one tomato, not 6 oz. of tomato; (2) We may have substituted more common ingredients; or (3) We may have adjusted the quantities of some ingredients to further improve the nutrition profile.

Unfamiliar ingredients

When an ingredient is included that might be unfamiliar to the "average" cook, we've given some explanation and direction for finding it. If you need further explanation, please call the restaurant, a cooking school, or a specialty market. Or use your creativity and try your own substitutions!

Talk to us!

We wish you enjoyment and satisfaction, challenge and variety in experimenting with the recipes included. We're eager to get your feedback on the recipes included – please return the questionnaire at the back of your book!

Recipes

Recipe Index
By Type of Cuisine

Salads

Apple-Chicken Salad – *Thai Specialty 2*   131
Avocado, Grapefruit and Shrimp Salad – *Top of the Cove*   132
Chicken Fajita Salad – *Mi Ranchito*   133
Pan Roasted King Salmon Salad – *J Taylor's at L'Auberge Del Mar Resort & Spa*   134
Steamed White Sea Bass Salad – *Café Pacifica*   135
Zone Salad – *Sisley Italian Kitchen*   136

Fish

Ceviche de Pescado – *El Torito*   137
Charbroiled Fish Tacos – *Wahoo's Fish Taco*   138
Drambui Salmon with Roasted Winter Vegetables – *The Brigantine*   139
Flash Grilled Ahi Tuna – *Tutto Mare*   140
Huli Huli Salmon – *Dave & Buster's*   141
Roasted Chile Honey Fish with Cucumber Salsa – *Indigo Grill*   142
Salmon Burgers – *Crest Café*   143
Salmon Wrap – *Susan's Healthy Gourmet*   144
Steamed Fish with Black Beans & Ginger – *The Fish Market*   145
Summer Sautéed Halibut with Pepper Strawberry Salsa & Belgian Endive
                                            – *The French Gourmet*   146

Other Seafood

Ceviche with Citrus Marinade (Appetizer) – *Fresh Seafood Restaurant & Bar*   147
Imperial Shrimp – *Chin's Szechwan Cuisine*   148
Indonesian Tiger Shrimp Skewers with Tomato Horseradish Sauce & Mango Salsa
                                            – *Roppongi*   149
Jumbo Sea Scallops – *G5-George's on Fifth*   150
Riso al Profumo di Mare – *Il Fornaio*   151
Seared Sea Scallops & Sweet Pea Risotto – *910 Restaurant*   152
Shrimp & Lobster Potstickers with Lemongrass Ponzu Glaze (Appetizer)
                                            – *Blue Point Coastal Cuisine*   153
Shrimp Fra Diavolo – *Lotsa Pasta*   154
Spiedino di Gamberi con Riccoli de Capra – *Harry's Bar & American Grill*   155
Wok Seared Garlic Shrimp – *Azzura Point at Loews Coronado Bay Resort & Spa*   156

Recipe Index, continued

Poultry & Eggs

Battuta Di Pollo – *Prego Ristorante*   157
Big Scramble – *St. Germain's Café*   158
Chicken Biryani – *Star of India*   159
Lettuce Wraps with Plum Sauce – *Newport Beach Brewing Company*   160
Mushroom Chicken – *Pick Up Stix*   161
Pollo a la Plancha – *Andre's Cuban Restaurant*   162

Pasta

Basil Pasta Primavera – *Ki's Restaurant & Juice Bar*   163
Capellini al Pomodoro Fresco – *Pane e Vino*   164
Linguini with Pesto Shrimp – *Pizza Nova*   165
Spaghetti all Vongole Veraci – *Trattoria La Strada*   166

Vegetarian, Vegetables and Side Dishes

Butternut Squash – *Café Santorini*   167
Grilled Herbed Vegetables – *Henry's Marketplace*   168
Kashk-e Bademjan (Appetizer) – *Bandar Fine Persian Cuisine*   169
Roasted Vegetable Terrine – *Trellises Garden Grill at the Town & Country Hotel*   170
Salsa Fresca – *Rubio's*   171
Singapore Curry – *World Curry*   172
Spicy Roasted Eggplant with Sesame & Honey – *Whole Foods Markets*   173
Spicy Tofu with Fresh Basil – *rice Jones*   174
Thai Tofu Stir fry – *Wild Note Café*   175
Vegetable Biryani – *Café India*   176
Veggie Wraps – *Brockton Villa*   177
Whole Earth Casserole – *Angie's Cuisine Italiano*   178

Dessert

Strawberry Rhubarb Crepes Leucadia – *Leucadia Pizzeria*   179

Recipes

Recipe Index

by Restaurant Name

Andre's Cuban Restaurant – Pollo a la Plancha   162
Angie's Cuisine Italiano (Orange County) – Whole Earth Casserole   178
Azzura Point at Loews Coronado Bay Resort & Spa – Wok Seared Garlic Shrimp   156

Bandar Fine Persian Cuisine – Kashk-e Bademjan (Appetizer)   169
Blue Point Coastal Cuisine – Shrimp & Lobster Potstickers with
                 Lemongrass Ponzu Glaze (Appetizer)   153
The Brigantine – Drambui Salmon with Roasted Winter Vegetables   139
Brockton Villa – Veggie Wraps   177

Café India – Vegetable Biryani   176
Café Pacifica – Steamed White Sea Bass Salad   135
Café Santorini (Los Angeles) – Butternut Squash   167
Chin's Szechwan Cuisine – Imperial Shrimp   148
Crest Café – Salmon Burgers   143

Dave & Buster's – Huli Huli Salmon   141

El Torito – Ceviche de Pescado   137

The Fish Market – Steamed Fish with Black Beans & Ginger   145
The French Gourmet – Summer Sautéed Halibut with Pepper Strawberry Salsa…   146
Fresh Seafood Restaurant & Bar – Ceviche with Citrus Marinade (Appetizer)   147

G5-George's on Fifth – Jumbo Sea Scallops   150

Harry's Bar & American Grill – Spiedino di Gamberi con Riccoli de Capra   155
Henry's Marketplace – Grilled Herbed Vegetables   168

Il Fornaio – Riso al Profumo di Mare   151
Indigo Grill – Roasted Chile Honey Fish with Cucumber Salsa   142

Recipe Index, continued

J. Taylor's at L'Auberge Del Mar Resort & Spa – Pan Roasted King Salmon Salad   134

Ki's Restaurant & Juice Bar –Basil Pasta Primavera   163

Leucadia Pizzeria – Strawberry Rhubarb Crepes Leucadia   179
Lotsa Pasta – Shrimp Fra Diavolo   154

Mi Ranchito – Chicken Fajita Salad   133

Newport Beach Brewing Co. (Orange County)– Lettuce Wraps with Plum Sauce   160
910 Restaurant – Seared Sea Scallops & Sweet Pea Risotto   152

Pane e Vino (Orange County) – Capellini al Pomodoro Fresco   164
Pick Up Stix – Mushroom Chicken   161
Pizza Nova – Linguini with Pesto Shrimp   165
Prego Ristorante – Battuta Di Pollo   157

rice Jones – Spicy Tofu with Fresh Basil   174
Roppongi – Indonesian Tiger Shrimp Skewers with Tomato Horseradish Sauce…   149
Rubio's – Salsa Fresca   171

St. Germain's Cafe – Big Scramble   158
Sisley Italian Kitchen (Los Angeles)– Zone Salad   136
Star of India – Chicken Biryani   159
Susan's Healthy Gourmet – Salmon Wrap   144

Thai Specialty 2 (Orange County)– Apple-Chicken Salad   131
Top of the Cove – Avocado, Grapefruit and Shrimp Salad   132
Trattoria La Strada – Spaghetti all Vongole Veraci   166
Trellises Garden Grill at the Town & Country Hotel – Roasted Vegetable Terrine   170
Tutto Mare – Flash Grilled Ahi Tuna   140

Wahoo's Fish Taco – Charbroiled Fish Tacos   138
Whole Food's Market – Spicy Roasted Eggplant with Sesame & Honey   173
Wild Note Café – Thai Tofu Stir Fry   175
World Curry – Singapore Curry   172

Recipes

APPLE-CHICKEN SALAD 🍎

Nutrition Information per Serving:

✓✓ CALORIES: Excellent Choice (195) ✓✓ CHOLESTEROL: Excellent Choice (35 mg)
✓✓ FAT: Excellent Choice (4 g)   SODIUM: Moderate (765 mg)
         PROTEIN: 16 g, CARBOHYDRATE: 26 g, FIBER: 4 g

This nutrition analysis corresponds to the recipe below. The restaurant version may differ.

Ingredients (4 servings):

6 oz. chicken breast
2 Tbs. fish sauce
2 Tbs. lime juice
2 Tbs. sugar
2 green apples, peeled, cored & diced

2 carrots, shredded
1 cup sliced red onion
2 Tbs. chopped green onion
6 Tbs. ($^3/_8$ cup) chopped cilantro
2 Tbs. cashews, dry roasted & salted

Directions:

1. Grill chicken breast or sauté with non-stick spray. Cool and shred the chicken.
2. Mix fish sauce, lime juice and sugar together.
3. Mix apples, carrots, onions, cilantro and shredded chicken together.
4. Pour fish sauce mixture over apple mixture and stir gently.
5. Garnish with cashews and serve.

Recipe supplied by:

Thai Specialty 2
RESTAURANT

Thai Specialty 2
13572 Newport Ave.
Tustin, CA 92780
(714) 731-1711

🍎 at least 2 fruit/vegetable servings

Recipes

Avocado, Grapefruit and Shrimp Salad

Ingredients (4 servings):

6 cups water
½ cup white wine
3 Tbs onion, diced
1 Tbs. carrot, diced
1 Tbs. celery, chopped
1¼ lb shrimp, peeled, deveined

2 black peppercorns
2 pink/red grapefruit
12 cups spinach
¼ red cup onion
1 avocado
salt & pepper to taste (not in analysis)

Dressing

2 tsp. oil, olive, extra virgin
2 Tbs. vinegar, red wine

1 Tbs. mustard, dijon
3 Tbs. water

Directions:

Salad:
1. Bring water, white wine, onion, carrot, celery and black peppercorn to a boil.
2. Add shrimp and cook for 6 minutes. Shock shrimp in an ice bath.
3. Meanwhile, prepare the grapefruit. First grate and set aside 1 Tbsp. grapefruit zest.
4. Then, supreme the grapefruit by cutting off the thick peel where it meets the flesh, then cutting between the thin membranes to release the segments, and squeeze the membranes, reserving the juice.
5. Combine the spinach and red onion in large bowl. Toss with half the dressing to moisten well. Divide the spinach mixture among 4 plates.
6. Distribute the remaining grapefruit sections, avocado and shrimp on top of each salad.
7. Serve the extra dressing on the side.

Dressing:
1. Fill a 2-cup measure to the half-cup level with grapefruit sections and juice.
2. Add the oil, vinegar, mustard and water. Puree using a stick blender.
3. Stir in the zest, add salt (not included in analysis) and pepper to taste and set aside.

Recipe supplied by:

Top of the Cove
216 Prospect Street
La Jolla, CA 92037
(858) 454-7779

Ŏ at least 2 fruit/vegetable servings

CHICKEN FAJITA SALAD 🍎

As seen on KFMB-TV

Nutrition Information per Serving:

✓ CALORIES: Good Choice (585)   ✓ CHOLESTEROL: Good Choice (125 mg)
✓ FAT: Good Choice (19 g)   SODIUM: Moderate (950 mg)
PROTEIN: 52 g, CARBOHYDRATE: 54 g, FIBER: 13 g

This nutrition analysis corresponds to the recipe below. The restaurant version may differ.

Ingredients (2 servings):

1 tomato
1 or 2 pasilla chilies, diced
1 medium onion, diced
1 Tbs. unsalted butter
12 oz. skinless chicken breast
pinch pepper and garlic powder

¼ cup fajita sauce
    (available at most grocery stores)
2 corn tortillas
1 cup (8 oz.) refried black beans
8 cups romaine lettuce
2 oz. low-moisture mozzarella cheese

Directions:

1. Dice tomato and set aside. Mix onion and pasilla chili together and set aside.
2. Slice chicken breast into thin strips and season with a pinch of garlic powder and black pepper.
3. Heat sauté pan and add butter.
4. Add chicken breast to pan and brown for approximately 11 minutes or until cooked thoroughly.
5. Once chicken is cooked, add onion/pasilla mixture. Cover with lid and cook for 1 minute.
6. Add fajita sauce to pan and stir to combine.
7. Heat tortillas in heavy skillet or griddle until slightly puffy.
8. Arrange on plates in the following order: puffed tortilla, refried black beans, lettuce, mozzarella cheese, chicken, and diced tomato.

Recipe supplied by:

MI RANCHITO
Authentic Mexican Cuisine

Mi Ranchito
12812 Rancho Penasquitos Blvd.
San Diego, CA 92129
(858) 484-4548

🍎 at least 2 fruit/vegetable servings

Recipes

As seen on KFMB-TV

Pan Roasted King Salmon Salad

with arugula and warm mushroom vinaigrette

Nutrition Information per Serving:

✓✓ CALORIES: Excellent Choice (405) ✓ CHOLESTEROL: Good Choice (80 mg)
✓ FAT: Good Choice (24 g)♥ ✓✓ SODIUM: Excellent Choice (175 mg)
PROTEIN: 36 g, CARBOHYDRATE: 14 g, FIBER 4 g

This nutrition analysis corresponds to the recipe below. The restaurant version may differ.
♥ primarily unsaturated fat

Ingredients (4 servings):

¼ cup extra virgin olive oil
9 cups wild mushrooms
½ Tbs. garlic, minced
1 Tbs. sliced shallots
1 Tbs. fresh thyme, chopped

¼ cup aged balsamic vinegar
4 wild salmon filets, 5 oz. each
black pepper and salt to taste (salt
 not included in analysis)
10 oz. baby arugula (2 bags)

Directions:

1. Clean the mushrooms and slice thin.
2. Heat a sauté pan over medium heat and add half the olive oil.
3. Sauté mushrooms until tender. Add the garlic, shallots and thyme. Sauté for 1 min.
4. Add balsamic vinegar, salt (if desired, not included in analysis) and pepper and set aside.
5. Heat a sauté pan over medium heat and add remaining olive oil.
6. Season salmon with salt (if desired, not included in analysis) and pepper and pan roast until cooked medium.
7. For presentation, toss the mushroom vinaigrette with arugula and divide between four dinner plates.
8. Place salmon on top of the salad and serve.

Recipe supplied by:

J. Taylor's
in L'Auberge Del Mar Resort & Spa
1540 Camino Del Mar
Del Mar, CA 92014
(858) 259-1515

🍎 at least 2 fruit/vegetable servings

As seen on KFMB-TV

STEAMED WHITE SEA BASS SALAD 🍎

with Granny Smith apples, dried cranberries and baby arugula,
tossed with Red Beet Vinaigrette and drizzled with lemon-caper yogurt.

Nutrition Information per Serving:

✓ CALORIES: Good Choice (570)   ✓ CHOLESTEROL: Good Choice (85 mg)
✓ FAT: Good Choice (19 g)♥   ✓✓ SODIUM: Excellent Choice (300 mg)
PROTEIN: 42 g, CARBOHYDRATE: 61 g, FIBER: 5 g

This nutrition analysis corresponds to the recipe below. The restaurant version may differ.
♥ primarily unsaturated fat

Ingredients (4 servings):

4 sea bass fillets, 7oz. each
¼ cup plain yogurt
juice of ½ lemon or lime
1 Tbs. capers, finely chopped
pinch salt and pepper
8 cups chopped arugula
2 Granny Smith apples, diced
1 cup dried cranberries
1 cup bean sprouts
1 medium red onion, chopped

Red Beet Vinaigrette:

1 medium cooked beet, sliced
¼ cup red wine vinegar
¼ cup honey
½ small shallot, chopped
pinch salt
pinch black pepper
¼ cup vegetable oil

Directions:

1. Heat water in a steamer to just before boiling (when the steam starts to rise). Place fish in the steamer with a dash of seasoning (not included in analysis) on one side. Cook fish for a total of 5 minutes or until medium rare in texture.
2. While fish is cooking, prepare the lemon-caper yogurt by mixing the yogurt, lemon (or lime) juice, capers, salt & pepper thoroughly in a bowl.
3. Prepare the Red Beet Vinaigrette by placing all ingredients except oil in a blender and blend until smooth. Then add vegetable oil slowly.
4. Prepare the salad by mixing together the arugula, apples, dried cranberries, bean sprouts, and onion. Toss with Red Beet Vinaigrette.
5. Place the salad in the center of each of the 4 plates.
6. Place the fish on top of the salad and drizzle the lemon-caper yogurt on top.

Recipe supplied by:

Cafe
PACIFICA

Cafe Pacifica
2414 San Diego Ave.
San Diego, CA 92110
(619) 291-6666

🍎 at least 2 fruit/vegetable servings

Recipes

ZONE SALAD 🍎

Sliced gourmet grilled apple chicken sausage tossed with tomatoes, apples, pears and mixed baby greens, garnished with sweet peas.

Nutrition Information per Serving:

✓✓ CALORIES: Excellent Choice (380)   ✓ CHOLESTEROL: Good Choice (80 mg)
✓ FAT: Good Choice (16 g)   SODIUM: High (1270 mg)
PROTEIN: 32 g, CARBOHYDRATE: 35 g, FIBER: 9 g

This nutrition analysis corresponds to the recipe below. The restaurant version may differ.

Ingredients (2 servings):

8 oz. (5 cups) mixed baby greens   12 oz. cooked apple chicken sausage,
1 to 2 chopped roma tomatoes (6 oz.)   sliced§
1 pear, sliced   Dijon mustard dressing (not included
1 apple, sliced   in analysis – use sparingly)

¾ cup green peas, blanched (steamed lightly)

Directions:

1. Toss ingredients except peas and dressing.
2. Garnish with peas and serve dressing on the side or add dressing sparingly.

§Apple chicken sausage is available at most grocery stores

Recipe supplied by:

Sisley Italian Kitchen

www.sisleykitchen.com

Los Angeles: 10800 W. Pico Blvd.   (310) 446-3030
Sherman Oaks: 15300 Ventura Blvd.   (818) 905-8444
Thousand Oaks: 446 W. Hillcrest Dr.   (805) 777-7511
Valencia: 24201 W. Valencia Blvd.   (661) 287-4444

CEVICHE DE PESCADO 🍎

Nutrition Information per Serving:

✓✓ CALORIES: Excellent Choice (280)   ✓✓ CHOLESTEROL: Excellent Choice (45 mg)
✓✓ FAT: Excellent Choice (7 g)♥   ✓✓ SODIUM: Excellent Choice (245 mg)*
PROTEIN: 22 g, CARBOHYDRATE: 34 g, FIBER: 11 g

Every 10 weeks El Torito highlights cuisine from a different region of Mexico;
this recipe was part of El Torito's specials from Veracruz.

♥ Primarily unsaturated fat   * if you do not add optional salt

Ingredients (2 servings):

8 oz. sea bass, diced ¼ inch
6 Tbs. fresh lime juice
pinch salt
2 Tbs. red onions, diced ¼ inch
¼ cup tomatoes, diced ¼ inch
1 tsp. fresh jalapeños, chopped fine
1 tsp. fresh cilantro, coarsely chopped

½ cup mango, peeled, diced ¼ inch
1½ tsp. jalapeño juice, from can
¼ tsp. dry oregano, crumbled
2 Tbs. fresh squeezed orange juice
2 slices avocado
2 cilantro sprigs
2 fresh lime halves

1 tsp. salt (optional, not included in analysis)

Directions:

1. Marinate fish in lime juice with a pinch of salt for 3 hours, stirring occasionally.
2. Rinse fish with cold water and drain well.
3. Place marinated fish in a glass bowl, add the remaining ingredients and mix well.
4. Divide ceviche between 2 martini glasses. Top each with an avocado slice and cilantro sprig.
5. Squeeze lime halves over ceviche.
6. Serve with tostaditas or tortilla chips and bottled hot sauce if desired (not included in analysis).

Recipe supplied by:

El Torito
With San Diego area locations in Chula Vista,
Encinitas, La Jolla, La Mesa, Mira Mesa,
Mission Valley, Oceanside and Rancho Bernardo.

Recipes

CHARBROILED FISH TACO

Nutrition Information per Serving:

✓✓ CALORIES: Excellent Choice (225)   ✓✓ CHOLESTEROL: Excellent Choice (50 mg)
✓✓ FAT: Excellent Choice (4 g)   ✓ SODIUM: Good Choice (340 mg)
              PROTEIN: 15 g, CARBOHYDRATE: 27 g, Fiber: 3g

This nutrition analysis corresponds to the recipe below. The restaurant version may differ.

Ingredients (4 servings):

½ lb. fresh mahi mahi fillets (¾-1 inch thick)   2 oz. cabbage, shredded
pinch of garlic salt   4 oz. salsa
8 corn tortillas   2 limes, quartered
1 oz. shredded cheese (Jack and/or cheddar)   cilantro (optional)

Directions:

1. Season fish with pinch of garlic salt.
2. Grill each side over medium heat until done. Divide into 4 portions.
3. Heat tortillas in pan and keep warm.
4. Fill tortillas with fish and top with cheese, cabbage, and salsa. In the restaurant the tacos are made using a double layer of corn tortillas. Alternatively, you can divide the filling evenly between all 8 tortillas to make 2 tacos per serving that contain less filling per taco.
5. Garnish with lime and cilantro.

Recipe supplied by:

wahoos.com

Wahoo's Fish Taco

La Jolla: 639 Pearl Street   (858) 459-0027
Encinitas: 1006 N. El Camino Real #C   (760) 753-5060
Point Loma: 3944 W. Pt. Loma Blvd. #A   (619) 222-0020
Mission Valley: 2195 Station Village Way #A   (619) 299-4550

Visit www.wahoos.com for a list of all locations.

Drambuie Salmon with Roasted Winter Vegetables

As seen on KFMB-TV

Nutrition Information per Serving:

✓ CALORIES: Good Choice (215) ✓✓ CHOLESTEROL: Excellent Choice (1 mg)
✓ FAT: Good Choice (8 g)♥ ✓ SODIUM: Good Choice (195 mg)
PROTEIN: 7 g, CARBOHYDRATE: 34 g, FIBER 10 g

This nutrition analysis corresponds to the recipe below. The restaurant version may differ.

♥ primarily unsaturated fat

Ingredients (4 servings):

24 oz. salmon
2 medium carrots
2 medium parsnips
1 large turnip
1 medium beet
½ yellow onion
½ leek
1 Tbs. olive oil

Marinade:

2 Tbs. minced ginger
2 Tbs. minced leeks
2 cups Drambuie
2 peppercorns, crushed
1 cup water
2 Tbs. low-sodium soy sauce

Directions:

Salmon:

1. Combine the ingredients for the marinade.
2. Cut salmon into 6 oz. portions and place in a glass or ceramic dish. Cover with marinade and chill for 12 hours.
3. Pan roast the salmon in a heavy skillet to caramelize the sugars.
4. Finish salmon in a hot oven, if needed.
5. Deglaze pan with marinade and pour over fish just before serving.

Root Vegetables:

1. Wash vegetables & pat dry. Peel and cut into strips. Add olive oil & toss to coat.
2. Season with a pinch of salt (not included in analysis) and pepper to taste.
3. Place vegetables in a large pan and roast in a 300-degree oven until they begin to caramelize and are tender. Take care not to overcook them.
4. Serve immediately.

Recipe supplied by:

The Brigantine

Pt. Loma: 2725 Shelter Island Dr. (619) 224-2871
Coronado: 1333 Orange Ave. (619) 435-4166
Del Mar: 3263 Camino del Mar (858) 481-1166
La Mesa: 9350 Fuerte Dr. (619) 465-1935
Escondido: 421 W. Felicita (760) 743-4718
Poway: 13455 Poway Rd. (858) 486-3066

at least 2 fruit/vegetable servings

Recipes

FLASH GRILLED AHI TUNA 🍎

Nutrition Information per Serving:

✓✓ CALORIES: Excellent Choice (360)   ✓ CHOLESTEROL: Good Choice (80 mg)
✓✓ FAT: Excellent Choice (10 g)♥   ✓✓ SODIUM: Excellent Choice (110 mg)
PROTEIN: 44 g, CARBOHYDRATE: 27 g, FIBER: 6 g

This nutrition analysis corresponds to the recipe below. The restaurant version may differ
♥primarily unsaturated fat.

Ingredients (4 servings):

4 filets of ahi tuna, 6-oz each
1 cup cherry tomatoes
1½ cups mandarin oranges

1 lb. (10 cups) assorted baby greens
1 Tbs. olive oil
salt (not in analysis) & pepper to taste

Raspberry Champagne Vinaigrette (makes 2 cups)
1 medium shallot
¼ cup raspberry vinegar
2 Tbs. champagne vinegar
2 Tbs. champagne
¼ cup orange juice
1 Tbs. honey

³/₈ cup raspberry puree (or blend ½
    pound frozen raspberries & add
    ¼ cup extra orange juice)
½ cup extra virgin olive oil
½ bunch green onions, sliced

Sweet Pepper Relish
1 yellow pepper (julienne or dice)
1 red pepper (julienne or dice)
4 Tbs. fresh basil (cut in thin strips)

2 tsp. unsalted butter
1 tsp. honey

Directions:

1. Raspberry-Champagne Vinaigrette: Blend the shallot, both vinegars, champagne, raspberry puree, orange juice & honey in a blender. While blending, slowly add the oil. Turn off blender. Add green onions. Extra dressing will last in refrigerator 10 – 14 days.
2. Prepare the sweet pepper relish by combining all the ingredients included.
3. Pre-heat grill.
4. Toss together the baby greens, mandarin oranges, cherry tomatoes, and vinaigrette.
5. Split the salad evenly onto 4 plates.
6. Brush both sides of the tuna with the oil and season as desired with salt (not included in analysis) and pepper.
7. Place tuna onto pre-heated grill. Cook tuna 3 minutes on both sides.
8. Slice tuna onto salad. Top with ½ cup sweet pepper relish & 1 Tbs. dressing per person.

Recipe supplied by:

Tutto Mare
4365 Executive Drive
San Diego, CA 92121
(858) 597-1188

🍎 at least 2 fruit/vegetable servings

Huli Huli Salmon

As seen on KFMB-TV

Nutrition Information per Serving:

✓ CALORIES: Good Choice (490)   ✓ CHOLESTEROL: Good Choice (120 mg)
✓ FAT: Good Choice (18 g)♥   SODIUM: Moderate (885 mg)
PROTEIN: 46 g, CARBOHYDRATE: 33 g, FIBER 1 g

This nutrition analysis corresponds to the recipe below. The restaurant version may differ.
♥ primarily unsaturated fat

Ingredients (4 servings):

Huli Huli Marinade
¾ cup tamari (soy) sauce
1 tsp. sesame oil
1 tsp. minced garlic
½ cup sugar
1 tsp. minced ginger
1 Tbs. chopped green onions
½ Tbs. chopped cilantro
1 tsp. chopped red pepper
⅓ cup frozen pineapple concentrate

Huli Huli Glaze
¼ cup Huli Huli Marinade (recipe
    on left column)
¼ cup ketchup
¼ cup honey

Salmon
4 salmon filets, 8-oz. each
4 tsp. oil for grill

Recipes

Directions:

1. Prepare the marinade by combining all ingredients listed above under "marinade" and mixing well.
2. Prepare the glaze by combining the ingredients listed above under "glaze" and mixing well (use ¼ cup of the Huli Huli Marinade mix).
3. Place the salmon filets in the remaining Huli Huli Marinade and allow to sit refrigerated – overnight if possible.
4. Place the marinated salmon filets on an oiled grill and cook both sides till done. Place salmon on plates and drizzle Huli Huli Glaze over the salmon.
5. Recommended sides: green beans and your choice of rice or potato (not included in analysis).

Recipe supplied by:

Dave & Buster's
2931 Camino del Rio North
San Diego, CA 92108
(619) 280-7115
www.daveandbusters.com

ROASTED CHILE HONEY FISH
WITH CUCUMBER SALSA ☝

Nutrition Information per Serving:

✓ CALORIES: Good Choice (560)　　✓ CHOLESTEROL: Good Choice (105 mg)
✓ FAT: Good Choice (16 g)　　✓ SODIUM: Good Choice (410 mg)
PROTEIN: 45 g, CARBOHYDRATE: 58 g, FIBER: 4 g
Use fish of your choice; analysis is for salmon. The restaurant version may differ.

Ingredients (4 servings):

3 Tbs. chopped fresh red chili peppers
¹/₃ cup honey
2 tsp. dried guajillo chili peppers
1 tsp. water
4 fish filets, 6-oz. each
16 oz. cooked spaghetti noodles
　　(6 oz. dry weight before cooking)
2 oz. Cotija cheese

3 cucumbers, chopped
½ red bell pepper, chopped
½ yellow bell pepper, chopped
½ medium onion, chopped
1 to 2 jalapeno peppers, minced
2 Tbs. fresh dill sprigs
2 Tbs. lime juice

Directions:

1. Honey-chile glaze: Mix red chili peppers, honey, guajillo chili peppers and water.
2. Coat salmon filets with chile honey glaze.
3. Roast or grill salmon until desired doneness.
4. Cook spaghetti according to package instructions.
5. Toss spaghetti with Cotija cheese.
6. Cucumber Salsa: Combine chopped cucumber, bell peppers, onion, jalapeno peppers, dill and lime juice.
7. Serve salmon with spaghetti and cucumber salsa on the side.

Salsa can be made ahead of time if desired.

Recipe supplied by:

Indigo Grill
1536 India Street
San Diego, CA 92101
(619) 234-6802

　　☝ at least 2 fruit/vegetable servings

Salmon Burgers

As seen on KFMB-TV

Nutrition Information per Serving:

✓ CALORIES: Good Choice (590)   ✓ CHOLESTEROL: Good Choice (95 mg)
✓ FAT: Good Choice (21 g)♥   SODIUM: High (1050 mg)
PROTEIN: 42 g, CARBOHYDRATE: 56 g, FIBER 5 g

This nutrition analysis corresponds to the recipe below. The restaurant version may differ.
♥ primarily unsaturated fat

Ingredients (6 servings):

2 pounds salmon, ground
8 green onions, chopped
2 Tbs. capers
2 Tbs. lemon juice
2 tsp. tarragon
2 tsp. Dijon mustard
2 tsp. horseradish
½ tsp. salt

1 tsp. pepper
1 cup bread crumbs
6 Tbs. light mayonnaise
6 onion hamburger buns
½ avocado
6 pieces lettuce
6 pieces tomato
3 sprays cooking spray

Directions:

1. Combine the first ten ingredients in a medium bowl.
2. Add the mayonnaise and mix well. Form into 6 patties.
3. Put cooking spray into the pan and sauté patties for about 3 minutes on each side.
4. Place on top of the onion bun; top with avocado.
5. Serve with lettuce and tomato on the side.

Recipe supplied by:

Crest Cafe
425 Robinson Ave.
San Diego, CA 92103
(619) 295-2510

Recipes

Salmon Wrap 🍎

Salmon, cucumbers, fresh dill and capers in a green onion wrap, served with an apple.

Nutrition Information per Serving (per ½ wrap):

✓✓ Calories: Excellent Choice (330)   ✓✓ Cholesterol: Excellent Choice (45 mg)
✓✓ Fat: Excellent Choice (10 g)♥   ✓ Sodium: Good Choice (590 mg)
Protein: 21 g, Carbohydrate: 42 g, Fiber: 12 g

This nutrition analysis corresponds to the recipe below. The restaurant version may differ.
♥ primarily unsaturated fat

Ingredients (2 half-wrap servings):

4 ounces salmon filet
½ cucumber
¼ cup nonfat mayonnaise
pinch white pepper
1 tsp. fresh chopped dill

1 tsp. capers
1 green onion tortilla (10 inch)
1½ cups romaine lettuce
2 medium apples

Directions:

1. Bake salmon at 375° for 20-25 minutes or until flaky.
2. Seed and peel cucumber. Cut into 1 inch slices, then into julienne style pieces.
3. In a medium bowl, combine mayonnaise, pepper, dill, capers, and cucumber.
4. Flake salmon into pieces and mix into mayonnaise mixture.
5. Using a 10-inch green onion tortilla (or preference), spread mixture over half of the tortilla.
6. Top with chopped romaine lettuce and roll up.
7. Cut wrap in half and serve ½ wrap with an apple for each person.

Additional serving suggestions: add melon, salad or vegetables (not in analysis).

Recipe supplied by:

SUSAN'S HEALTHY GOURMET
FRESH • DELICIOUS • DELIVERED

Susan's Healthy Gourmet
(858) 456-1366,
(888) EZ-MEALS (396-3257)
Conveniently located pick-up locations
throughout San Diego County.

🍎 at least 2 fruit/vegetable servings

STEAMED FISH WITH
BLACK BEANS & GINGER

Nutrition Information per Serving:

✓ CALORIES: Good Choice (460)   ✓✓ CHOLESTEROL: Excellent Choice (75 mg)
✓ FAT: Good Choice (20 g)♥   SODIUM: High (1245 mg)*
        PROTEIN: 53 g, CARBOHYDRATE: 15 g, FIBER: 5 g

This nutrition analysis corresponds to the recipe below. The restaurant version may differ.
♥primarily unsaturated fat   *Sodium is higher with fermented (Oriental) black beans

Ingredients (2 servings):

1 pound halibut, seabass or roughy
1 tsp. minced garlic
2 Tbs. fresh ginger, cut in matchsticks
2 Tbs. black beans or
    Oriental (fermented) black beans

³/₈ cup white wine
¼ cup low sodium sauce
2 Tbs. sesame oil
¼ cup chopped green onion
1 cup steamed vegetables

Directions:

1. Score fish filets in diamond shape, half the depth of the filets.
2. Place in small boat and rub with garlic.
3. Add ginger, black beans, wine, soy sauce and sesame oil.
4. Steam until fish is cooked (flaky, but not overcooked).
5. Garnish with green onions.
6. Serve on large platter with steamed vegetables.

Recipe supplied by:

The Fish Market
640 Via de la Valle, Del Mar, CA 92075
(858) 755-2277

750 N. Harbor Dr., San Diego, CA 92101
(619) 232-3474

☺ at least 2 fruit/vegetable servings

As seen on KFMB-TV

SUMMER SAUTÉED HALIBUT WITH PEPPER STRAWBERRY SALSA AND GRILLED BELGIAN ENDIVE 🍎

Nutrition Information per Serving:

✓✓ CALORIES: Excellent Choice (390)   ✓✓ CHOLESTEROL: Excellent Choice (75 mg)
✓✓ FAT: Excellent Choice (13 g)♥   SODIUM: Moderate (560 mg)
PROTEIN: 50 g, CARBOHYDRATE: 19 g, Fiber: 6 g

This nutrition analysis corresponds to the recipe below. The restaurant version may differ.
♥ Primarily unsaturated fat

Ingredients (4 servings):

Halibut:
1½ Tbs. olive oil
1½ Tbs. flour
1½ lemon, sliced
4 filets of halibut, 8 oz. each
1½ Tbs. lemon pepper

Pepper Strawberry Salsa:
24 strawberries
2 tsp. of black whole peppercorn
1 tsp. olive oil
dash of salt
4 scallions (green onions)
juice of 1 lemon

Endive:
4 Belgian endives cut in half lengthwise
¾ tsp. olive oil
½ tsp. red wine vinegar
squeeze of ½ a lemon (save the zest)
½ clove garlic
½ medium chopped shallot
½ tsp. sugar
zest of ½ lemon
salt and pepper to taste (salt & pepper not included in analysis)

Directions:

Endive: Mix the ingredients together and drizzle over endives. Let sit for ½ hour. Grill on BBQ for 5 minutes on each side. (Can be made ahead of time and re-heated in the oven)

Salsa: Cut strawberries and scallions into 1/8 – ¼ inch pieces. Mix all ingredients. Set aside.

Halibut:
1. Mix flour and lemon pepper in a bowl. Lightly coat each fillet with flour mixture.
2. Heat sauté pan and add olive oil.
3. Place fish in heated pan. Cook until bottom side is golden brown.
4. Turn fish over and squeeze lemon slices over fillets. Leave lemon slices on top of each fish fillet. Cover pan with snug fitting lid to prevent steam from escaping. Cook for 7-10 minutes. Moisture will collect inside pan and make a tangy glaze.
5. Place fish on warm place and spoon glaze and salsa on top. Serve with Endive.

Recipe supplied by:

The French Gourmet
Social and Business Catering Solutions

The French Gourmet
960 Turquoise Street
San Diego, CA 92109

🍎 at least 2 fruit/vegetable servings

SCALLOP CEVICHE WITH
CITRUS MARINADE (APPETIZER) 🍎

Nutrition Information per Serving:†
✓✓ CALORIES: Excellent Choice (130)   ✓ CHOLESTEROL: Good Choice (35 mg)
✓✓ FAT: Excellent Choice (1 g)♥   SODIUM: High (450 mg)
PROTEIN: 17 g, CARBOHYDRATE: 15 g, FIBER: 1 g

This nutrition analysis corresponds to the recipe below. The restaurant version may differ.
† Side dish guidelines are ⅓ of entrée guidelines   ♥ primarily unsaturated fat

Ingredients (4 servings):

1 lb. scallops, diced
1 cup orange juice
½ cup lemon juice
½ cup lime juice
1 cup cucumber, diced

¼ cup red onion, diced
1 cup mango, diced
½ cup tomato, diced
2 Tbs. mint, chopped
¼ cup cilantro, chopped

Directions:

1. Combine scallops and all citrus juices.
2. Marinate in the refrigerator for about 3 hours or until the scallops become opaque.
3. Add the remaining ingredients.
4. Season with salt and pepper to taste (not included in analysis).

Recipe supplied by:

Fresh Seafood Restaurant & Bar
1044 Wall Street
La Jolla, CA 92037
(858) 551-7575
www.freshseafoodrestaurant.com

🍎 at least 1 fruit/vegetable serving for side dishes

Recipes

IMPERIAL SHRIMP 🍎

Nutrition Information per Serving:

✓✓ CALORIES: Excellent Choice (245) CHOLESTEROL: Moderate (280 mg)
✓✓ FAT: Excellent Choice (9 g)♥ SODIUM: Moderate (695 mg)
PROTEIN: 33 g, CARBOHYDRATE: 8 g, FIBER: 4 g

This nutrition analysis corresponds to the recipe below. The restaurant version may differ.
♥Primarily unsaturated fat

Ingredients (4 servings):

1 Tbs. cooking oil
1¼ lb. shrimp, deveined & butterflied
2 cups broccoli, chopped
1½ cup mushrooms, sliced
¾ cup snow peas
½ tsp. garlic, fresh, minced
½ tsp. ginger, fresh, minced

½ tsp. salt
¼ tsp. sugar
1 Tbs. rice cooking wine
¼ tsp. white pepper
¼ cup chicken broth, no salt added
2 tsp. corn starch
1 Tbs. sesame oil

Directions:

1. Heat oil in a skillet over medium-high heat.
2. Add shrimp and quickly sauté until it just starts to turn pink. Do not cook through. Remove from skillet.
3. In a separate pot, parboil vegetables. Do not overcook.
4. Combine remaining ingredients except cornstarch and sesame oil in skillet and stir.
5. Add shrimp and vegetables. Stir-fry until shrimp is done.
6. Add sesame oil and then cornstarch to thicken sauce.

Recipe supplied by:

Chin's Szechwan Cuisine

Carlsbad: 2958 Madison St. (760) 434-7115
Encinitas: 1506 Encinitas Blvd. (760) 753-3903
Escondido: 445 N. Escondido Blvd. (760) 480-4115
Oceanside: 4140 Oceanside Blvd. (760) 631-4808
Oceanside: 2241 El Camino Real (760) 439-3600
Rancho Bernardo: 15721A Bernardo Hts. Pky. (858) 676-0166
San Marcos: 631 S. Rancho Santa Fe Rd. (760) 591-9648
Scripps Ranch: 9978 Scripps Ranch Blvd. (858) 566-0031
Vista: 600 E. Vista Way (760) 732-3880

🍎 at least 2 fruit/vegetable servings

Indonesian Tiger Shrimp Skewers with Tomato Horseradish Sauce & Mango Salsa ♨

As seen on KFMB-TV

Nutrition Information per Serving:

✓✓ CALORIES: Excellent Choice (345)   CHOLESTEROL: Moderate (220 mg)
✓✓ FAT: Excellent Choice (9 g)♥   SODIUM: Moderate (955 mg)
PROTEIN: 27 g, CARBOHYDRATE: 41 g, FIBER: 2 g

This nutrition analysis corresponds to the recipe below. The restaurant version may differ.

♥ primarily unsaturated fat

Ingredients (4 servings):

4 bamboo skewers – soaked in water
16 tiger shrimp (16/20 count, peeled & deveined)
1 fresh ripe mango, peeled & finely chopped
2 ripe roma tomatoes, seeded & chopped
½ bunch cilantro, chopped
¼ cup rice wine vinegar
2 Tbs. sugar

½ oz chives
2 Tbs. olive oil
8 oz (1 cup) tomato ketchup
1 Tbs. (or to taste) wasabi powder*
2 Tbs. fresh lemon juice
2 Tbs. horseradish sauce

* Available at Asian grocery stores

Directions:

Shrimp:
1. Soak wooden bamboo skewers in water.
2. Place shrimp on skewer pushing along back from tail to top.
3. Season skewers with salt, pepper, chopped chives and olive oil.
4. Cook skewers on grill (charcoal) or gas with wooden skewers away from heat.
5. Turn skewers to cook evenly on all sides.

Salsa: Dissolve sugar and rice wine vinegar in bowl. Add mango, tomatoes and chopped cilantro.

Tomato Horseradish Sauce: Mix wasabi powder with water to form a wet paste. Add ketchup, horseradish and lemon juice. Place tomato horseradish sauce in ramekin.

Serve skewers on plate with mango salsa.

Recipe supplied by:

Roppongi Restaurant & Sushi Bar
875 Prospect Street
La Jolla, CA 92037
(858) 551-5252

♨ at least 2 fruit/vegetable servings

JUMBO SEA SCALLOPS ♆

Pan seared scallops with watercress, new potatoes, sun dried tomatoes & green goddess dressing.

Nutrition Information per Serving:

✓ CALORIES: Good Choice (660)   CHOLESTEROL: Moderate (165 mg)
✓ FAT: Good Choice (20 g)♥   SODIUM: High (1300 mg)
          PROTEIN: 44 g, CARBOHYDRATE: 86 g, FIBER: 9 g

This nutrition analysis corresponds to the recipe below. The restaurant version may differ.

♥ primarily unsaturated fat

Ingredients (4 servings):

1¼ lb. scallops
2 eggs
4 Tbs. flour
2 Tbs. oil
½ cup panko (Japanese) breadcrumbs
4 new potatoes (8 oz.)
½ bunch raw watercress (approx. 2 cups)
1 medium large tomato, diced
4 oz. sun dried tomatoes, diced

Green Goddess Dressing
½ bunch watercress
2 to 3 leaves fresh basil
2 Tbs. lemon juice
¼ tsp. salt
1½ cups olive oil
pepper to taste

Directions:

<u>Scallops</u>: Whip eggs. Dip scallops in flour, then egg, then breadcrumbs. Add oil to sauté pan and heat. Sauté scallops for 3 minutes on each side.

<u>New Potatoes:</u> Steam or boil.

<u>Dressing</u>: Place all ingredients in blender except the oil. Blend ingredients together, adding a little oil at a time until all oil is mixed in.

<u>Assembling the dish:</u>
1. Clean the watercress and place in the center of each of four plates.
2. Top watercress with diced tomato.
3. Slice the potatoes into "coins." Place each cooked scallop on a potato "coin" and arrange around the plate.
4. Sprinkle sun dried tomatoes on top of scallops.
5. Drizzle 1 Tbs. dressing over each dish. Save remaining dressing for future use.

Recipe supplied by:

Georges on 5 Fifth
Steak • Seafood • Entertainment

G5 – Georges on Fifth
835 Fifth Avenue
San Diego, CA 92101
(619) 702-0444

♆ at least 2 fruit/vegetable servings

RISO AL PROFUMO DI MARE

As seen on KFMB-TV

Nutrition Information per Serving:

✓ CALORIES: Good Choice (615)   CHOLESTEROL: Moderate (250 mg)
✓ FAT: Good Choice (24 g)   SODIUM: High (1115 mg)
       PROTEIN: 49 g, CARBOHYDRATE: 53 g, FIBER: 2 g

This nutrition analysis corresponds to the recipe below. The restaurant version may differ.
This item is only available on the regional menu.

Ingredients (2 servings):

8 oz. shrimp
2 Tbs. olive oil
2 cloves garlic, crushed
8 oz. manila clams (including shells)
pinch of ground chili pepper flakes
½ tsp. parsley (chopped)
4 oz. white wine
4 oz. clam juice

Risotto
2 shallots or small onions, chopped
½ cup uncooked risotto rice
20 oz. fish stock
½ tsp. orange peel (chopped fine,
    no white!)
1 Tbs. butter (unsalted)
sprigs of parsley

Directions:

1. Peel, de-vein and cut the shrimp. Set aside.
2. In a sauté pan, put 1 Tbs. olive oil and the garlic. Cook garlic until light brown.
3. Add the clams, chili flakes, half of the chopped parsley, white wine, and clam juice. Sauté until the clams open. Filter excess liquid off the clam mix.
4. Make the risotto by putting chopped shallots into a sauté pan with 1 Tbs. oil. Cook for one minute, then add the risotto rice and cook for 2 more minutes.
5. Add fish stock and the filtered juice from the clams a little at a time, stirring well between additions. Continue until rice is cooked nearly to desired consistency.
6. Add the shrimp several minutes before the risotto is ready.
7. Finish with orange zest, remaining parsley, and butter. Let rest for one minute.
8. Presentation: serve on 12-inch plates. Arrange clams around the risotto and garnish with a parsley sprig.

Recipe supplied by:

Il Fornaio
1333 First Street, Coronado 92118   (619) 437-4911
1555 Camino del Mar, Del Mar 92014   (858) 755-8876

 at least 2 fruit/vegetable servings

SEARED SEA SCALLOPS & SWEET PEA RISOTTO

Nutrition Information per Serving:

✓ CALORIES: Good Choice (630)   ✓✓ CHOLESTEROL: Excellent Choice (50 mg)
✓✓ FAT: Excellent Choice (12 g)♥   ✓ SODIUM: Good Choice (480 mg)
PROTEIN: 33 g, CARBOHYDRATE: 102 g, FIBER: 5 g

This nutrition analysis corresponds to the recipe below. The restaurant version may differ.
♥primarily unsaturated fat

Ingredients (4 servings):

1½ Tbs. canola oil
1 leek, diced
1 pound Arborio or canaroli rice
¼ cup white wine
2 cups chicken stock
1 cup fresh green peas

1 lemon, zested
1 Tbs. unsalted butter
1 Tbs. chives, minced
1 pound scallops (12 pieces)
¼ cup parmesan cheese, fresh grated

Directions:

1. Bring chicken stock to a boil and keep warm.
2. In a sauté pan on medium heat, add ½ Tbs. oil. Add diced leeks and sweat on low heat until tender. Try not to brown and stir often.
3. Add rice and toast for 1 to 2 minutes, stirring often.
4. Add wine and deglaze until mixture is dry, stirring often.
5. Add enough chicken stock to cover rice and stir.
6. Keep adding stock in small batches until rice becomes al dente (15 - 20 min).
7. Stir in peas and continue to cook for 1 to 2 minutes.
8. Add a little stock or water to loosen rice.
9. Add lemon zest, part of the grated cheese (save some for garnish), butter, and chives, and stir well. Risotto should be a loose and creamy consistency. Add more stock if needed.
10. Season the scallops with a pinch of salt and pepper on both sides.
11. Heat a medium sized sauté pan on medium high heat. Add 1Tbs. oil. Once the pan is hot, add scallops and sear until golden brown on both sides (about 2 minutes on each side). Set on a plate with a paper towel. Keep warm.
12. Place risotto in the center of a platter, place scallops around risotto and serve family style or serve in individual bowls. Garnish with grated parmesan cheese.

Recipe supplied by:

NINE-TEN

Nine-Ten Restaurant
910 Prospect Street
La Jolla, CA 92037
(858) 964-5400

☼ at least 2 fruit/vegetable servings

SHRIMP & LOBSTER POTSTICKERS WITH LEMONGRASS PONZU GLAZE (APPETIZER)

As seen on KFMB-TV

Ingredients (4 servings):

Potstickers:
½ lb. shrimp (raw), peeled & deveined
4 oz. lobster meat, chopped
½ tsp. garlic, chopped fine
½ tsp. ginger, chopped fine
½ tsp. lemongrass, chopped fine
¹/8 tsp. lime leaf, chopped fine
¹/3 cup cilantro, chopped fine
1 tsp. sambal
1 Tbs. olive oil
16 gyoza wrappers

Lemongrass Jalapeno Ponzu Glaze:
½ cup low sodium soy sauce
¼ cup orange juice
½ lime, juiced
¹/3 cup mirin
¼ each jalapeno, julienned
¼ lemongrass, sliced very fine
¼ cup cilantro, chopped fine

Directions:
1. Combine all ingredients in a bowl and mix by hand.
2. Place 1 tsp. of potsticker mix into each gyoza wrapper. Seal wrapper.
3. Sauté 4 to 8 potstickers at a time in olive oil. After lightly browned, add a few Tbs. water and let potstickers steam another 1 to 2 minutes to finish cooking. Remove with tongs and drain. Repeat for remaining potstickers.

Lemongrass Jalapeno Ponzu Glaze:
1. Combine all ingredients together in saucepot. Bring to a boil.
2. Add cornstarch slurry and whisk in thoroughly. Let cool.
3. Drizzle over or serve alongside potstickers.

Recipe supplied by:

BLUE POINT
COASTAL CUISINE

Blue Point Coastal Cuisine
565 Fifth Avenue
San Diego, CA 92101
(619) 233-6623

Recipes

As seen on KFMB-TV

SHRIMP FRA DIAVOLO 🍎

Nutrition Information per Serving:

✓✓CALORIES: Excellent Choice (445)   CHOLESTEROL: High (305 mg)
✓✓ FAT: Excellent Choice (6 g)♥   SODIUM: High (1055 mg)
      PROTEIN: 41 g, CARBOHYDRATE: 52 g, FIBER: 4 g
This nutrition analysis corresponds to the recipe below. The restaurant version may differ.
♥primarily unsaturated fat

Ingredients (2 servings):

14 jumbo shrimp
1 tsp. garlic butter
4 oz. fresh linguini (uncooked)

1½ cups Fra Diavolo Sauce:
(the following recipe makes enough for you to save some for additional uses)

Fra Diavolo Sauce

4½ cups clam juice
½ cup white wine
1 oz. garlic
1¾ cups marinara sauce
¼ tsp. ground black pepper
½ Tbs. crushed red pepper

½ cup concentrated crushed tomatoes
    or ¼ cup tomato paste
½ Tbs. lime juice, fresh squeezed
¼ cup fresh parsley
¼ cup fresh cilantro
¼ cup fresh basil leaves
¼ cup fresh oregano

Directions:

1. Place linguini in boiling water for 1 minute and set aside.
2. Cook the shrimp by sautéing them in the garlic butter.
3. Pour clam juice into a medium size pot and put on high heat.
4. Puree garlic cloves and wine in a blender, and then add to pot.
5. Add the remaining ingredients to pot except for fresh herbs.
6. Combine and chop finely the herbs and set aside.
7. Bring to a boil and reduce heat to a simmer. Simmer for 30 minutes.
8. Add fresh herbs and simmer for another 5 minutes.
9. Add the cooked pasta to the sauce, along with the shrimp cooked in garlic butter.

Recipe supplied by:

Lotsa Pasta
Fresh Pasta • Restaurant • Market

Lotsa Pasta
1762 Garnet Ave.
San Diego, CA 92109
(858) 581-6777

154 *Healthy Dining in San Diego*   🍎 at least 2 fruit/vegetable servings

As seen on
KFMB-TV

Spiedino di Gamberi con Riccioli di Capra

Skewers of grilled prawns, goat cheese filled zucchini,
served on beds of roasted peppers & greens.

Nutrition Information per Serving:

✓✓ Calories: Excellent Choice (435)   Cholesterol: High (375 mg)
  ✓ Fat: Good Choice (25 g)♥   Sodium: Moderate (810 mg)
    Protein: 45 g, Carbohydrate: 4 g, Fiber 1 g

This nutrition analysis corresponds to the recipe below. The restaurant version may differ.

♥ primarily unsaturated fat

Ingredients (4 servings):

Lemon Vinaigrette:
1 Tbs. lemon juice
3 Tbs. olive oil
pinch salt
pinch pepper

Other Ingredients:
12 medium-sized prawns, peeled & deveined
1 zucchini
¾ cup grated goat cheese
4 wooden skewers
4 oz. (about 1½ cups) mixed lettuce
2 bell peppers

Directions:

1. Roast bell peppers in 450° oven until skin blisters (5 to 10 minutes). Peel off skin and chop.
2. Cook the prawns in boiling water with salt for 2 minutes.
3. Slice zucchini top to bottom.
4. Place one Tbs. of grated goat cheese on the zucchini slice and roll up.
5. Make skewers by beginning with a prawn first, followed by a zucchini "roll." Repeat 2 more times to make 6 items per skewer.
6. Season with salt (optional, not included in analysis) and pepper.
7. Cook on the grill for 3 minutes.
8. Serve on a bed of roasted peppers and mixed greens tossed with the Lemon Vinaigrette dressing.

Recipe supplied by:

HARRY'S BAR
and American Grill ®

Harry's Bar & American Grill
4370 La Jolla Village Drive
San Diego, CA 92121
(858) 373-1252

Recipes

WOK SEARED GARLIC SHRIMP AND DUNGENESS CRAB-GINGER RISOTTO 🍎

Nutrition Information per Serving:

✓ CALORIES: Good Choice (710) ✓ CHOLESTEROL: Good Choice (100 mg)
FAT: Moderate (27 g) SODIUM: High (1870 mg)
PROTEIN: 28 g, CARBOHYDRATE: 92 g, FIBER: 4 g

This nutrition analysis corresponds to the recipe below. The restaurant version may differ.

Ingredients (2 servings):

6 large tiger shrimp
2 Tbs. roasted garlic paste (or minced garlic)
2 tsp. olive oil

1 cup pea shoots
2 oz. crab meat
½ fresh mango, cut into strips

Risotto:

2 Tbs. olive oil
2 garlic cloves, minced
2 oz. Maui sweet onion, minced
2 inch Awapuhi (ginger), peeled/minced
5 cups clam juice
2 Tbs. coconut milk

2 stalks lemon grass, bruised & cut in thirds
6 oz. (¾ cup) Arborio rice (dry weight)
1 Tbs. butter
2 Tbs. Parmigiano Reggiano cheese
2 scallions, sliced
2 Tbs. spring peas

Directions:

1. Sauté the minced garlic in olive oil, add Maui sweet onions, and cook until tender.
2. Add Awapuhi (ginger) and Arborio rice. Cook on low heat, until the rice is translucent.
3. In a separate pot, combine clam juice, coconut milk, and lemon grass and bring to a boil, then turn down to a low simmer.
4. Turn up heat on rice to medium-high, ladle in hot stock, until it covers the rice. There may be extra coconut/clam stock.
5. Constantly stir risotto with a wooden spoon. Let liquid absorb until au sec (almost dry).
6. Repeat process (adding stock and letting it absorb) until risotto is near tender. Remove from heat.
7. Add butter and Parmigiano Reggiano cheese.
8. Fold in half of the crab meat, scallions, and spring peas. Keep warm.
9. Season with salt (not included in analysis) and pepper to taste.
10. In a separate pan, add olive oil and sear shrimp on high with roasted garlic paste. Set aside.
11. In a medium bowl, mix pea shoots, remaining crab meat and mango. Season mango salad with olive oil and salt/pepper (not included in analysis).
12. Place risotto in center of plates. Arrange 3 shrimp around risotto on each plate. Then place pea shoots, crab meat and mango salad on top of risotto. Optional: Garnish with scallion oil (not included in analysis).

Recipe supplied by:

LOEWS
CORONADO BAY RESORT
SAN DIEGO

Azzura Point

at Loews Coronado Bay Resort & Spa
4000 Coronado Bay Rd., Coronado CA 92118
(619) 424-4406

🍎 at least 2 fruit/vegetable servings

BATTUTA DI POLLO 🍎

Ingredients (2 servings):

2 skinless chicken breasts, 5 oz. each
pinch fresh rosemary
pinch fresh sage
¼ tsp. salt
¼ tsp. black pepper
2 tsp. olive oil

½ medium tomato
2½ cups romaine lettuce
½ cup chopped portabella mushroom
2 thin-medium slices of avocado
¼ cup balsamic vinegar

Directions:

1. Pound the chicken breasts.
2. Season with fresh rosemary, sage, salt, pepper and olive oil. Then grill.
3. Toss the tomato, greens and portabella mushroom in balsamic vinegar.
4. Top with grilled chicken breast and top with avocado slices. Serve.

Recipe supplied by:

Prego Ristorante
1370 Frazee Road
San Diego, CA 92108
(619) 294-4700

🍎 at least 2 fruit/vegetable servings

As seen on KFMB-TV

BIG SCRAMBLE 🍎

Nutrition Information per Serving:

✓✓ CALORIES: Excellent Choice (375)   ✓✓ CHOLESTEROL: Excellent Choice (0 mg)
✓✓ FAT: Excellent Choice (5 g)♥   SODIUM: Moderate (695 mg)
              PROTEIN: 27 g, CARBOHYDRATE: 59 g, FIBER: 4 g

This nutrition analysis corresponds to the recipe below. The restaurant version may differ.
♥Primarily unsaturated fat

Ingredients (2 servings):

12 oz. Eggbeaters or 12 egg whites
1 tsp. canola oil
2 Tbs. onions
¼ bell pepper
2 large mushrooms

¼ medium tomato
2 cups fresh fruit
4 slices whole-wheat bread
Salt & pepper to taste
   (salt not included in analysis)

Directions:

1. Slice or chop fresh tomatoes, bell pepper, onion and mushrooms. Blot with paper towel if needed.
2. Sauté these ingredients in a hot frying pan using canola oil, or spray on canola oil or Pam cooking spray, just enough oil to coat the pan.
3. Once vegetables are sautéed, add Eggbeaters or egg whites. Scramble till cooked.
4. Serve with 2 slices of whole-wheat toast and fresh fruit.

Recipe supplied by:

St. Germain's Cafe
1010 S. Hwy. 101
Encinitas, CA 92024
(760) 753-5411

CHICKEN BIRYANI

As seen on KFMB-TV

Nutrition Information per Serving:

✓✓ CALORIES: Excellent Choice (400) ✓ CHOLESTEROL: Good Choice (140 mg)
✓✓ FAT: Excellent Choice (15 g) ✓✓ SODIUM: Excellent Choice (145 mg)
PROTEIN: 52 g, CARBOHYDRATE: 11 g, FIBER 2 g

This nutrition analysis corresponds to the recipe below. The restaurant version may differ.

Ingredients (4 servings):

2 lb. boneless, skinless chicken breast
1 Tbs. oil
1 Tbs. cumin seeds
1 Tbs. crushed coriander
2 medium tomatoes
2 medium onions
1 Tbs. ginger and garlic paste

½ Tbs. turmeric powder
1 tsp. garam masala
1 Tbs. green chilies
1 cup hot water
1 Tbs. fresh cilantro
Salt to taste (not included in analysis)

Directions:

1. Cut the chicken into 1-inch pieces.
2. Heat the oil in a pan and add the cumin and coriander. When they start popping, add garlic and ginger paste, then the chopped onions, and cook until they turn golden brown.
3. Add the chopped tomatoes and green chilies, along with the garam masala and turmeric. Mix everything well and cook for about a minute. Add the chicken pieces and cook for approximately 3 more minutes.
4. If you like curry to be diluted, then add water, cover with a lid, and boil for 5-6 minutes on low flame.
5. When cooked, garnish with fresh chopped cilantro.
6. Serve with basmati rice (not included in analysis).

Recipe supplied by:

Star of India

Pacific Beach: 1820 Garnet Avenue (858) 483-1372
Del Mar: 3860 Valley Center Drive (858) 792-1111
Downtown: 423 F Street (619) 234-8000

Star of India Express/Royal India Express

4545 La Jolla Village Dr., E22 (858) 453-5300
1640 Camino Del Rio North, FC7 (619) 501-9999
423 Horton Plaza, Unit 379 (619) 269-9999

Recipes

LETTUCE WRAPS WITH PLUM SAUCE 🍎

Nutrition Information per Serving:

✓ CALORIES: Good Choice (495)
✓✓ FAT: Excellent Choice (10 g)
✓ CHOLESTEROL: Good Choice (130 mg)
SODIUM: Moderate (865 mg)
PROTEIN: 58 g, CARBOHYDRATE: 47 g, FIBER: 12 g

This nutrition analysis corresponds to the recipe below. The restaurant version may differ.

Ingredients (2 servings):

Plum Sauce
¼ cup plum sauce (commercially bottled)
2 Tbs. hoisin sauce
1 tsp. sesame oil
pinch crushed red pepper
¼ tsp. ginger
1 Tbs. soy sauce
1 tsp. orange juice
1 green onion, sliced

Lettuce Wraps
2 chicken breasts, 6 oz. each
1 head of lettuce
2 cups shredded carrots
2 cups bean sprouts
1 cucumber, sliced into thin strips

Directions:

1. For the plum sauce, combine all ingredients and blend well.
2. Grill chicken and slice into thin strips.
3. Remove the larger leaves from the head of lettuce (about ½ of the head) for this recipe. Discard smaller leaves or save for another use.
4. Place lettuce leaves, chicken strips, carrots, sprouts and cucumber in sections on plates.
5. Serve sauce on the side. Each person can prepare his/her own wraps and dip in sauce or spread sauce within the lettuce wraps.

Recipe supplied by:

Newport Beach Brewing Co.
2920 Newport Blvd.
Newport Beach, CA 92663
(949) 675-8449

MUSHROOM CHICKEN ♨

Nutrition Information per Serving:

✓✓ CALORIES: Excellent Choice (175)   ✓✓ CHOLESTEROL: Excellent Choice (60 mg)
✓✓ FAT: Excellent Choice (2 g)   ✓✓ SODIUM: Excellent Choice (145 mg)
PROTEIN: 26 g, CARBOHYDRATE: 12 g, FIBER: 2 g

This nutrition analysis corresponds to the recipe below. The restaurant version may differ.

Ingredients (2 servings):

7 oz. white meat chicken, diced
1 carrot, cut (½ cup)
1 small zucchini, cut (½ cup)
6 oz. sliced mushrooms (2 cups)
1 green onion, chopped
2 Tbs. white cooking wine

¹/₃ cup chicken broth (no salt added)
pinch each, garlic & ginger
dash white pepper
1 Tbs. corn starch
1 Tbs. water
drop sesame oil

Directions:

1. Blanch or steam chicken, carrots, zucchini, and mushrooms, and set aside.
2. In sauté pan, combine green onion, wine, broth, garlic, ginger and pepper and heat until almost boiling.
3. Mix cornstarch with water.
4. Add chicken-vegetable mix and cornstarch mix to sauté pan and cook 1 to 2 minutes until cornstarch is thickened.
5. Add drop of sesame oil for flavor.
6. Serving suggestion: serve with rice or noodles (not included in analysis).

Recipe supplied by:

Pick Up Stix

San Diego area locations: Carlsbad, Carmel Mountain Ranch, Chula Vista, Clairemont Mesa, Del Mar, El Cajon, Encinitas, Escondido, Hillcrest, La Jolla, La Mesa, Mira Mesa, Mission Valley, Murphy Canyon, Pacific Beach, Point Loma, Scripps Ranch, Torrey Highlands, and Vista. Please visit www.pickupstix.com.

♨ at least 2 fruit/vegetable servings

POLLO A LA PLANCHA

Ingredients (2 servings):

2 skinless chicken breasts, 7 oz. each
¼ cup lemon juice
1 small brown onion, cut into wedges
4 cloves minced garlic

2 Tbs. olive oil
pinch of fresh ground pepper
salt to taste (not included in analysis)

Directions:

1. Pound chicken breasts to about half an inch in thickness and as even as possible.
2. Pour lemon juice over the chicken breast, as evenly as possible.
3. Hand rub chicken with garlic.
4. Add salt and pepper as desired (salt not included in analysis).
5. Place olive oil in skillet and bring up to medium heat.
6. Place chicken breast in pan for about 1 to 2 minutes on each side (or until done), along with onions, so that they contribute taste to the chicken breasts.
7. Serve with beans and/or fresh vegetables (not included in analysis).

Recipe supplied by:

Andre's Restaurant
1235 Morena Blvd.
San Diego, CA 92110
(619) 275-4114

BASIL PASTA PRIMAVERA ☺

Tri-colored rotelli pasta sautéed with extra virgin olive oil, seasonal veggies, fresh basil, garlic, parmesan cheese and topped with chopped tomatoes.

Nutrition Information per Serving:

✓ CALORIES: Good Choice (530)   ✓✓ CHOLESTEROL: Excellent Choice (10 mg)
✓✓ FAT: Excellent Choice (8 g)   ✓✓ SODIUM: Excellent Choice (285 mg)
PROTEIN: 23 g, CARBOHYDRATE: 91 g, FIBER: 9 g

This nutrition analysis corresponds to the recipe below. The restaurant version may differ.

Ingredients (4 servings):

1 lb. tri-color rotelli pasta, dry
2 cups broccoli, chopped
2 cups cauliflower, chopped
1 red bell pepper, chopped
1 green bell pepper, chopped
½ Tbs. olive oil

1 bunch basil, chopped
¼ cup white wine
4 cloves garlic, minced
2 tomatoes, chopped
½ cup parmesan cheese

Directions:

1. Cook pasta according to package directions and set aside.
2. Steam vegetables (feel free to substitute any other favorite veggies).
3. Heat oil in a large pan. Add garlic and sauté for a few seconds.
4. Add cooked pasta, chopped basil, steamed vegetables and chopped tomatoes.
5. Sauté, stirring occasionally for a few minutes (until thoroughly mixed and heated).
6. Serve in 4 large serving bowls.
7. Sprinkle each dish with 2 Tbs. parmesan cheese.

Recipes

Recipe supplied by:

Ki's Restaurant & Juice Bar
2591 South Coast Hwy. 101
Cardiff, CA 92007
(760) 436-5236

☺ at least 2 fruit/vegetable servings

Capellini al Pomodoro Fresco

Ingredients (4 servings):

12 oz. capellini pasta (dry weight)
1 lb. fresh ripe Roma tomatoes
¼ cup olive oil
4 cloves garlic, thinly sliced
½ cup chopped fresh basil leaves

⅛ tsp. pepper
salt to taste (not included in analysis)
grated parmesan or romano cheese
   (optional, not included in analysis)

Directions:

1. Remove skins from tomatoes by piercing with a paring knife on the tip and then putting in boiling water for 15 to 20 seconds. Drain, peel and dice the tomatoes and set aside.
2. Cook the pasta according to package instructions.
3. While pasta is cooking, sauté the garlic, tomatoes, and basil over medium heat until almost cooked. Add pepper. Add salt to taste (optional, not included in analysis).
4. When the pasta is cooked "al dente," rinse, drain and place back in cooking pan.
5. Add the tomato mix, toss well, and serve.
6. Sprinkle with grated cheese (optional, not included in analysis).

Recipe supplied by:

Pane e Vino
240 S. Brea Blvd.
Brea, CA 92821
(714) 256-7779
www.panevino.biz

As seen on KFMB-TV

LINGUINI WITH PESTO SHRIMP 🍎

Nutrition Information per Serving:

✓ CALORIES: Good Choice (650)   ✓ CHOLESTEROL: Good Choice (145mg)
✓ FAT: Good Choice (25 g)   ✓ SODIUM: Excellent Choice (425 mg)
PROTEIN: 34 g, CARBOHYDRATE: 70 g, FIBER: 5 g
This nutrition analysis corresponds to the recipe below. The restaurant version may differ.

Ingredients (2 servings):

3 oz. linguini pasta (dry weight)
2 tsp. salted butter
6 oz. shrimp, peeled & de-veined
4 tsp. pignoli (pine) nuts
2 tsp. garlic

16 oz. pesto
2 Tbs. sun-dried tomatoes
Basil for garnish
Optional garnish: Fresh parmesan
    cheese (not included in analysis)

Directions:

1. Prepare linguini according to package instructions.
2. Sauté shrimp in butter.
3. Add pine nuts and garlic and sauté until browned.
4. Add the pesto and sun-dried tomatoes.
5. Garnish with fresh parmesan cheese (not included in analysis) and basil.

Recipe supplied by:

PIZZA NOVA

Pizza Nova

Hillcrest: 3955 Fifth Ave. (Village Hillcrest)   (619) 296-6682
Point Loma: 5050 N. Harbor Dr. (on the bay)   (619) 226-0268
Solana Beach: 945 Lomas Santa Fe Dr.   (858) 259-0666

🍎 at least 2 fruit/vegetable servings

Recipes

As seen on KFMB-TV

SPAGHETTI ALLE VONGOLE VERACI

(with fresh Manila clams).

Nutrition Information per Serving:

✓ CALORIES: Good Choice (605)   ✓ CHOLESTEROL: Good Choice (85 mg)
✓✓ FAT: Excellent Choice (14 g)♥   ✓ SODIUM: Good Choice (410 mg)
PROTEIN: 43 g, CARBOHYDRATE: 69 g, FIBER: 4 g

This nutrition analysis corresponds to the recipe below. The restaurant version may differ.

♥ primarily unsaturated fat

Ingredients (4 servings):

6 cups cooked spaghetti pasta (9 oz. dry)   splash of vodka
1½ Tbs. olive oil   1 cup white wine
3 cloves garlic, chopped   6 Tbs. (³/₈ cup) clam juice
up to 2 tsp. red chili flakes (optional to taste)   fresh ground pepper to taste
36 oz. (2 lb. 4 oz.) Manila clams   ²/₃ cup parsley, fresh chopped

Directions:

1. Cook pasta according to instructions.
2. In a medium size frying pan, bring the extra virgin olive oil to high temperature.
3. Add chopped garlic cloves and red chili flakes.
4. Add the fresh clams (in the shell) to the oil and garlic, toss, and cook for about 1 minute.
5. Add vodka and flambé till the flames extinguish.
6. Add white wine, clam juice, and freshly ground pepper.
7. Cook on high heat for about 4 minutes, or until sauce is reduced.
8. Add fresh chopped parsley.
9. Toss the spaghetti with the sauce in the pan for about 1 minute.

Recipe supplied by:

TRATTORIA LA STRADA
CUCINA TOSCANA

Trattoria La Strada
702 Fifth Ave.
San Diego, CA 92101
(619) 238-3400
www.trattorialastrada.com

☼ at least 2 fruit/vegetable servings

BUTTERNUT SQUASH ♨

Roasted Mediterranean vegetables with brown rice and wilted greens in a baked butternut squash.

Nutrition Information per Serving:†

✓✓ CALORIES: Excellent Choice (200)   ✓✓ CHOLESTEROL: Excellent Choice 0 mg)
✓✓ FAT: Excellent Choice (7 g)♥   ✓✓ SODIUM: Excellent Choice (15 mg)
PROTEIN: 4 g, CARBOHYDRATE: 34 g, FIBER: 2 g

This nutrition analysis corresponds to the recipe below. The restaurant version may differ.
† Side dish guidelines are ¹/3 of entrée guidelines

Ingredients (4 servings):

2 lbs. butternut squash (2 small squash)
¼ zucchini, grilled
2 large slices eggplant, grilled
2 cups chopped seasonal vegetables

1½ cups field greens, steamed
2 Tbs. oil
²/₃ cup cooked brown rice

Directions:

1. Prepare rice according to package directions.
2. Cut butternut squash in half. Fill baking dish with about 1 inch of water. Place squash in baking dish (seed side into water). Bake at 400° until squash is soft (about 40 minutes).
3. Slice zucchini and eggplant, brush with oil and grill until done (or sauté in oil or grill without added oil, if preferred). After grilling, dice into small pieces and add vegetables to the rice.
4. Steam seasonal vegetables.
5. Wilt field greens (in steamer or microwave).
6. After butternut squash has finished baking, remove seeds. Stuff rice in the center of the butternut squash.
7. Place squash on plate. Place steamed vegetables on one side of squash and the wilted greens on the other side. Enjoy!

Recipe supplied by:

Cafe Santorini
64 W. Union Street
Pasadena, CA 91103
(626) 564-4200
www.cafesantorini.com

♨ at least 1 fruit/vegetable serving for side dishes

GRILLED HERBED VEGETABLES 🍎

Nutrition Information per Serving:

✓✓ CALORIES: Excellent Choice (127)   ✓✓ CHOLESTEROL: Excellent Choice (0 mg)
✓✓ FAT: Excellent Choice (7 g)♥   ✓✓ SODIUM: Excellent Choice (300 mg)
PROTEIN: 3 g, CARBOHYDRATE: 15 g, FIBER: 5 g

This nutrition analysis corresponds to the recipe below. The restaurant version may differ.

♥primarily unsaturated fat

Ingredients (2 servings):

1 Tbs. olive oil
1 fresh garlic clove
¼ tsp. salt
1 tsp. ground basil leaves
½ cup fresh cubed eggplant
½ cup fresh crookneck squash slices

½ cup fresh zucchini squash slices
½ cup fresh snap green peas
½ cup fresh chopped red onion
½ cup fresh sliced sweet green bell pepper
½ cup fresh sliced sweet red bell pepper
½ cup fresh sliced sweet yellow bell pepper

Directions:

1. In a medium-sized mixing bowl combine the olive oil, garlic, basil, and salt.
2. Add vegetables to oil mixture, tossing to coat.
3. Spoon vegetable mixture onto a 24x12-inch piece of heavy foil.
4. Bring opposite edges of foil together; seal tightly with a double fold. Fold in remaining ends to completely enclose vegetables, leaving a little space for steam to build.
5. Grill vegetable packet on a grill rack directly over medium-hot coals about 20 minutes or until tender, turning the packet over halfway through cooking time.

Recipe supplied by:

Henry's Farmers Market

12 locations in San Diego.
Visit www.henrysmarkets.com or
call (800) 494-9453 for the one nearest you.

🍎 at least 2 fruit/vegetable servings

KASHK-E BADEMJAN (APPETIZER)

Eggplant with yogurt.

Recipes

Nutrition Information per Serving:†

✓ CALORIES: Good Choice (215)   ✓✓ CHOLESTEROL: Excellent Choice (1 mg)
✓ FAT: Good Choice (8 g)♥   ✓ SODIUM: Good Choice (340 mg)
PROTEIN: 7 g, CARBOHYDRATE: 34 g, FIBER 10 g

This nutrition analysis corresponds to the recipe below. The restaurant version may differ.
† Side dish guidelines are ¹/3 of entrée guidelines   ♥ primarily unsaturated fat

Ingredients (4 servings):

3 medium eggplants
2 large yellow onions, peeled & sliced
5 cloves garlic, peeled and crushed
2 Tbs. dried mint flakes
1 tsp. turmeric

½ tsp. salt
¼ tsp. freshly ground black pepper
2 Tbs. extra virgin olive oil
½ cup plain non-fat yogurt

Directions:

1. Peel eggplants and cut into 4-6 slices each.
2. Brown the eggplant in a non-stick pan with 1 Tbs. olive oil. Remove from pan.
3. Brown the onions and garlic in 1 Tbs. oil. Add the turmeric, mint, salt and pepper.
4. Place the sliced eggplant on plates.
5. Top with yogurt and the onion/garlic/mint mixture.

Recipe supplied by:

FINE PERSIAN CUISINE

Bandar Fine Persian Cuisine
825 4ᵗʰ Ave.
San Diego, CA 92101
(619) 238-0101

at least 1 fruit/vegetable serving for side dishes

As seen on KFMB-TV

ROASTED VEGETABLE TERRINE 🍎

Nutrition Information per Serving:†

✓✓ CALORIES: Excellent Choice (135)   ✓✓ CHOLESTEROL: Excellent Choice (<5 mg)
✓ FAT: Good Choice (8 g)   ✓ SODIUM: Good Choice (115 mg)
PROTEIN: 4 g, CARBOHYDRATE: 14 g, FIBER: 5 g

This nutrition analysis corresponds to the recipe below. The restaurant version may differ.

† Side dish guidelines are ¹/₃ of entrée guidelines

Ingredients (8 servings):

1 eggplant
1 onion
1 red bell pepper
1 green bell pepper
1 yellow bell pepper
1 zucchini squash

1 yellow summer squash
¼ cup olive oil
1 cup chickpeas (canned garbanzos, drained)
½ cup fresh basil
¼ cup parmesan cheese
salt & pepper to taste
(not included in analysis)

Directions:

1. Cut eggplant and onion into ¼-inch slices.
2. Cut peppers into ½-inch strips and remove seeds.
3. Cut zucchini and squash lengthwise into ¼-inch thick strips.
4. Coat all prepped vegetables lightly in olive oil and layout on sheet pan.
5. If desired, sprinkle with salt (not included in analysis) and pepper.
6. Roast vegetables in 400-degree oven for 10 minutes. Set aside to cool.
7. Combine chickpeas, basil, parmesan, salt & pepper (if desired, not included in analysis) in blender & puree.

To assemble:
1. Line terrine or loaf pan(s) with plastic wrap. Layer the ingredients into the terrine or loaf pan(s) in the following order: red pepper, eggplant, onion, chickpea puree, yellow pepper, zucchini, yellow squash, green pepper.
2. Compress layers and seal with plastic wrap. Refrigerate for at least four hours.

To serve:
1. Remove terrine from pan and carefully remove plastic wrap. Slice into ¾-inch sections.
2. Serve as an hors d'oeuvre or as the salad course for a meal.

Recipe supplied by:

Trellises Garden Grille
Town and Country Hotel
500 Hotel Circle North
(619) 291-7131

170 *Healthy Dining in San Diego*   🍎 at least 1 fruit/vegetable serving for side dish

SALSA FRESCA 🍎

Recipe by Ralph Rubio, but not served in Rubio's restaurants.

Nutrition Information per Cup: †
✓✓ CALORIES: Excellent Choice (45)   ✓✓ CHOLESTEROL: Excellent Choice (0 mg)
✓✓ FAT: Excellent Choice (1 g)♥   ✓✓ SODIUM: Excellent Choice (15 mg)
PROTEIN: 2 g, CARBOHYDRATE: 10 g, FIBER: 2 g

♥primarily unsaturated fat   † Side dish guidelines are ¹/3 of entrée guidelines

Ingredients (Makes approx. 4 cups):

3 cups fresh chopped red tomatoes
½ cup fresh chopped sweet onion
2 Tbs. diced jalapeno peppers

¾ cups fresh chopped cilantro
4 Tbs. lime juice
1 tsp. ground cumin

Directions:

1. Rinse, core, and chop tomatoes.
2. Cut ends off of onions, peel, and chop.
3. Rinse jalapeños.
4. Break ends off all jalapeños and finely dice.
5. Rinse and chop cilantro.
6. Add lime juice and cumin.
7. Mix well.

Recipe supplied by Ralph Rubio of Rubio's Restaurants:

Rubio's San Diego area locations:

Carlsbad, Carmel Mountain Ranch, Chula Vista, College Grove, Coronado, Del Mar, Eastlake, El Cajon, Encinitas, Escondido, Fashion Valley, Grossmont Center, Kearny Mesa, La Jolla, Mira Mesa, Mission Bay, Mission Gorge, Mission Valley, Oceanside, Pacific Beach, Parkway Plaza, Point Loma, Poway, Ramona, Rancho Bernardo, Rancho Del Rey, Rancho San Diego, San Marcos, Scripps Ranch, SDSU, Solana Beach, Torrey Highlands, UCSD, UTC, Viejas, and Vista.

Visit rubios.com for a map to your local Rubio's.

🍎 at least 1 fruit/vegetable serving for side dishes

As seen on KFMB-TV

SINGAPORE CURRY 🍎

Nutrition Information per Serving:

✓✓ CALORIES: Excellent Choice (330)   ✓✓ CHOLESTEROL: Excellent Choice (0 mg)
✓✓ FAT: Excellent Choice (9 g) ♥   ✓ SODIUM: Good Choice (360 mg)
PROTEIN: 9 g, CARBOHYDRATE: 58 g, FIBER: 12 g

This nutrition analysis corresponds to the recipe below. The restaurant version may differ.

♥ primarily unsaturated fat

Ingredients (4 servings):

2 Tbs. olive oil
1 cup chopped onion
1 Tbs. fresh garlic
¼ cup curry powder (1 oz.)
1-2 tsp. Sambal chili paste
3 cups water
2 Tbs. brown sugar

1½ cups vegetable broth and/or liquid from canned garbanzos
3 cups carrots, diced
florets from 1 cauliflower
10 oz. chickpeas (canned garbanzos, drained)
1 lb. potatoes, diced

Directions:

1. Sauté onions with 1 Tbs. oil on medium-low heat until caramelized, about 20 – 40 minutes. Set aside.
2. Heat 1 Tbs. oil and sauté garlic for about a minute.
3. Add in curry powder and chili paste and sauté for another minute.
4. Place onions, garlic and spices from above, water, brown sugar and vegetable broth in a blender. Blend until smooth.
5. Put the sauce into a stockpot and bring to a low boil.
6. Add remaining vegetables and reduce heat to medium-low.
7. Cook for 45 – 60 minutes, stirring occasionally.
8. Serve with rice (not included in analysis).

Recipe supplied by:

World Curry
1433 Garnet Ave.
San Diego, CA 92109
(858) 270-9238

🍎 at least 2 fruit/vegetable servings

SPICY ROASTED EGGPLANT
WITH SESAME & HONEY 🍎

Ingredients (4-6 servings):

2 medium eggplants, peeled & diced
    into ¾ inch cubes (about 4 cups)
¹/₈ cup white or red miso
¾ cup Roasted Sesame-Honey Dressing

½ tsp. salt
¼ tsp. freshly ground pepper
1 large red pepper, seeded & diced
½ cup fresh chopped cilantro

Roasted Sesame-Honey Dressing

¹/₈ cup tamari
¼ cup water
4 cloves garlic, minced (2 tsp.)
¹/₈ cup ginger, fresh grated (2" piece)
1 cup canned pineapple juice

¹/₈ cup teriyaki sauce
2 tsp. toasted sesame oil
¼ cup white sesame seeds
¼ cup cider vinegar
3 Tbs. honey
½ tsp. Szechwan sauce

Directions:

1. Preheat oven to 450°. Place cubed eggplant in a large bowl.
2. Mix dressing ingredients well. In a small bowl, whisk the miso with ¾ cup dressing until well blended. Save remaining dressing for another meal or extra.
3. Add the miso mixture to the eggplant along with the salt and pepper. Toss lightly, and let marinate at room temperature for about 20 minutes.
4. Drain off any excess liquid. Place the eggplant in a large baking pan. Roast for 15-20 minutes, or until edges of the eggplant have browned & eggplant is slightly firm, not mushy.
5. Remove & cool it in the pan. Place the eggplant in a large bowl. Gently mix in the red pepper & cilantro.
   Optional: Add more dressing to taste (not included in analysis).

Recipe from The Whole Foods Market Cookbook:

Whole Foods Market

711 University Ave., San Diego, CA 92103 (619) 294-2800
8825 Villa La Jolla Dr., La Jolla, CA 92037 (858) 642-6700

🍎 at least 1 fruit/vegetable servings for side dishes

SPICY TOFU WITH FRESH BASIL 🍎

Nutrition Information per Serving:

✓✓ CALORIES: Excellent Choice (385)   ✓✓ CHOLESTEROL: Excellent Choice (0 mg)
✓✓ FAT: Excellent Choice (13 g)♥   ✓✓ SODIUM: Moderate (745 mg)*
PROTEIN: 22 g, CARBOHYDRATES: 47 mg, FIBER: 3 g

This nutrition analysis corresponds to the recipe below. The restaurant version may differ.
♥primarily unsaturated fat   *without optional salt

Ingredients (2 servings):

½ cup rice
14 oz. firm tofu, drained
3 tsp. cooking oil
1–2 tsp. chopped garlic
½ medium onion, peeled and sliced
8 oz. fresh mushrooms, sliced
1 Tbs. soy sauce

1 Tbs. water
1–2 tsp. sambal chili sauce
salt to taste (optional, not in analysis)
½ cup coarsely chopped cinnamon
    basil (Thai basil)
1 tsp. chopped green onion

Directions:

1. Steam rice or cook according to package instructions.
2. Cut tofu into ¼-inch slices.
3. Heat 1 tsp. oil in a nonstick skillet over medium high heat and cook tofu about 2 minutes on each side.
4. In a nonstick wok, heat the remaining 2 tsp. oil over high heat. Sauté the onion for 1 to 2 minutes; add garlic, prepared tofu, and mushrooms. Cook for 2 minutes.
5. Add soy sauce, chili sauce, salt (optional) and water. Cook another minute.
6. Remove from heat. Add basil and green onion. Serve with steamed rice.

Recipe supplied by:

rice Jones
3687 Fifth Avenue, San Diego, CA 92103
(619) 291-1887

🍎 at least 2 fruit/vegetable servings

THAI TOFU STIR FRY 🍎

Nutrition Information per Serving:

✓ CALORIES: Good Choice (500) ✓✓ CHOLESTEROL: Excellent Choice (0 mg)
   FAT: Moderate (26 g)   SODIUM: Moderate (625 mg)
   PROTEIN: 20 g, CARBOHYDRATE: 54 g, FIBER: 7 g
This nutrition analysis corresponds to the recipe below. The restaurant version may differ.

Ingredients (4 servings):

12 oz. firm tofu, cubed & drained   1 stalk & head broccoli (8 oz.), chopped
4 carrots, short cut   1 medium zucchini, moon shape cut
              1 pound sticky (sweet) rice (approx. 1 cup uncooked)
                      4 cups spinach, cleaned well
    Red cabbage and sesame seeds for garnish (not included in analysis)

Ponzu Sauce

1 1/3 Tbs. soy sauce   1/3 cup sliced green onions
2 2/3 Tbs. rice vinegar   1/4 cup chopped cilantro
1/2 Tbs. minced ginger   1 tsp. sesame oil
1/2 tsp. minced garlic   1 1/4 Tbs. honey
1/2 tsp. red chili flakes

Spicy Peanut Sauce

1 cup coconut milk   1/2 Tbs. sambal chili paste
2 Tbs. peanut butter

Directions:

1. Prepare sticky rice according to package.
2. Heat sesame oil in sauté pan until hot.
3. Sauté tofu for about 2-3 minutes or until golden.
4. Add ingredients for Ponzu Sauce along with carrots, zucchini, and broccoli
   and cook until vegetables are tender.
5. Add Spicy Peanut Sauce.
6. Season with salt and pepper, if desired (optional, not included in analysis).
7. Serve with sticky rice and arrange spinach around plate.
8. Garnish with red cabbage and sesame seeds.

Recipe supplied by:

Wild Note Cafe
43 South Cedros Ave.
Solana Beach, CA 92075
(858) 720-9000

🍎 at least 2 fruit/vegetable servings

Recipes

VEGETABLE BIRYANI 🍎

Vegetables sautéed with onions and bell peppers, cooked with basmati rice, topped with raisins and nuts. This vegetarian dish is served hot and can be accompanied with salad, chutney and raita of your choice (not included in analysis).

Nutrition Information per Serving:

✓✓ CALORIES: Excellent Choice (280) ✓✓ CHOLESTEROL: Excellent Choice (0 mg)
✓✓ FAT: Excellent Choice (8 g)♥ ✓✓ SODIUM: Excellent Choice (95 mg)
PROTEIN: 6 g, CARBOHYDRATE: 48 g, FIBER: 4 g
This nutrition analysis corresponds to the recipe below. The restaurant version may differ.

♥ primarily unsaturated fat

Ingredients (4 Servings):

1 cup basmati rice
1½ Tbs. vegetable oil
½ cup onion, chopped
1 tsp. garlic, minced
1 tsp. ginger, minced
⅛ tsp. salt (or to taste)
½ green chili, chopped
½ bell pepper, chopped

½ cup finely diced carrots
¾ cup broccoli crowns, chopped
¾ cup small cauliflower flowerets
2 tsp. curry paste#
1-4 tsp. garam masala#
1 cup chopped cilantro
¼ cup raisins
¼ cup nuts (cashews/almonds)

An Indian spice available at Indian and specialty stores and at Henry's Marketplace.

Directions:

1. Precook rice by boiling 1½ cups water with 1 cup basmati rice on low heat, until water is absorbed.
2. In large pot, heat oil and sauté onions, garlic, ginger, salt and chili.
3. Add vegetables and curry paste.
4. Add rice and let vegetables & rice cook together for about 2 to 5 minutes on low heat.
5. Add salt and garam masala to taste.
6. Top with cilantro, nuts and raisins.

Recipe supplied by:

Cafe India
Fine Indian Cuisine

Cafe India
3760-5 Sports Arena Blvd.
San Diego, CA 92109
(619) 224-7500

🍎 at least 2 fruit/vegetable servings

VEGGIE WRAPS 🍎

Crunchy veggies with hummus, wrapped in colorful tortillas.

Nutrition Information per Serving:

✓ CALORIES: Good Choice (590)   ✓✓ CHOLESTEROL: Excellent Choice (0 mg)
✓ FAT: Good Choice (25 g)♥   SODIUM: Moderate (965 mg)
        PROTEIN: 18 g, CARBOHYDRATE: 75 g, FIBER: 13 g

This nutrition analysis corresponds to the recipe below. The restaurant version may differ.

♥ primarily unsaturated fat

Ingredients (4 servings):

Hummus
1 ½ cups canned garbanzos
2 Tbs. tahini
1 Tbs. fresh lemon juice
1 garlic clove
3 Tbs. olive oil
pinch salt

Veggie Mix
6 cups arugula
2 cups bean sprouts
1/3 medium jicama, shredded
1/3 red bell pepper, chopped
1/3 green bell pepper, chopped
1 carrot, shredded
2/3 cup chopped cilantro

4 spinach tortillas (3.6 oz. each)
8 oz. alfalfa sprouts

Directions:
1. Blend hummus ingredients in a blender until smooth.
2. Divide ingredients between 4 tortillas and wrap.

Recipe supplied by:

"The Dr. Rodes/Brockton Villa House"
~ The La Jolla Historical Society ~ *circa 1894*

Brockton Villa Restaurant
1235 Coast Blvd.
La Jolla, CA 92037
(858) 454-7393

🍎 at least 2 fruit/vegetable servings

Recipes

WHOLE EARTH CASSEROLE 🍎

Spaghetti in marinara with onions, mushrooms, zucchini, green bell pepper, alfalfa sprouts, black olives and tomatoes, covered with cheese and oven baked.

Nutrition Information per Serving:

✓✓ CALORIES: Excellent Choice (395) ✓✓ CHOLESTEROL: Excellent Choice (15 mg)
✓ FAT: Good Choice (17 g)   SODIUM: Moderate (805 mg)##
PROTEIN: 15 g, CARBOHYDRATE: 49 g, FIBER: 5 g

This nutrition analysis corresponds to the recipe below. The restaurant version may differ.
Use low-salt marinara sauce for lower sodium value

Ingredients (4 servings):

6 oz. dry spaghetti (dry weight)
1 medium white onion, chopped
1 green bell pepper, chopped
1 medium zucchini, chopped
6 oz. fresh mushrooms, sliced

1 medium tomato, chopped
1/3 cup alfalfa sprouts
6 oz. black olives (15-20 large), chopped
26 oz. marinara sauce
4 oz. part skim milk mozzarella cheese

Directions:

1. Cook spaghetti according to directions. Rinse and drain.
2. Spray pan with non-stick spray. Sauté onion, bell pepper, zucchini, mushrooms and tomato. Add alfalfa sprouts and olives.
3. Mix vegetables, marinara sauce, and spaghetti together and place in baking dish.
4. Top with cheese and bake at 350° for 10 to 15 minutes until cheese melts.

Recipe supplied by:

Angie's Cuisine Italiano
14425 Newport Ave.
Tustin, CA 92780
(714) 832-3434

🍎 at least 2 fruit/vegetable servings

STRAWBERRY RHUBARB CREPES LEUCADIA

Nutrition Information per Serving:†

CALORIES: Moderate (270)   ✓ CHOLESTEROL: Good Choice (35 mg)
✓✓ FAT: Excellent Choice (4 g)   ✓ SODIUM: Good Choice (125 mg)
PROTEIN: 8 g, CARBOHYDRATE: 53 g, FIBER: 4 g

This nutrition analysis corresponds to the recipe below. The restaurant version may differ.

† Side dish guidelines are 1/3 of entrée guidelines

Ingredients (6 servings of 2 crepes each):

2 cups nonfat milk
1 cup white flour
2 large egg whites (raw)
1 medium whole egg (raw)
1 Tbs. vegetable oil
1 Tbs. fresh grated orange peel
1/8 tsp. salt
4 cups fresh diced rhubarb

2 Tbs. lemon juice
1/2 cup raspberries
1 Tbs. corn starch
1 vanilla bean
2/3 cup sugar
2 cups strawberries
1 Tbs. powdered sugar
(optional; not included in analysis)

Directions:

Crepes:

1. Put the first seven ingredients in a blender and blend until smooth.
2. Spray crepe pan or nonstick skillet with fat free pan spray and heat over medium flame until pan starts to smoke slightly. Pour enough crepe batter to thinly coat pan.
3. When edges of crepe appear firm, flip and cook until center of crepe is fully cooked.
4. Repeat until all crepes are done.

Filling:

1. Place the rhubarb, lemon juice, raspberries and cornstarch in a heavy saucepan.
2. Split and scrape vanilla bean and add to pot. Pour sugar over contents and let stand for 15 minutes, i.e., until juices begin to extract from rhubarb.
3. Bring mixture to a boil over high heat, stirring constantly. Reduce heat to low, cover and simmer, stirring occasionally, until rhubarb is tender & liquid is thickened, about 7-10 minutes.
4. Remove from heat and fold in strawberries.
5. To assemble: fold crepes into quarters and place 2 on a plate. Spoon strawberry-rhubarb mixture over crepes. Dust with powdered sugar (optional).

Recipe supplied by Chef Nikki Schaeffer of:

Pizzeria & Italian Restaurant

Leucadia Pizzeria:
Encinitas: 315 S. Coast Hwy. 101   (760) 942-2222
La Jolla/UTC: 7748 Regents Rd   (858) 597-2222
Rancho Santa Fe: 16085 San Dieguito Rd.   (858) 759-2222
Carmel Mt. Ranch: 12075 Carmel Mtn. Rd.   (858) 675-2222

at least 1 fruit/vegetable serving for side dish

Recipes

Part IV

Health Resource Guide

It's probably easier to live a more healthful lifestyle in Southern California than anywhere in the country. The agreeable climate, gentle pace, health-conscious mindset, and accessibility to health-oriented products and services all promote a healthier way of life.

Healthful living includes more than healthy dining. So in the Health Resource Guide that follows, you'll find an array of "tools" to further support your healthful lifestyle. We think you'll find this guide useful, informative and interesting and recognize the Health Resource Guide companies and organizations for their contribution to a healthier community.

Index

1.	American Cancer Society	182
2.	American Council on Exercise	183
3.	American Diabetes Association	184
4.	American Heart Association	185
5.	California 5-A-Day for Better Health Campaign	186
6.	Henry's Farmers Market	187
7.	San Diego County Certified Farmers' Markets	188
8.	San Diego Dietetic Association	189
9.	San Diego Nutrition Network	190
10.	Specialty Produce	191
11.	Taking Control of Your Diabetes (TCOYD)	192
12.	YMCA	193

Resources

AMERICAN CANCER SOCIETY

NUTRITION, EXERCISE & CANCER

1.800.ACS.2345
www.cancer.org

Hope.Progress.Answers.

THE BASICS

Poor diet and physical inactivity may be responsible for one of every three cancer deaths. The numbers of people overweight and obese have increased dramatically in California: About 57% were overweight or obese in 2003, compared to 38% in 1984. The number of teenagers who are overweight is about 29%; that's almost one-third of all teens. In general, men are more likely to be overweight than women, though women are more likely to be obese.

The American Cancer Society recommends eating at least five servings of fruits and vegetables each day. Few Californians meet this recommendation. In general, people who eat fast food on a regular basis eat fewer fruits and vegetables.

Regular physical activity is also strongly recommended. In 2003, only one of every three California adults reported having engaged in physical activity for 30 minutes or more at least five times a week.

NUTRITION GUIDELINES

- Eat five or more servings of fruits and vegetables each day. Choose whole grains in preference to processed grains.

- Limit your consumption of red meats, especially those processed and high in fat.

- Adults should engage in at least moderate activity for 30 minutes or more on five or more days of the week; Children and teens at least 60 minutes.

- Stay within your healthy weight range. Balance caloric intake with physical activity.

- If you drink alcoholic beverages, limit consumption.

- Public, private and community organizations should work to create social and physical environments that support the adoption and maintenance of healthful nutrition and physical activity behaviors.

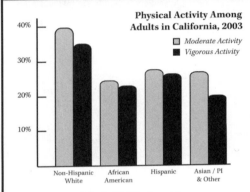

Less Than 1/2 of Californians are Exercising Regularly

Physical Activity Among Adults in California, 2003

Moderate Activity
Vigorous Activity

Non-Hispanic White / African American / Hispanic / Asian / PI & Other

Note: Data are age-adjusted to the 1990 California population
Source: California Behavioral Risk Study
Prepared by the California Department of Health Services, Cancer Surveillance Section

1/3 OF CANCER DEATHS MAY BE CAUSED BY POOR DIET & INACTIVITY

Most Californians are Overweight

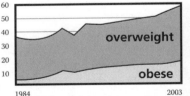

Percentage of Overweight Californians is On the Rise

57.3%
2003

38%
1984

Many Californians are not Physically Active

In 2003, only **one** out of **three** California adults reported being engaged in moderate physical activity for 30 minutes or more at least five times a week.

Source: American Cancer Society and California Cancer Registry

Think of her as an exercise machine with hair.

ACE CERTIFIED

ACE Certified: The Mark of Quality
Look for the ACE symbol of excellence
in fitness training and education.
For more information, visit our website:
www.ACEfitness.org

You don't have to join a gym to get a workout. Recent studies show that every hour of moderate physical activity can add two hours to your life. So there's no need to radically alter your exercise habits to improve your health, and live longer! Just enjoy everyday activities like walking the dog. Washing the car. Cutting the grass. Playing golf. Or just taking the stairs instead of the elevator.

Don't sweat it if spinning classes aren't your style. Just get out and do something physical each day. You'll feel better, and live longer. Besides, the stair climber at the gym won't fetch your newspaper.

A Public Service Message brought to you by the American Council on Exercise,
a not-for-profit organization committed to the promotion of safe and effective exercise.

America's Authority on Fitness™

4851 PARAMOUNT DRIVE, SAN DIEGO, CA 92123 USA

(800) 825-3636 X653 | WWW.ACEFITNESS.ORG

AMERICAN DIABETES ASSOCIATION

San Diego Office:
225 Broadway, Suite 1120
San Diego, CA 92101
(619) 234-9897 x7432
Matt Bean

American Diabetes Association.
Cure • Care • Commitment®

The American Diabetes Association is the nation's leading nonprofit health organization providing diabetes research, information and advocacy. The mission of the organization is to "prevent and cure diabetes, and to improve the lives of all people affected by diabetes." To fulfill this mission, the American Diabetes Association funds research, publishes scientific findings, and provides information, education programs and other services to people with diabetes, their families, health care professionals, and the public.

The 1-800-DIABETES program is the cornerstone of the Association's information programs. 1-800-DIABETES is a toll-free help line for people who have questions and concerns about diabetes. Through 1-800-DIABETES, people can request information and literature about diabetes-related topics, including exercise, nutrition and self-management.

Check out our website! www.diabetes.org

Call 1-800-DIABETES

For the most *up-to-date* information related to diabetes, including information about:

- Daily Health Maintenance
- Diet and Nutrition
- Long-term Complications
- Exercise
- And More

AMERICAN HEART ASSOCIATION

American Heart Association
9404 Genesee Ave., Suite 240
La Jolla, CA 92037
(858) 410-3850

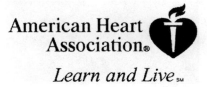

The American Heart Association's Dietary Guidelines: At-A-Glance

Achieve an overall healthy eating pattern.
- Choose an overall balanced diet with foods from all major food groups, emphasizing fruits, vegetables and grains.
- Consume a variety of fruits, vegetables and grain products:
  - At least 5 daily servings of fruits and vegetables.
  - At least 6 daily servings of grain products, including whole grains.
- Include fat-free and low-fat dairy products, fish, legumes, poultry and lean meats.
- Eat at least two servings of fish per week.

Achieve a healthy body weight.
- Maintain a level of physical activity that achieves fitness and balances energy expenditure with caloric intake; for weight reduction, expenditure should exceed intake.
- Limit foods that are high in calories and/or low in nutritional quality, including those with a high amount of added sugar.

Achieve a desirable cholesterol level.
- Limit foods with a high content of saturated fat and cholesterol. Substitute with grains and unsaturated fat from vegetables, fish, legumes and nuts.
- Limit cholesterol to 300 milligrams (mg) a day for the general population, and 200 mg a day for those with heart disease or its risk factors.
- Limit *trans* fatty acids. Trans fatty acids are found in foods containing partially hydrogenated vegetable oils, such as packaged cookies, crackers and other baked goods; commercially prepared fried foods and some margarines.

Achieve a desirable blood pressure level.
- Limit salt intake to less than 6 grams (2,400 mg sodium) per day, slightly more than one teaspoon a day.
- If you drink, limit alcohol consumption to no more than one drink per day for women and two drinks per day for men.

The American Heart Association is the nation's largest voluntary health agency that fights heart disease and stroke through lifesaving research and education. For more information on education, volunteering or donations, call your local San Diego office at (858) 410-3850 or visit our web site at www.americanheart.org.

CALIFORNIA 5 A DAY CAMPAIGN
601 N. 7th Street, P.O. Box 942732, MS-662
Sacramento, CA 94234-7320

When making healthy dining decisions, think color! A variety of colorful fruits and vegetables provide the vitamins, minerals and fiber your body needs to maintain good health and high energy. Plus, eating fruits and vegetables can protect against the effects of aging and reduce the risk of cancer and heart disease.

Through outreach and educational activities, the *California 5 a Day—for Better Health! Campaign* empowers Californians to consume fruits and vegetables every day and be physically active at least 30 minutes a day for adults and 60 minutes a day for children.

So next time you enjoy a meal out with friends or family, remember to put more color in your life by reaching for nature's answer to better health.

For more information about the California 5 a Day Campaign, visit www.ca5aday.com or call 1-888-EAT-FIVE

HENRY'S FARMERS MARKET

12 locations in San Diego.
Visit www.henrysmarkets.com or call 800-494-9453 for the one nearest you.

Henry's is known for its farm-fresh produce at great prices, but did you know that Henry's also carries bulk-bin items like healthy cereals, beans and pastas? Try our all-natural beef with no added chemicals or artificial ingredients. We also carry the finest poultry and the freshest seafood in town. Henry's own sprouted breads are delivered fresh daily! We also have one of Southern California's largest selections of natural vitamins and supplements, natural cosmetics and much more, like…

* Save an additional 10% off retail on all major brands of vitamins and supplements, herbs, natural cosmetics, body care products and books when you purchase $100 or more of these items.

* Wednesday's are double ad days. **Double the number of items on sale.**

* Ad items can be viewed by going to our web site: www.henrysmarkets.com

* **20** locations to serve you in San Diego, Orange, and San Bernardino Counties

In a nutshell, Henry's is quality products, great prices friendly and knowledgeable people — all for you!

Trust
Henry's Farmers Market
For Life™

Resources

SAN DIEGO COUNTY
CERTIFIED FARMERS' MARKETS

Take a bite of San Diego's fresh produce! More than 6,000 farmers work to make agriculture a billion-dollar industry in San Diego County. Many of our county's growers operate small family farms, with 65% harvesting nine acres or less. They have developed a reputation for quality, high-value specialty crops. Visiting one of the Farmers' Markets in San Diego County allows you to experience agriculture. These Farmers' Markets are certified by the State, ensuring that the produce is being sold by the grower, is grown in California, and meets all California quality standards. These criteria ensure that you receive the freshest produce for the right price. For more information, including updates on times and places, please visit the San Diego Farm Bureau's website at www.sdfarmbureau.org.

CERTIFIED FARMERS' MARKETS SCHEDULE

Tuesday:
Coronado: 2:30–6 pm, Corner of 1st & B Sts. (Old Ferry Landing)
Escondido: 2–6 pm, Grand Ave. between Broadway and Kalmia St.
UCSD/La Jolla: 10 am–2 pm (Sept.–June), UCSD Price Ctr., Lyman Lane & Library Walk

Wednesday:
Carlsbad: 2– 5 pm, Roosevelt St. between Grand Ave. & Carlsbad Village Dr.
Ocean Beach: 4–7 pm (Winter), 4–8 pm (Sum.), Newport Ave. between Cable & Bacon Sts.

Thursday:
Chula Vista: 3–6:30 pm (Winter), 3–7 pm (Summer), 3rd Ave. & Center St.
El Cajon Marketplace: 3–6 pm (7 pm in summer) Orange Ave. & Main St.
North Park: 4–7 pm, North Park Way and Granada
Oceanside: 9 am–12:30 pm, Pier View Way between Coast Hwy. & Ditmar St.
San Diego (Horton Plaza): 11 am–3 pm (March to mid-Oct.), 225 Broadway

Friday:
Chula Vista (Eastlake): 3–7 pm, 1360 Eastlake Parkway
La Mesa: 3–6 pm, 8300 block of Allison Ave. (East of Spring St.)
Rancho Bernardo: 9 am–12 pm, Bernardo Winery at 13330 Paseo del Verano Norte

Saturday:
Carlsbad:8 am–noon, Roosevelt St between Grand Ave & Carlsbad Village Dr.
Chula Vista: 9 am–2 pm, Southwestern College parking lot "O" at 900 Otay Lakes Rd.
Clairemont: 3–6:30 pm, Lindbergh Schweitzer Elem. School, Balboa Ave. & Hathaway St.
Del Mar: 1–4 pm, City Hall Parking Lot, Camino Del Mar between 10th & 11th Sts.
Pacific Beach: 8 am–12 pm, Promenade Mall, Mission Blvd. between Reed & Pacific B. Dr.
Point Loma: 9–1 pm, Womble Rd. & Truxtun Rd. in High Tech High School parking lot
Poway: 8 am–noon, Old Poway Park, Corner of Midland & Temple
Scripps Ranch: 9 am–1 pm, Ellen Browning Elem. School at 10380 Spring Canyon Rd.
Vista: 7:45–11 am, Corner of Eucalyptus & Escondido Ave. (City Hall parking lot)

Sunday:
Hillcrest: 9 am–1 pm, Corner of Normal & Lincoln Sts. (DMV parking lot)
La Jolla: 9 am–2 pm, La Jolla Elementary School (Girard & Genter)
Leucadia/Encinitas: 10 am–2 pm, Paul Ecke Elementary at Union St & Vulcan St.
San Diego (Downtown): 9 am–1 pm, Third Ave & J St.
Solana Beach: 2–5 pm, 410 Cedros Ave.

SAN DIEGO DIETETIC ASSOCIATION

The San Diego Dietetic Association (SDDA) is a professional organization of nutrition experts dedicated to promoting healthy lifestyles through the encouragement of good eating habits and physical activity. To locate a Registered Dietitian in your area, contact the National Center for Nutrition and Dietetics at 1-800-366-1665 or online at http://www.eatright.org.

SDDA's website address is http://www.dietitian.org/sdda_home.htm.

Good nutrition is important through every stage of life, from conception to the "golden years." A Registered Dietitian can help you improve your overall health.

You may need a Registered Dietitian if ...

 ... You are eating for 2

... The media has you confused about nutrition

... You are tired of eating on the run

... Want to make changes in your life that will lead to a healthier lifestyle

... You have ? ? ? ? ? about food labels

SAN DIEGO NUTRITION NETWORK

(760) 436-6162 Tel
(760) 436-6409 Fax
www.sdnnonline.org

The San Diego Nutrition Network is a collaboration of over

70 health, nutrition and physical activities programs.

MISSION: To unite, educate and advocate for healthier food choices and increased physical activity for the people of San Diego County.

MEETING WELL: Please encourage your workplace or organization to join the growing coalition of organizations that promote a healthier San Diego. Organizations signing the "Meeting Well" policy agree to:

- Include healthy options (like fruit juice or water & fruits or vegetables) at all business/organization meetings at which meals or snacks are served.

- Provide physical activity breaks when meetings run longer than 90 minutes.

For more information, call (760) 436-6162 or visit www.sdnnonline.org.

Add one more serving of fruits/vegetables each day!

SPECIALTY PRODUCE

www.specialtyproduce.com

5245 Lovelock St.
San Diego, CA 92110
(619) 295-3173
www.specialtyproduce.com

Specialty Produce is San Diego's top foodservice and retail produce supplier. At any given time, we stock hundreds of different produce items. Specialty Produce has been family owned and operated for over twenty years.

Our business was built by providing the highest quality fruits and vegetables to many of San Diego's best restaurants. **Our doors are now open to the public** – so if you're looking for exotic, unusual, or hard-to-find products, want to enjoy top quality produce, or are looking for a fun and interesting produce experience, please visit us!

You're also invited to **access our website (www.specialtyproduce.com)**, updated daily, which offers a virtual encyclopedia of information on over 800 types of produce (including, for example, 25 types of apples and 18 types of pears). For each item, along with a photo, you'll find information concerning:

- Seasons/availability

- Current facts

- Description/taste

- Nutritional value

- Applications

- History/geography

- Ethnic/cultural information

- Restaurants currently featuring this product

You may also register for our **free weekly e-newsletter** by logging on to our website, www.specialtyproduce.com.

We welcome new ideas and partnerships from all levels of the culinary industry. Please contact us at 619-295-3173.

Resources

TAKING CONTROL OF YOUR DIABETES

1110 Camino Del Mar, Suite B
Del Mar, CA 92014
(858) 755-5683
www.TCOYD.org

Taking Control of Your Diabetes is a not-for-profit educational organization. Our mission is to educate and motivate people with diabetes to take a more active role in their condition, in order to live healthier, happier, and more productive lives.

We invite you to participate in the following **Taking Control of Your Diabetes** programs:

- The annual conference – a dynamic, informative day featuring presentations by highly qualified health professionals, educational exhibit booths, health screenings, lunch, and more, all designed to help those with diabetes better understand and manage their condition. The conference will be held at the San Diego Convention Center on November 18, 2006.

- The mini series – two-hour evening sessions including two lectures on topics of interest, a refreshment break, and time to meet with other "blood brothers and sisters." The mini-series is held every other month at The Preuss School, on campus at UCSD.

For more information, please visit www.TCOYD.org or call **Taking Control of Your Diabetes** at (858) 755-5683.

Resources

Part V

Advisory Board
Members

Healthy Dining's Distinguished Advisory Board

The following individuals serve on Healthy Dining's Advisory Board. Each advisor completes a review of one of our publications – the San Diego, Orange County, or Los Angeles edition – and provides feedback and suggestions. The Healthy Dining team is proud, honored, and fortunate to gain the input of such a distinguished group. We thank every Advisory Board member for his or her commitment to this important community health program.

Margot J. Aiken, MD, FRCPC, FACE. Dr. Aiken is a board certified internist and endocrinologist in clinical practice with Scripps Health and XIMED Medical Group. Dr. Aiken is involved in education programs and professional societies related to infertility, menopause and endocrinology. She is a member of numerous professional organizations including The American Association of Clinical Endocrinology, The American Society of Reproductive Medicine, The Pacific Coast Reproductive & Endocrine Society and The International Menopause Society.

Marilyn Biggica, Instructor of Foods & Nutrition, San Diego Community College. Marilyn teaches low-fat cooking at San Diego Community College and is active in the Community College District, where she serves on the Academic Senate and Advisory Committee. Marilyn is an active member of the International Association of Cooking Professionals. She also advises restaurants about healthier alternatives on their menus, and teaches that healthy food can taste good, as reflected in her cookbook, *101 Ways to Eat for Health and Pleasure*.

Mary Donkersloot, RD, Nutrition Therapist. Mary is a Beverly Hills-based consulting nutritionist who treats clients dealing with diabetes, weight control, eating disorders, and fitness and nutrition issues. She is the author of *The Simply Gourmet Diabetes Cookbook* and *Fast-Food Diet, Quick and Healthy Eating*. Mary is also the nutrition consultant for numerous national food corporations.

Lisa Dougherty, Owner of Whole Body Fitness in Costa Mesa and Past President, Nutrition and Fitness Council of Orange County Inc. Lisa has an extensive background in nutrition and fitness. She graduated from the Fitness Instructor Program at UC Irvine, and is a certified ACE personal trainer and Lifestyle and Weight Management Consultant. She has designed a unique 6-week lifestyle weight management program with a focus on daily physical activity and weekly goal setting. You can learn more about all of Lisa's services or sign up for her newsletter at www.wholebodyfitness.biz.

Karen C. Duester, MS, RD, President, Food Consulting Company. Karen has expertise in food composition, nutrition analysis and food labeling regulations. In 1993, she founded Food Consulting Company, which now serves over 1000 clients worldwide, primarily in the packaged food industry, but also restaurateurs and recipe publishers. In addition to fulfilling client orders for nutrition analysis, nutrition facts labels, ingredient/allergen statements and other regulation-compliant food label content, the company maintains a full-service website at foodlabels.com and publishes a popular monthly e-newsletter Food Label News that covers government actions for food labels.

Judith Ewing, Adult Education Instructor, San Diego Community College District. With a Bachelor's degree in Home Economics, Judith is involved in a variety of projects and programs related to health. For the past 31 years, she has been an Instructor at the San Diego Community College, where she teaches cooking classes. Judy has been a member of the American Association of Family & Consumer Sciences for over 30 years. She also does appliance demonstrations.

Mary Felando, MS, RD, Cardiac Rehab Dietitian, Cedars-Sinai Medical Center, Los Angeles. With a Master's degree in Human Nutrition from Cornell University, Mary has worked in the nutrition field for 25 years. Currently employed as a cardiovascular nutrition specialist at Cedars-Sinai Medical Center in Los Angeles, she is responsible for the development and implementation of the nutrition component of one of the largest cardiac rehabilitation programs in the country.

Gail C. Frank, DrPH, RD, CHES, Professor of Nutrition, Cal. State University, Long Beach. Gail has been active in the fields of nutrition and health for over 30 years. Along with directing many programs at Cal State Univ., Long Beach, Gail is an Adjunct Professor of Primary Care and Internal Medicine at Univ. of Calif., Irvine. She is active in several professional organizations and served as the Media Spokesperson for the American Dietetic Association for 19 years. Gail has had over 800 media interviews, including the *LA Times*, *Orange County Register*, CNN, NPR, "Dateline NBC," KABC, *US News & World Report* and *USA Today*.

Linda Gigliotti, MS, RD, CDE, Program Director, University of California, Irvine, Weight Management Program. Linda is a registered dietitian with a degree in education and extensive experience in outpatient and community education. Her expertise is in weight management and lifestyle modification, working with clients to make choices to manage their health. She is a certified diabetes educator and has received certification from the American Dietetic Association in both adult and childhood and adolescent weight management.

Annette Globits, R.D., Nutrition Educator and Counselor. Annette graduated from Cornell University, completed her internship at the University of Michigan Medical Center, and has worked as a dietitian at the UCLA Medical Center and the Los Alamitos Medical Center. She teaches classes on various subjects from weight reduction to nutrition during pregnancy and has lectured extensively throughout the community. She now operates a private practice in nutrition and believes "What you eat can make a difference."

Robyn L. Goldberg, R.D., Private Practice. Robyn began her career at Cedars-Sinai Medical Center in Los Angeles as the inpatient dietitian in the Department of Cardiology. She currently has her own private practice in Beverly Hills, where she specializes in medical conditions, disordered eating, preventative nutrition and athletes maximizing optimal nutrition. Robyn promotes opportunity to excel in personal health and fitness maintenance through a lecture series in association with several medical groups. She serves as a Nutrition Consultant for the Celiac Disease Foundation and is the nutritionist for the Susan Krevoy Eating Disorders Program.

De'Anna Gullotta, Mrs. California, United States, 2002-2003 and Mrs. Southern California, America, 2003-2004. De'Anna is the community spokesperson for the Ronald McDonald house and works with The Special Olympics. She does public speaking on healthy food choices, volunteerism and breast cancer awareness. De'Anna is also a part-time model and voiceover artist and was previously a stuntwoman and actress for a variety of television shows.

Greg Hernandez, Executive Director, Lifestyles Health & Fitness Consulting. Greg is an ACE Gold Certified Clinical Exercise Specialist in practice for 9 years and has provided health, fitness and nutrition services for several Southern California hospitals, medical groups, companies, and individuals. He is a former president and current board member of the Orange County Wellness Coalition and owner of Salsa Swing Connection Dance Studio in Costa Mesa. With a commitment to motivating the "inactive" population to adopt a healthy lifestyle, he has worked to develop new programs for the American Cancer Society, the American Diabetes Association, and the American Heart Association.

Adv. Board

Steve Karfaridis, Director of Operations, Wahoo's Fish Taco. Steve was born and raised on the coast of northern Greece. In 1974, he immigrated to the US, where he earned a Bachelor's Degree in Business Administration and Molecular Biology. He has been involved in the restaurant industry for the better part of the last 30 years as a line cook, server, chef, general manager and consultant. He has been with Wahoo's Fish Taco for over 15 years, where he was promoted to district manager and then partner and Director of Operations, helping the company to grow from two locations to 23 in two states. He enjoys being part of the drive to provide restaurant guests with healthier, fresher, better dining choices.

Kay Kimball, RN, MSN, OCN. Coordinator, Cancer Resource Centers/Patient Education & Support Services, Palomar Pomorado Health. Kay is an oncology certified nurse. She maintains the Cancer Resource Centers at Palomar Medical Center and Pomerado Hospital in North San Diego County. Through these centers she coordinates patient education classes addressing the prevention, detection, diagnosis and treatment of cancer. Information on nutrition is always offered as part of an 8-week I Can Cope program presented 3 times yearly and co-sponsored by Palomar Pomorado Health and the American Cancer Society.

Jeffrey Krebs, MD, FACP. Dr. Krebs has been practicing Internal Medicine in San Diego County since 1989. He is an Associate Clinical Professor of Medicine at the UCSD School of Medicine. Dr. Krebs has served on the Council of the San Diego County Medical Society and is past Chair of the California Medical Association's Young Physician Section. As a former competitive athlete, Dr. Krebs has always had an interest in nutrition.

Rieva Lesonsky, Senior Vice President/Editorial Director, Entrepreneur Media, Inc. Rieva has over 20 years experience at Entrepreneur Media, currently serving as SVP/Editorial Director of Entrepreneur magazine and entrepreneur.com. Rieva served on the Small Business Administration's (SBA) National Advisory Council from 1994 - 2000. The SBA has also honored her as a Small Business Media Advocate and a Woman in Business Advocate. For five years, Business News Reporter has named her one of the Top 100 Most Influential Journalists.

Randy Lopez, Vice President of Marketing, The Ruby Restaurant Group. Randy has been involved in the food industry for over 20 years. At Ruby's Diner, he is responsible for all marketing, advertising and public relations functions. Previous experience includes executive marketing positions at Buca Inc. and Del Taco. A stage IV colon cancer survivor and Board Member of the Colon Cancer Alliance, Lopez was spokesperson for various campaigns supporting cancer awareness and screening. Having an interest in menu development and nutrition, he has also developed public relations programs with the American Dietetic Association.

Phyllis Ann Marshall, FCSI, President, FoodPower, Inc. Phyllis is a foodservice industry consultant specializing in concept development and strategic plans to increase sales and profits of restaurants. She holds a BA degree from Cornell University and has extensive experience in the areas of market positioning, menu development, merchandising and four-walls marketing. Phyllis develops growth strategies with an eye to adding new profit centers and establishing brands. She assists shopping centers with the development of new food service and the retrofitting of existing properties in order to create destination restaurant locations.

April Morgan, VP of Sports and Fitness, The Sports Club Company. April has over 20 years experience in the fitness industry and holds a Bachelor's degree in Commercial Recreation. In her current position, she oversees all member programs such as private training, group exercise, nutrition, sports and children's programs for The Sports Club Company, which operates upscale health and fitness clubs throughout the country under The Sports Club/LA name.

Mae Ng, MPH, CHES, Director of Mission Delivery, American Cancer Society. Mae received her Bachelor's degree in Exercise Science from USC and MPH from Loma Linda University. She is responsible for all Nutrition, Physical Activity, Tobacco Prevention and Wellness Programs for the California Division. She has been with the American Cancer Society since 1998 and also serves on several statewide committees including the California Task Force on Youth and Workplace Wellness, the Cancer Prevention and Nutrition Services Joint Steering Committee and that group's Executive Committee.

Paula Partch, MS, RD, CDE, Health Educator, St. Joseph Heritage Healthcare. Paula received a BS degree in Dietetics from UC Davis and a Masters degree in Nutrition from the University of Arizona. She has worked in the field of dietetics for over 25 years. Her health educator role focuses on nutrition counseling in the areas of diabetes, gestational diabetes, weight management, and cardiovascular health. She values the behavior changes her clients need to incorporate to support healthy eating and finds the *Healthy Dining* publication a valuable tool to be used.

Vicki Pepper, MS, RD, Marketing & Promotions Coordinator, Kaiser Permanente Preventive Medicine. Vicki has worked for Kaiser Permanente's Positive Choice Wellness Center since 1987. She teaches nutrition and weight management for the wellness center. In addition, she coordinates the marketing and promotion for the Department of Preventive Medicine, which includes the Positive Choice Wellness Center and Health Appraisal.

Elyse Resch, MS, RD, FADA, Nutrition Therapist. Elyse is a Fellow of the American Dietetic Association and has been in private practice in Beverly Hills for over 23 years, specializing in eating disorders, intuitive eating and preventative nutrition. She is the co-author of *Intuitive Eating* (St. Martin's Press 1995, 2003) and does regular speaking engagements. She is a certified child and adolescent obesity expert and was the treatment team nutritionist on the Eating Disorder Unit at Beverly Hills Medical Center. She participates in a variety of organizations and activities including the Sports, Cardiovascular and Wellness Nutrition Practice Group of the American Dietetic Association, The International Association of Eating Disorder Professionals, and National Association of Anorexia Nervosa and Associated Disorders.

Joan W. Rupp, MS, RD, Director, Project LEAN and Director, Didactic Program in Dietetics & Lecturer, Dept. Exercise & Nutritional Sciences, San Diego State University. Joan is an Assistant Clinical Professor in the Department of Family & Preventative Medicine at the University of California, San Diego and a Lecturer and Director of the Didactic Program in Dietetics in the Department of Exercise & Nutritional Sciences at San Diego State University. Her interests involve advocacy for health policy and environmental changes in schools, restaurants, worksites, grocery stores, communities and the media to increase access to healthy food and physical activity programs.

John Ryan, General Manager, Walt's Wharf Restaurant. John has been in the food industry business for over 20 years. He is a firm believer in healthy dining and its counterpart, physical fitness. His position at Walt's Wharf has been a perfect fit, with a menu emphasizing freshness and healthy choices. John, wife Dana and two sons have many fitness accomplishments that currently include swimming and triathlon competition.

Adv. Board

Mary Ryzner, MS, RD, Clinical and Consultant Dietitian. Since receiving her Master's Degree in Nutrition in 1988 from California State University, Northridge, Mary has worked as a Clinical and Consultant Dietitian for various hospitals and healthcare centers. She also has her own business, specializing in fitness and wellness. Mary is active in the San Diego Dietetic Association and is the event coordinator for the Nutrition Fuels Fitness 5K/10K Run/Walk. She is also the team coordinator for the San Diego Track Club Masters Women's Team.

Jamie Steele, President & Fitness Director, Steele Bodies. Jamie has been in the health and fitness industry for over 20 years. His company, Steele Bodies, a personalized fitness, wellness and nutrition program, specializes in high-intensity training principles. Jamie has owned and operated 10 health and fitness facilities in California and Arizona and worked in upper level management and business development for a large California health and fitness chain.

Christopher Trela, Journalist, *OC Metro Magazine*/"Metro Menus". Christopher is the restaurant writer for "Metro Menus" and the performing arts columnist for *OC Metro Magazine*. He also writes about Health & Fitness for *OC Metro*, and writes a monthly column called "A Slice of Orange" (about life in the OC) for *Coast Magazine*. He is a freelance writer and photographer for many local magazines, serves as Director of Marketing for Balboa Performing Arts Theater, and is the owner of TrelaVisions Creative Services and TrelaPR.

Evelyn Tribole, MS, RD, Nutritionist for LifetimeTV.com. Evelyn is an award-winning registered dietitian, with a nutrition counseling practice in Irvine, CA. She has written six books including the million-copy bestseller *Healthy Homestyle Cooking* and *Intuitive Eating* (co-author). She is currently the nutritionist for LifetimeTV.com and was contributing editor for *Shape* magazine where her monthly column, *Recipe Makeovers*, appeared for 11 years. Tribole was the nutrition expert for Good Morning America and was a national spokesperson for the American Dietetic Association for 6 years.

Bruce Vancil, Director, American Cancer Society's Orange County Region. Bruce has worked for the American Cancer Society since 1982 in social work, patient counseling, ethnic outreach, legislative advocacy, research promotion, and related activities. He serves on many community-based coalitions, including the Orange County Breast Cancer Coalition (currently president), the Breast Cancer Detection Partnership, Cancer Genetics Research Advisory Board, Tobacco Use Prevention Coalition, Nutrition Alert Coalition, and a committee advising use of tobacco settlement funds. He is also the So. Calif. Chapter President of the Steamship Historical Society of America, a member of the group's National Board of Directors and an avid fan of the Queen Mary and other old steamships.

Part VI

Other Editions in the
Healthy Dining
Book Series,

Questionnaire &
Book Order Form
with Discount,

Notes to Restaurants

Other

Healthy Dining in *Orange County*
Participating Restaurants:

Acapulco
Angie's Cuisine Italiano
The Back Bay Rowing & Running Club
Baja Fresh Mexican Grill
The Beach House
BeachFire Bar & Grill
Blackboard Bistro
Bluewater Grill
Café Chin Chin
Café de France
Café Heidelberg
Café Vienna
California Wok
Charo Chicken
Chin's Chinese Kitchen
The Culinary Wrap
Daphne's Greek Café
Diho Siam
El Pollo Loco
El Torito
Ferdussi Taste of Persia
Finbars Italian Kitchen
The Fish Market
The Fisherman's Restaurant
Fitness Grill
Fitness Pizza
The Flame Broiler
Gelson's Market
Green Parrot Café
The Gypsy Den
The Health Emporium
Henry's Marketplace
Ho Sum Bistro
il Farro Caffe Trattoria
J.T. Schmid's
Jamba Juice

Koo Koo Roo
La Salsa
Luciana's Ristorante
Luigi's D'Italia
Marrakesh
McCormick & Schmick's
McKenna's on the Bay
Melissa's/World Variety Produce, Inc.
Mother's Market & Kitchen
Newport Beach Brewing Co.
The Old Spaghetti Factory
Pane e Vino Trattoria
Pascal Epicerie & Wine
Pascal Restaurant
Pat & Oscar's
Pick Up Stix
Red Rock Chili Co.
Round Table Pizza
Royal Khyber
Ruby's Diner
Sammy's Woodfired Pizza
Santa Monica Seafood
Souplantation
The Sundried Tomato
Susan's Healthy Gourmet
Taco Bell
The Taco Company
Thai Dishes
Thai Specialty 2
Vie de France
Wahoo's Fish Taco
Walt's Wharf
Whole Foods Market
Yard House
Z Pizza

To order any of the Healthy Dining editions, see pages 205-206 or call (858) 541-2049.

Healthy Dining in *Los Angeles*
Participating Restaurants:

Acapulco
Baja Fresh Mexican Grill
BlackBoard Bistro
Bluewater Grill
Border Grill
Buona Vita
Café Luna
Café Santorini
California Wok
Chandra Thai
Changs of Brentwood
Chaya Brasserie & Chaya Venice
Chili My Soul
Chili's
Chin Chin
China Grill
Ciudad
Claim Jumper
Cuvee
Daily Grill
Edward's Steakhouse
El Pollo Loco
El Torito
Factor's Famous Deli
Farm, The
Finbars Italian Kitchen
Flame Broiler, The
Four Seasons Hotel - Gardens Restaurant
Gaetano's Restaurant
Gelson's Market
Havana Mania
Hotel Bel Air
Il Fornaio
il forno
Il Moro
Jamba Juice
Junior's Restaurant & Deli
Kabuki Japanese Restaurant
Kate Mantilini
Kincaid's Bay House
King's Fish House
La Salsa
Lisa's Bon Appétit

Malvasia
Maria's Italian Kitchen
McCormick & Schmick's
McKenna's On the Bay
Mi Piace
Misto Caffé and Bakery
More Than Waffles
Old Spaghetti Factory, The
Pat & Oscar's
Pick Up Stix
Pinot Bistro
Pradeep's
Real Food Daily
Riviera Mexican Grill
Rock'N Fish
Rosti
Round Table Pizza
Rubio's Fresh Mexican Grill
Ruby's Diner
Sammy's Woodfired Pizza
Santa Monica Seafood
Shenandoah Café
Sisley Italian Kitchen
Souplantation
Spot Natural Food Restaurant, The
Susan's Healthy Gourmet
Tacone
The Farm
The Flame Broiler
The Old Spaghetti Factory
The Spot Natural Food Restaurant
Think Fish
Twin Palms
Wahoo's Fish Taco
Wasabi Japanese Restaurant
Westin Century Plaza Hotel –
    Breeze Restaurant
Westin Century Plaza Hotel –
    Café Mystique
Whole Foods Market
Wokcano Asian Café
Xi'an Healthy Chinese Cuisine
Z Pizza

To order any of the Healthy Dining editions, see pages 205-206 or call (858) 541-2049.

Other

$5.00 OFF
your next purchase of *Healthy Dining*

We want to know more about you and your thoughts about Healthy Dining. So we'll give you $5.00 off your next copy of *Healthy Dining* if you'll return this questionnaire (information is confidential). To thank you, we will contact you when new editions are published and offer $5.00 off the retail price. You may also order now at the discount price (see reverse side).

1. How did you learn about *Healthy Dining in San Diego*?

    ____ Newspaper   ____ Family or Friend   ____ Dietitian
    ____ Radio   ____ Restaurant   ____ Personal Trainer/Fitness Ctr.
    ____ Television   ____ Health Organization   ____ Special Event _____
    ____ Internet   ____ Physician   ____ Workplace
    ____ Store _____   ____ Other _____

2. Are you on any of these special diets?

    ____ Weight loss   ____ Low-cholesterol   ____ Diabetic   ____ General health-conscious
    ____ Low-fat   ____ Low-sodium   ____ Vegetarian   ____ Other _____

3. Please rate the following features of the book:

	Very helpful	Moderately helpful	Not needed
Chapters on general nutrition	____	____	____
Specific menu items available at restaurants	____	____	____
Numerical values of fat, calories, cholesterol, etc.	____	____	____
"Excellent Choice" (✔✔) and "Good Choice" (✔) categories	____	____	____
Restaurant coupons	____	____	____
Chefs' recipes section	____	____	____

4. Please list your favorite restaurants from this book:

5. What other restaurants would you like to see in the next edition?

6. Please list your favorite recipes from the book:

7. On average, how many times <u>per month</u> do you dine out? _____ Do you use the coupons? ____

8. Is this book primarily used by: ___ female ___ male ___ both ____ how many?

9. What is the age of the primary user of this book?
    ____ Under 30   ____ 30 to 45   ____ 45 to 60   ____ over 60

10. What other food or health-related publications do you read? (*Health Magazine, Berkeley Wellness, Nutrition Action Healthletter, Eating Well, Cooking Light,* etc.)

11. If you or any of your contacts would like information about fund-raising, seminars, or wholesale prices for Healthy Dining, please provide your phone number or e-mail _____

    Other Comments?

Please complete name and address on reverse side, fold and mail. Photocopy acceptable. SD7

Fold on lines with address on outside.

Name: _____

Address: _____

_____

Stamp

Healthy Dining
8305 Vickers Street, Suite 106
San Diego, CA 92111

Special **$5.00 OFF** *Healthy Dining* **books.**

Order as many as you want at the special discount! It's our thank-you for answering our questionnaire.
You will also receive the $5.00 discount on future editions. Orders normally processed within 1 week.

Quantity		Price
_____ *Healthy Dining in San Diego*	$19.95 - $5.00 discount = $14.95	_____
_____ *Healthy Dining in Orange County*	$19.95 - $5.00 discount = $14.95	_____
_____ *Healthy Dining in Los Angeles*	$19.95 - $5.00 discount = $14.95	_____

Please call (858) 541-2049 for more information.

Shipping & Handling ($1.84 for 1st book + 24¢ each for additional books)   _____

Subtotal   _____

Tax (7¾% in San Diego)   _____

_____ Check enclosed   Phone (   ) _____   Total   _____

_____ VISA/Mastercard/AmEx # _____ exp._____ Signature_____

Please fill out questionnaire on reverse and your name & address above. If sending check, make to
Healthy Dining and fasten your check securely to this sheet or use a separate envelope. Thanks.

THANK YOU

Dear Restaurant Owner/Manager:

Thank you for participating in the **Healthy Dining** Program. Healthy choices and nutrition information are very important to us. We appreciate your dedication to your customers.

THANK YOU

Dear Restaurant Owner/Manager:

Thank you for participating in the **Healthy Dining** Program. Healthy choices and nutrition information are very important to us. We appreciate your dedication to your customers.

THANK YOU

Dear Restaurant Owner/Manager:

Thank you for participating in the **Healthy Dining** Program. Healthy choices and nutrition information are very important to us. We appreciate your dedication to your customers.

THANK YOU

Dear Restaurant Owner/Manager:

Thank you for participating in the **Healthy Dining** Program. Healthy choices and nutrition information are very important to us. We appreciate your dedication to your customers.

THANK YOU

Dear Restaurant Owner/Manager:

Thank you for participating in the **Healthy Dining** Program. Healthy choices and nutrition information are very important to us. We appreciate your dedication to your customers.

Healthy Dining

Healthy Dining is a community-wide program to encourage restaurants to offer a selection of great-tasting, healthful menu items. **Healthy Dining**'s nutrition experts provide the restaurant industry with nutrition guidance, expertise and nutrition analysis services.

(858) 541-2049   **www.healthy-dining.com**

Healthy Dining

Healthy Dining is a community-wide program to encourage restaurants to offer a selection of great-tasting, healthful menu items. **Healthy Dining**'s nutrition experts provide the restaurant industry with nutrition guidance, expertise and nutrition analysis services.

(858) 541-2049   **www.healthy-dining.com**

Healthy Dining

Healthy Dining is a community-wide program to encourage restaurants to offer a selection of great-tasting, healthful menu items. **Healthy Dining**'s nutrition experts provide the restaurant industry with nutrition guidance, expertise and nutrition analysis services.

(858) 541-2049   **www.healthy-dining.com**

Healthy Dining

Healthy Dining is a community-wide program to encourage restaurants to offer a selection of great-tasting, healthful menu items. **Healthy Dining**'s nutrition experts provide the restaurant industry with nutrition guidance, expertise and nutrition analysis services.

(858) 541-2049   **www.healthy-dining.com**

Healthy Dining

Healthy Dining is a community-wide program to encourage restaurants to offer a selection of great-tasting, healthful menu items. **Healthy Dining**'s nutrition experts provide the restaurant industry with nutrition guidance, expertise and nutrition analysis services.

(858) 541-2049   **www.healthy-dining.com**

Please leave the following notes with your favorite restaurants.

PLEASE JOIN

Dear Restaurant Owner/Manager:

Healthy choices and nutrition information are very important to me and my family. We hope you will participate in the **Healthy Dining** Program. Please call **(858) 541-2049**. Thank you!

PLEASE JOIN

Dear Restaurant Owner/Manager:

Healthy choices and nutrition information are very important to me and my family. We hope you will participate in the **Healthy Dining** Program. Please call **(858) 541-2049**. Thank you!

PLEASE JOIN

Dear Restaurant Owner/Manager:

Healthy choices and nutrition information are very important to me and my family. We hope you will participate in the **Healthy Dining** Program. Please call **(858) 541-2049**. Thank you!

PLEASE JOIN

Dear Restaurant Owner/Manager:

Healthy choices and nutrition information are very important to me and my family. We hope you will participate in the **Healthy Dining** Program. Please call **(858) 541-2049**. Thank you!

PLEASE JOIN

Dear Restaurant Owner/Manager:

Healthy choices and nutrition information are very important to me and my family. We hope you will participate in the **Healthy Dining** Program. Please call **(858) 541-2049**. Thank you!

Healthy Dining

Healthy Dining is a community-wide program to encourage restaurants to offer a selection of great-tasting, healthful menu items. **Healthy Dining's** nutrition experts provide the restaurant industry with nutrition guidance, expertise and nutrition analysis services.

(858) 541-2049   **www.healthy-dining.com**

Healthy Dining

Healthy Dining is a community-wide program to encourage restaurants to offer a selection of great-tasting, healthful menu items. **Healthy Dining's** nutrition experts provide the restaurant industry with nutrition guidance, expertise and nutrition analysis services.

(858) 541-2049   **www.healthy-dining.com**

Healthy Dining

Healthy Dining is a community-wide program to encourage restaurants to offer a selection of great-tasting, healthful menu items. **Healthy Dining's** nutrition experts provide the restaurant industry with nutrition guidance, expertise and nutrition analysis services.

(858) 541-2049   **www.healthy-dining.com**

Healthy Dining

Healthy Dining is a community-wide program to encourage restaurants to offer a selection of great-tasting, healthful menu items. **Healthy Dining's** nutrition experts provide the restaurant industry with nutrition guidance, expertise and nutrition analysis services.

(858) 541-2049   **www.healthy-dining.com**

Healthy Dining

Healthy Dining is a community-wide program to encourage restaurants to offer a selection of great-tasting, healthful menu items. **Healthy Dining's** nutrition experts provide the restaurant industry with nutrition guidance, expertise and nutrition analysis services.

(858) 541-2049   **www.healthy-dining.com**

Please leave the following notes with your favorite restaurants.

PLEASE JOIN

Dear Restaurant Owner/Manager:

Healthy choices and nutrition information are very important to me and my family. We hope you will participate in the **Healthy Dining** Program. Please call **1-800-266-2049**. Thank you!

PLEASE JOIN

Dear Restaurant Owner/Manager:

Healthy choices and nutrition information are very important to me and my family. We hope you will participate in the **Healthy Dining** Program. Please call **1-800-266-2049**. Thank you!

PLEASE JOIN

Dear Restaurant Owner/Manager:

Healthy choices and nutrition information are very important to me and my family. We hope you will participate in the **Healthy Dining** Program. Please call **1-800-266-2049**. Thank you!

PLEASE JOIN

Dear Restaurant Owner/Manager:

Healthy choices and nutrition information are very important to me and my family. We hope you will participate in the **Healthy Dining** Program. Please call **1-800-266-2049**. Thank you!

PLEASE JOIN

Dear Restaurant Owner/Manager:

Healthy choices and nutrition information are very important to me and my family. We hope you will participate in the **Healthy Dining** Program. Please call **1-800-266-2049**. Thank you!

Healthy Dining

Healthy Dining is a community-wide program to encourage restaurants to offer a selection of great-tasting, healthful menu items. **Healthy Dining's** nutrition experts provide the restaurant industry with nutrition guidance, expertise and nutrition analysis services.

1-800-266-2049   **www.healthy-dining.com**

Healthy Dining

Healthy Dining is a community-wide program to encourage restaurants to offer a selection of great-tasting, healthful menu items. **Healthy Dining's** nutrition experts provide the restaurant industry with nutrition guidance, expertise and nutrition analysis services.

1-800-266-2049   **www.healthy-dining.com**

Healthy Dining

Healthy Dining is a community-wide program to encourage restaurants to offer a selection of great-tasting, healthful menu items. **Healthy Dining's** nutrition experts provide the restaurant industry with nutrition guidance, expertise and nutrition analysis services.

1-800-266-2049   **www.healthy-dining.com**

Healthy Dining

Healthy Dining is a community-wide program to encourage restaurants to offer a selection of great-tasting, healthful menu items. **Healthy Dining's** nutrition experts provide the restaurant industry with nutrition guidance, expertise and nutrition analysis services.

1-800-266-2049   **www.healthy-dining.com**

Healthy Dining

Healthy Dining is a community-wide program to encourage restaurants to offer a selection of great-tasting, healthful menu items. **Healthy Dining's** nutrition experts provide the restaurant industry with nutrition guidance, expertise and nutrition analysis services.

1-800-266-2049   **www.healthy-dining.com**

Part VI

Coupons

See pages 205-206 for special offer on
additional *Healthy Dining* books!

Healthy
Dining

Healthy
Dining

Healthy
Dining

Healthy
Dining

Healthy
Dining

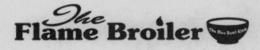

 Healthy
Dining

 Healthy
Dining

 Healthy
Dining

 Healthy
Dining

 Healthy
Dining

--

Healthy
Dining

Healthy
Dining

Healthy
Dining

Healthy
Dining

Healthy
Dining

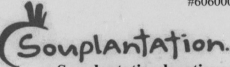

 Healthy
Dining

 Healthy
Dining

 Healthy
Dining

 Healthy
Dining

 Healthy
Dining

Healthy
Dining

Healthy
Dining

Healthy
Dining

Healthy
Dining

Healthy
Dining

Part VIII

Indexes

Restaurant Menu Indexes
Cuisine   226
Location   228
Alphabetical   232

Other Indexes
Health Resource Guide 181
Recipe Index   123

Index by Cuisine

American, Family
Arby's 48
Brockton Villa 53
Chili's Grill & Bar 57
Claim Jumper Restaurant 60
Crest Café 61
Dave and Buster's 63
G5-Georges on Fifth 71
Leucadia Pizzeria & Italian Restaurant 81
Pat & Oscar's 90
Ruby's Diner 101
Sizzler 106
Souplantation 107
Spoons Grill & Bar 108

Asian Fusion
Roppongi Restaurant & Sushi Bar 97

California
Azzura Point and Market Café at
    Loews Coronado Bay Resort & Spa 82
150 Grand Cafe 88
The Prado at Balboa Park 93
Sammy's Woodfired Pizza 103
Trellises Garden Grille at the
    Town & Country Hotel 114
Wild Note Café 89
Zanzibar Cafe 120
Zocalo Grill 121

Cajun
Gulf Coast Grill 72

Chinese
Chin's Szechwan Cuisine 58
Pick Up Stix 91

Contemporary American
J. Taylor's Restaurant at the L'Arberge
    Del Mar Resort and Spa 76

Continental
St. Germain's Cafe 102

Cuban/Latin American
Andrés Cuban Restaurant 45

Fast Food – see Quick Serve

Fine Dining
Blue Point Coastal Cuisine 51
G5-Georges on Fifth 71
Harry's Bar and American Grill 73
Nine-Ten Restaurant 87
150 Grand Cafe 88
The Prado at Balboa Park 93
Top of the Cove 112

French
The French Gourmet 69

Greek
Yanni's Bistro 119

Home Delivery
Susan's Healthy Gourmet 110

Indian
Cafe India 54
Royal India Express 99
Star of India 99

Italian
Harry's Bar and American Grill 73
Il Fornaio 74
Leucadia Pizzeria & Italian Restaurant 81
Lotsa Pasta 84
Pizza Nova 92
Prego Ristorante 94
Trattoria La Strada 113
Tutto Mare 115
Yanni's Bistro 119

Juice Bar
Jamba Juice 78
Ki's Restaurant & Juice Bar 79

Index by Cuisine, continued

Korean
The Flame Broiler   67

Latin and Italian Fusion
The Prado at Balboa Park   93

Mediterranean
The Prado at Balboa Park   93
Yanni's Bistro   119

Mexican, Southwest
Antonios Hacienda Mexican Rest.   47
Baja Fresh   49
Chile Peppers   56
Chili's Grill & Bar   57
El Pollo Loco   64
El Torito   65
Fred's Mexican Café   68
La Salsa   80
Los Cabos Mexican Mesquite Grill   83
Mi Ranchito   86
Ranchos Cocina   95
Rubio's Fresh Mexican Grill   100
Santana's Mexican Grill   105
Tierrasanta Mexican Restaurant   47
Tio Leo's   111
Wahoo's Fish Taco   116

Pacific Rim
Indigo Grill   75
Kemo Sabe   75
Pacific Coast Grill   89

Persian
Bandar Persian Cuisine   50

Pizza
Leucadia Pizzeria & Italian Restaurant   81
Pat & Oscar's   90
Pizza Nova   92
Round Table Pizza   98
Sammy's Woodfired Pizza   103

Quick Serve, Fast Casual, Fast Food
Arby's   48
Baja Fresh   49
Chile Peppers   56
El Pollo Loco   64
The Flame Broiler   67
Jamba Juice   78
La Salsa   80
Mi Ranchito   86
Pick Up Stix   91
Rubio's Fresh Mexican Grill   100
Subway   109
Wahoo's Fish Taco   116

Seafood
Anthony's Fish Grotto   46
Blue Point Coastal Cuisine   51
The Brigantine   52
Cafe Pacifica   55
The Fish Market   66
Fresh Seafood Restaurant & Bar   70
McCormick & Schmick's   85
Pacific Coast Grill   89
SandCrab Cafe   104
Tutto Mare   115

Specialty
World Curry   118

Steakhouse
G5-Georges on Fifth   71

Vegetarian, Health & Natural
Cilantro Live!   59
Daily's Restaurant   62
Jimbo's…Naturally!   78
Ki's Restaurant & Juice Bar   79
Lotsa Pasta   84
Ranchos Cocina   95
Souplantation   107
Susan's Healthy Gourmet   110
Whole Foods Market   117

Vietnamese
Rice Jones   96

Index by Location

All Locations
Subway 109
Susan's Healthy Gourmet 110

Alpine/Viejas
Rubio's Fresh Mexican Grill 100

Bay Park – see Old Town, Morena

Chula Vista, Bonita, National City, Rancho Del Rey, South Bay
Anthony's Fish Grotto 46
Arby's 48
Chili's Grill & Bar 57
Cilantro Live! 59
El Pollo Loco 64
El Torito 65
Jamba Juice 77
Pat & Oscar's 90
Pick Up Stix 91
Rubio's Fresh Mexican Grill 100
Sizzler 106

Cardiff – see Del Mar

Carlsbad – see Oceanside

Clairemont – see Kearny Mesa

College Area, Mission Gorge, Del Cerro
Arby's 48
El Pollo Loco 64
Rubio's Fresh Mexican Grill 100
Souplantation 107
Tio Leo's 111

Coronado
Azzura Point and Market Café at
   Loews Coronado Bay Resort & Spa 82
The Brigantine 52
Il Fornaio 74
La Salsa 80
Rubio's Fresh Mexican Grill 100

Del Cerro – see College Area

Del Mar, Solana Beach, Cardiff
The Brigantine 52
El Pollo Loco 64
The Fish Market 66
Il Fornaio 74
J. Taylor's Restaurant at the L'Arberge
   Del Mar Resort and Spa 76
Jamba Juice 77
Jimbo's...Naturally! 78
Ki's Restaurant & Juice Bar 79
La Salsa 80
Leucadia Pizzeria & Italian Restaurant 81
Los Cabos Mexican Mesquite Grill 83
Pacific Coast Grill 89
Pat & Oscar's 90
Pick Up Stix 91
Pizza Nova 92
Round Table Pizza 98
Rubio's Fresh Mexican Grill 100
Sammy's Woodfired Pizza 103
Souplantation 107
Star of India 99
Tio Leo's 111
Wild Note Café 89

Downtown, Gaslamp, Harbor Island
Anthony's Fish Grotto 46
Baja Fresh 49
Bandar Persian Cuisine 50
Blue Point Coastal Cuisine 51
El Pollo Loco 64
The Fish Market 66
Fred's Mexican Café 68
G5-Georges on Fifth 71
Indigo Grill 75
Jamba Juice 77
Kemo Sabe 75
La Salsa 80
McCormick & Schmick's 85
Pat & Oscar's 90
Royal India Express 99
Rubio's Fresh Mexican Grill 100
Sammy's Woodfired Pizza 103
Star of India 99
Trattoria La Strada 113
Zanzibar Cafe 120

Index by Location, continued

Old Town, Morena, Bay Park

Andrés Cuban Restaurant	45
Cafe Pacifica	55
Fred's Mexican Café	68
Santana's Mexican Grill	105
Tio Leo's	111
Zocalo Grill	121

Pacific Beach

Fred's Mexican Café	68
The French Gourmet	69
Jamba Juice	77
La Salsa	80
Lotsa Pasta	84
Pick Up Stix	91
Round Table Pizza	98
Rubio's Fresh Mexican Grill	100
Santana's Mexican Grill	105
Star of India	99
World Curry	118
Zanzibar Cafe	120

Point Loma, Midway, Ocean Beach

Arby's	48
Baja Fresh	49
The Brigantine	52
Cafe India	54
Chili's Grill & Bar	57
El Pollo Loco	64
Jamba Juice	77
Pick Up Stix	91
Pizza Nova	92
Ranchos Cocina	95
Rubio's Fresh Mexican Grill	100
Santana's Mexican Grill	105
Sizzler	106
Souplantation	107
Wahoo's Fish Taco	116

Poway, Rancho Bernardo, Carmel Mt.

Baja Fresh	49
The Brigantine	52
Claim Jumper Restaurant	60
Chile Peppers	56

continued on next column

Poway, R. Bernardo, Carmel Mt., cont'd.

Chili's Grill & Bar	57
Chin's Szechwan Cuisine	58
El Pollo Loco	64
El Torito	65
Jamba Juice	77
Leucadia Pizzeria & Italian Restaurant	81
Mi Ranchito	86
Pat & Oscar's	90
Pick Up Stix	91
Round Table Pizza	98
Rubio's Fresh Mexican Grill	100
Souplantation	107
Yanni's Bistro	119

R. Bernardo & R. Penasq. – see Poway

Ramona

Rubio's Fresh Mexican Grill	100
Sizzler	106

Rancho San Diego – see La Mesa

Rancho Santa Fe – see Del Mar

San Marcos – see Escondido

Santee – see El Cajon

Scripps Ranch – see Mira Mesa & Miramar

Solana Beach – see Del Mar

Temecula

Chile Peppers	56
Chili's Grill & Bar	57
Claim Jumper Restaurant	60
El Pollo Loco	64
Jamba Juice	77
Round Table Pizza	98
Rubio's Fresh Mexican Grill	100
Sizzler	106
Souplantation	107

Tierrasanta – see Murphy Canyon

Vista – see Oceanside

Alphabetical Index

Andrés Cuban Restaurant	45	Market Café at Loews Coronado Bay	82
Anthony's Fish Grotto	46	McCormick & Schmick's	85
Antonios Hacienda Mexican Rest.	47	Mi Ranchito	86
Arby's	48	Nine-Ten Restaurant	87
Azzura Point at Loews Coronado Bay	82	150 Grand Cafe	88
Baja Fresh	49	Pacific Coast Grill	89
Bandar Persian Cuisine	50	Pat & Oscar's	90
Blue Point Coastal Cuisine	51	Pick Up Stix	91
The Brigantine	52	Pizza Nova	92
Brockton Villa	53	The Prado at Balboa Park	93
Cafe India	54	Prego Ristorante	94
Cafe Pacifica	55	Ranchos Cocina	95
Chile Peppers	56	Rice Jones	96
Chili's Grill & Bar	57	Roppongi Restaurant & Sushi Bar	97
Chin's Szechwan Cuisine	58	Round Table Pizza	98
Cilantro Live!	59	Royal India Express	99
Claim Jumper Restaurant	60	Rubio's Fresh Mexican Grill	100
Crest Café	61	Ruby's Diner	101
Daily's Restaurant	62	St. Germain's Cafe	102
Dave and Buster's	63	Sammy's Woodfired Pizza	103
El Pollo Loco	64	SandCrab Cafe	104
El Torito	65	Santana's Mexican Grill	105
The Fish Market	66	Sizzler	106
The Flame Broiler	67	Souplantation	107
Fred's Mexican Café	68	Spoons Grill & Bar	108
The French Gourmet	69	Star of India	99
Fresh Seafood Restaurant & Bar	70	Subway	109
G5-Georges on Fifth	71	Susan's Healthy Gourmet	110
Gulf Coast Grill	72	The Brigantine	52
Harry's Bar and American Grill	73	The Fish Market	66
Henry's Farmers Market	179	The Flame Broiler	67
Il Fornaio	74	The French Gourmet	69
Indigo Grill	75	Tierrasanta Mexican Restaurant	47
J. Taylor's Restaurant at the L'Arberge Del Mar Resort and Spa	76	Tio Leo's	111
Jamba Juice	77	Top of the Cove	112
Jimbo's…Naturally!	78	Trattoria La Strada	113
Kemo Sabe	75	Trellises Garden Grille at the Town & Country Hotel	114
Ki's Restaurant & Juice Bar	79	Tutto Mare	115
L'Arberge Del Mar Resort & Spa	76	Wahoo's Fish Taco	116
La Salsa	80	Whole Foods Market	117
Leucadia Pizzeria & Italian Restaurant	81	Wild Note Café	89
Loews Coronado Bay Resort & Spa	82	World Curry	118
Los Cabos Mexican Mesquite Grill	83	Yanni's Bistro	119
Lotsa Pasta	84	Zanzibar Cafe	120
		Zocalo Grill	121